AS-Level Chemistry

AS Chemistry is seriously tricky — no question about that.
To do well, you're going to need to revise properly and practise hard.

This book has thorough notes on all the theory you need,
and it's got practice questions... lots of them.
For every topic there are warm-up and exam-style questions.

And of course, we've done our best to make the whole thing vaguely entertaining for you.

Complete Revision and Practice

Exam Board: OCR B

Editors:
Mary Falkner, Sarah Hilton, Paul Jordin, Sharon Keeley, Simon Little, Andy Park.

Contributors:
Antonio Angelosanto, Vikki Cunningham, Ian H. Davis, John Duffy, Max Fishel, Emma Grimwood, Richard Harwood, Lucy Muncaster, Glenn Rogers, David Scott, Derek Swain, Paul Warren, Chris Workman.

Proofreaders:
Barrie Crowther, Julie Wakeling

Published by CGP

ISBN: 978 1 84762 127 6

With thanks to Jan Greenway for the copyright research.

With thanks to Science Photo Library for permission to reproduce the photograph used on page 92.

Graph to show trend in atmospheric CO_2 Concentration and global temperature on page 89 based on data by EPICA Community Members 2004 and Siegenthaler et al 2005.

Groovy website: www.cgpbooks.co.uk
Jolly bits of clipart from CorelDRAW®
Printed by Elanders Ltd, Newcastle upon Tyne.

Based on the classic CGP style created by Richard Parsons.

Contents

How Science Works

The Scientific Process 2

Unit 1: Module 1 — The Elements of Life

The Atom 4
Atomic Models 6
Relative Mass 8
Nuclear Radiation 10
The Mole and Equations 12
Empirical and Molecular Formulas 14
Electron Shells and Atomic Spectra 16
Ionic Bonding 18
Covalent Bonding 20
Giant Covalent and Metallic Structures 22
Shapes of Molecules 24
The Periodic Table 26
Group 2 28

Unit 1: Module 2 — Developing Fuels

Gas Volumes and Entropy 30
Enthalpy Changes 32
Hess's Law 34
Measuring Enthalpy Changes 36
Catalysts 38
Organic Groups 40
Isomerism 42
Shapes of Organic Molecules 44
Catalysts and Petroleum 46
Fuels 48
Fuels of the Future 50

Unit 2: Module 1 — Elements from the Sea

More Calculations 52
Titrations 54
Electronic Structure 56
Oxidation and Reduction 59
Electronegativity 62
Intermolecular Forces 64
Ionisation Enthalpies 66
Group 7 — The Halogens 68
More About The Halogens 70
The Chemical Industry 72
Halogenoalkanes 74
More About Halogenoalkanes 76

Unit 2: Module 2 — The Atmosphere

Giant Structures 78
Reaction Rates 80
More on Reaction Rates 82
Reversible Reactions 84
The Atmosphere 86
The Greenhouse Effect 88
Halogenoalkanes and CFCs 90
Ozone 92

Unit 2: Module 3 — The Polymer Revolution

Addition Reactions of Alkenes 94
Alcohols and Other Organic Chemicals 97
Hydrogen Bonding 100
Polymers 102
E/Z isomerism 104
Infrared Spectroscopy 106

Practical and Investigative Skills 108

Answers 111

Index 120

Periodic Table 122

The Scientific Process

'How Science Works' is all about the scientific process — how we develop and test scientific ideas. It's what scientists do all day, every day (well except at coffee time — never come between scientists and their coffee).

*Scientists Come Up with **Theories** — Then **Test Them**...*

Science tries to explain **how** and **why** things happen. It's all about seeking and gaining **knowledge** about the world around us. Scientists do this by **asking** questions and **suggesting** answers and then **testing** them, to see if they're correct — this is the **scientific process**.

1) **Ask** a question — make an **observation** and ask **why or how** whatever you've observed happens.
   E.g. Why does sodium chloride dissolve in water?
2) **Suggest** an answer, or part of an answer, by forming a **theory** or a **model** (a possible **explanation** of the observations or a description of what you think is happening actually happening).
   E.g. Sodium chloride is made up of charged particles which are pulled apart by the polar water molecules.
3) Make a **prediction** or **hypothesis** — a **specific testable statement**, based on the theory, about what will happen in a test situation.
   E.g. A solution of sodium chloride will conduct electricity much better than water does.
4) Carry out **tests** — to provide **evidence** that will support the prediction or refute it.
   E.g. Measure the conductivity of water and of sodium chloride solution.

The evidence supported Quentin's Theory of Flammable Burps.

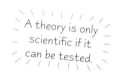

A theory is only scientific if it can be tested.

*...Then They **Tell** Everyone About Their **Results**...*

The results are **published** — scientists need to let others know about their work. Scientists publish their results in **scientific journals**. These are just like normal magazines, only they contain **scientific reports** (called papers) instead of the latest celebrity gossip.

1) Scientific reports are similar to the **lab write-ups** you do in school. And just as a lab write-up is **reviewed** (marked) by your teacher, reports in scientific journals undergo **peer review** before they're published.

   Scientists use standard terminology when writing their reports. This way they know that other scientists will understand them. For instance, there are internationally agreed rules for naming organic compounds, so that scientists across the world will know exactly what substance is being referred to. See page 41.
2) The report is sent out to **peers** — other scientists who are experts in the **same area**. They go through it bit by bit, examining the methods and data, and checking it's all clear and logical. When the report is approved, it's **published**. This makes sure that work published in scientific journals is of a **good standard**.
3) But peer review **can't guarantee** the science is **correct** — other scientists still need to **reproduce** it.
4) Sometimes **mistakes** are made and bad work is published. Peer review **isn't perfect** but it's probably the best way for scientists to self-regulate their work and to publish **quality reports**.

*...Then **Other Scientists** Will **Test** the Theory Too*

1) Other scientists read the published theories and results, and try to **test the theory** themselves. This involves:
   - Repeating the **exact same experiments**.
   - Using the theory to make **new predictions** and then testing them with **new experiments**.
2) If all the experiments in the world provide evidence to back it up, the theory is thought of as **scientific 'fact'** (for now).
3) If **new evidence** comes to light that **conflicts** with the current evidence the theory is questioned all over again. More rounds of **testing** will be carried out to try to find out where the theory **falls down**.

This is how the **scientific process works** — **evidence** supports a theory, loads of other scientists read it and test it for themselves, eventually all the scientists in the world **agree** with it and then bingo, you get to **learn** it.

This is exactly how scientists arrived at the structure of the atom (see pages 6-7) — and how they came to the conclusion that electrons are arranged in shells and orbitals (see page 56). It took years and years for these models to be developed and accepted — this is often the case with the scientific process.

The Scientific Process

If the **Evidence** Supports a Theory, It's **Accepted — for Now**

Our currently accepted theories have survived this '**trial by evidence**'. They've been tested **over and over again** and each time the results have backed them up. **BUT**, and this is a big but (teehee), they never become totally indisputable fact. Scientific **breakthroughs or advances** could provide new ways to question and test the theory, which could lead to **changes and challenges** to it. Then the testing starts all over again...

And this, my friend, is the **tentative nature of scientific knowledge** — it's always **changing** and **evolving**.

When CFCs were first used in fridges in the 1930s, scientists thought they were problem-free — well, why not? There was no evidence to say otherwise. It was decades before anyone found out that CFCs were actually making a whopping great hole in the ozone layer. See page 91-93.

Evidence Comes From **Lab Experiments...**

1) Results from **controlled experiments** in **laboratories** are **great**.
2) A lab is the easiest place to **control variables** so that they're all **kept constant** (except for the one you're investigating).
3) This means you can draw meaningful **conclusions**.

For example, if you're investigating how temperature affects the rate of a reaction you need to keep everything but the temperature constant, e.g. the pH of the solution, the concentration of the solution, etc.

...But You **Can't** Always do a Lab Experiment

There are things you **can't** study in a lab. And outside the lab controlling the variables is tricky, if not impossible.

- *Are increasing CO_2 emissions causing climate change?*
  There are other variables which may have an effect, such as changes in solar activity. You can't easily rule out every possibility. Also, climate change is a very **gradual process**. Scientists won't be able to tell if their predictions are correct for donkey's years.
- *Does drinking chlorinated tap water increase the risk of developing certain cancers?*
  There are always differences between groups of people. The best you can do is to have a **well-designed study** using **matched groups** — **choose two groups** of people (those who drink tap water and those who don't) which are **as similar as possible** (same mix of ages, same mix of diets etc). But you still can't rule out every possibility. Taking new-born identical twins and treating them identically, except for making one drink gallons of tap water and the other only pure water, might be a fairer test, but it would present huge **ethical problems**.

See pages 88-89 for more on climate change.

Samantha thought her study was very well designed — especially the fitted bookshelf.

Science Helps to Inform **Decision-Making**

Lots of scientific work eventually leads to **important discoveries** that **could** benefit humankind — but there are often **risks** attached (and almost always **financial costs**).

Society (that's you, me and everyone else) must weigh up the information in order to **make decisions** — about the way we live, what we eat, what we drive, and so on. Information is also be used by **politicians** to devise policies and laws.

- **Chlorine** is added to water in **small quantities** to disinfect it. Some studies link drinking chlorinated water with certain types of cancer. But the risks from drinking water contaminated by nasty bacteria are far, far greater. There are other ways to get rid of bacteria in water, but they're heaps **more expensive**.
- Scientific advances mean that **non-polluting hydrogen-fuelled cars** can be made. They're better for the environment, but are really expensive. Also, it'd cost a fortune to adapt the existing filling stations to store hydrogen.
- Pharmaceutical drugs are really expensive to develop, and drug companies want to make money. So they put most of their efforts into developing drugs that they can sell for a good price. Society has to consider the **cost** of buying new drugs — the **NHS** can't afford the most expensive drugs without **sacrificing** something else.

So there you have it — how science works...

Hopefully these pages have given you a nice intro to how science works, e.g. what scientists do to provide you with 'facts'. You need to understand this, as you're expected to know how science works yourselves — for the exam and for life.

The Atom

This stuff about atoms and elements should be ingrained on your brain from GCSE. You do need to know it perfectly though if you are to negotiate your way through the field of man-eating tigers which is AS Chemistry.

Atoms are made up of **Protons**, **Neutrons** and **Electrons**

All elements are made of **atoms**. Atoms are made up of 3 types of particle — **protons**, **neutrons** and **electrons**.

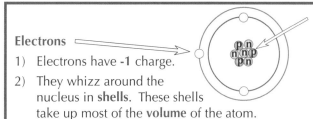

Electrons
1) Electrons have **-1** charge.
2) They whizz around the nucleus in **shells**. These shells take up most of the **volume** of the atom.

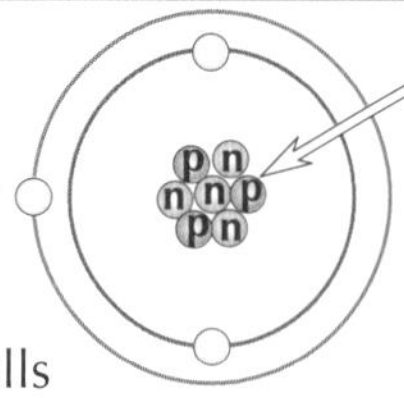

Nucleus
1) Most of the **mass** of the atom is concentrated in the nucleus.
2) The **diameter** of the nucleus is rather titchy compared to the whole atom.
3) The nucleus is where you find the **protons** and **neutrons**.

The mass and charge of these subatomic particles is **really small**, so **relative mass** and **relative charge** are used instead.

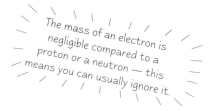

The mass of an electron is negligible compared to a proton or a neutron — this means you can usually ignore it.

Subatomic particle	Relative mass	Relative charge
Proton	1	+1
Neutron	1	0
Electron, e^-	$\frac{1}{2000}$	−1

Nuclear Symbols Show Numbers of **Subatomic Particles**

You can figure out the **number** of protons, neutrons and electrons from the **nuclear symbol**.

$$^{A}_{Z}\mathrm{X}$$

Mass number
This tells you the **total** number of **protons** and **neutrons** in the nucleus.

Element symbol

Atomic (proton) number
1) This is the number of **protons** in the nucleus — it identifies the element.
2) **All** atoms of the same element have the **same** number of protons.

Sometimes the atomic number is left out of the nuclear symbol, e.g. ^{7}Li. You don't really need it because the element's symbol tells you its value.

1) For **neutral** atoms, which have no overall charge, the number of electrons is **the same as** the number of protons.
2) The number of neutrons is just **mass number minus atomic number**, i.e. 'top minus bottom' in the nuclear symbol.

Nuclear symbol	Atomic number, Z	Mass number, A	Protons	Electrons	Neutrons
$^{7}_{3}Li$	3	7	3	3	7 – 3 = **4**
$^{80}_{35}Br$	35	80	35	35	80 – 35 = **45**
$^{24}_{12}Mg$	12	24	12	12	24 – 12 = **12**

"Hello, I'm Newt Ron..."

Ions have **Different** Numbers of **Protons and Electrons**

Negative ions have **more electrons** than protons...

E.g.

Br^-

The negative charge means that there's 1 more electron than there are protons.
Br has 35 protons (see table above), so Br^- must have 36 electrons.
The overall charge = +35 – 36 = –1.

...and **positive** ions have **fewer electrons** than protons. It kind of makes sense if you think about it.

E.g.

Mg^{2+}

The 2+ charge means that there's 2 fewer electrons than there are protons.
Mg has 12 protons (see table above), so Mg^{2+} must have 10 electrons.
The overall charge = +12 – 10 = +2.

The Atom

Isotopes are Atoms of the **Same Element** with Different Numbers of **Neutrons**

Make sure you **learn** this definition and totally **understand** what it means —

Isotopes of an element are atoms with the same number of protons but different numbers of neutrons.

Chlorine-35 and chlorine-37 are examples of isotopes.

$^{35}_{17}Cl$ — $35 - 17 = 18$ **neutrons**

The **atomic numbers** are the same. **Both** isotopes have 17 protons and 17 electrons.

Different mass numbers mean different numbers of neutrons.

$^{37}_{17}Cl$ — $37 - 17 = 20$ **neutrons**

1) It's the **number** and **arrangement** of electrons that decides the **chemical properties** of an element. Isotopes have the **same configuration of electrons**, so they've got the **same** chemical properties.
2) Isotopes of an element do have slightly different **physical properties** though, such as different densities, rates of diffusion, etc. This is because **physical properties** often depend more on the **mass** of the atom.

Here's another example — naturally occurring **magnesium** consists of 3 isotopes.

^{24}Mg (79%)	^{25}Mg (10%)	^{26}Mg (11%)
12 protons	12 protons	12 protons
12 neutrons	**13** neutrons	**14** neutrons
12 electrons	12 electrons	12 electrons

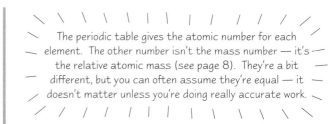

The periodic table gives the atomic number for each element. The other number isn't the mass number — it's the relative atomic mass (see page 8). They're a bit different, but you can often assume they're equal — it doesn't matter unless you're doing really accurate work.

Practice Questions

Q1 Draw a diagram showing the structure of an atom, labelling each part.

Q2 Define the term 'isotope' and give an example.

Q3 Draw a table showing the relative charge and relative mass of the three subatomic particles found in atoms.

Q4 Using an example, explain the terms 'atomic number' and 'mass number'.

Q5 Where is the mass concentrated in an atom, and what makes up most of the volume of an atom?

Exam Questions

Q1 Hydrogen, deuterium and tritium are all isotopes of each other.
  a) Identify one similarity and one difference between these isotopes. [2 marks]
  b) Deuterium can be written as ^{2}H. Determine the number of protons, neutrons and electrons in a neutral deuterium atom. [3 marks]
  c) Write the nuclear symbol for tritium, given that it has two neutrons. [1 mark]

Q2 This question relates to the atoms or ions A to D: A. $^{32}_{16}S^{2-}$, B. $^{40}_{18}Ar$, C. $^{30}_{16}S$, D. $^{42}_{20}Ca$.
  a) Identify the similarity for each of the following pairs, justifying your answer in each case.
    (i) A and B. [2 marks]
    (ii) A and C. [2 marks]
    (iii) B and D. [2 marks]
  b) Which two of the atoms or ions are isotopes of each other? Explain your reasoning. [2 marks]

Got it learned yet? — Isotope so...

This is a nice straightforward page just to ease you in to things. Remember that positive ions have fewer electrons than protons, and negative ions have more electrons than protons. Get that straight in your mind or you'll end up in a right mess. There's nowt too hard about isotopes neither. They're just the same element with different numbers of neutrons.

Atomic Models

Things ain't how they used to be, you know. Take atomic structure, for starters.

The **Accepted Model** *of the* **Atom** *Has* **Changed** *Throughout History*

The model of the atom you're expected to know (the one on page 4) is one of the currently **accepted** ones. In the past, completely different models were accepted, because they fitted the evidence available at the time:

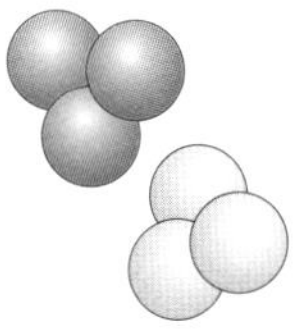

1) Some **ancient Greeks** thought that all matter was made from **indivisible particles**.
2) At the start of the 19th century John Dalton described atoms as **solid spheres**, and said that different spheres made up the different elements.
3) But as scientists did more experiments, our currently accepted models began to emerge, with modifications or refinements being made to take account of new evidence.

The Greek word atomos means 'uncuttable'.

Experimental Evidence *Showed that Atoms* **Weren't Solid Spheres**

In 1897 J J Thompson did a whole series of experiments and concluded that atoms **weren't** solid and indivisible.

1) His measurements of **charge** and **mass** showed that an atom must contain even smaller, negatively charged particles. He called these particles 'corpuscles' — we call them **electrons**.
2) The 'solid sphere' idea of atomic structure had to be changed. The new model was known as the '**plum pudding model**' — a positively charged sphere with negative electrons embedded in it.

positively charged 'pudding'
delicious pudding

Rutherford *Showed that the* **Plum Pudding** *Model Was* **Wrong**

1) In 1909 Ernest Rutherford and his students Hans Geiger and Ernest Marsden conducted the famous **gold foil experiment**. They fired **alpha particles** (which are positively charged) at an extremely thin sheet of gold.
2) From the plum pudding model, they were expecting **most** of the alpha particles to be deflected **very slightly** by the positive 'pudding' that made up most of an atom.
3) In fact, most of the alpha particles passed **straight through** the gold atoms, and a very small number were deflected **backwards** (through more than 90°). This showed that the plum pudding model **couldn't be right**.
4) So Rutherford came up with a model that **could** explain this new evidence — the **nuclear model** of the atom:

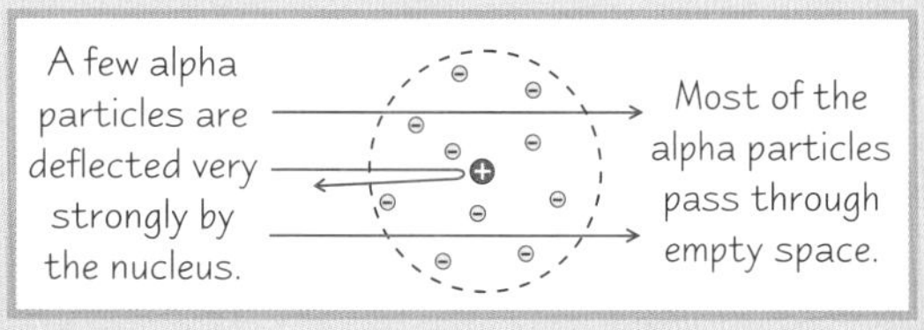
A few alpha particles are deflected very strongly by the nucleus.
Most of the alpha particles pass through empty space.

1) There is a **tiny, positively charged nucleus** at the centre of the atom, where most of the atom's mass is concentrated.
2) The nucleus is surrounded by a '**cloud**' of **negative electrons**.
3) Most of the atom is **empty space**.

Rutherford's **Nuclear Model** *Was* **Modified** *Several Times*

Rutherford's model seemed pretty convincing, but (there's always a but)... the scientists of the day didn't just say, "Well done Ernest old chap, you've got it", then all move to Patagonia to farm goats. No, they stuck at their experiments, wanting to be sure of the truth. (And it's just conceivable they wanted some fame and fortune too.)

1) Henry Moseley discovered that the charge of the nucleus **increased** from one element to another in units of one.
2) This led Rutherford to investigate the nucleus further. He finally discovered that it contained **positively charged** particles that he called **protons**. The charges of the nuclei of different atoms could then be explained — the atoms of **different elements** have a **different number of protons** in their nucleus.
3) There was still one problem with the model — the nuclei of atoms were **heavier** than they would be if they just contained protons. Rutherford predicted that there were other particles in the nucleus, that had **mass but no charge** — and the **neutron** was eventually discovered by James Chadwick.

This is nearly always the way scientific knowledge develops — **new evidence** prompts people to come up with **new, improved ideas**. Then other people go through each new, improved idea with a fine-tooth comb as well — modern '**peer review**' (see page 2) is part of this process.

Atomic Models

The **Bohr Model** Was a Further Improvement

1) Scientists realised that electrons in a '**cloud**' around the nucleus of an atom would **spiral down** into the nucleus, causing the atom to **collapse**. Niels Bohr proposed a new model of the atom with four basic principles:

   1) Electrons can only exist in **fixed orbits**, or **shells**, and not anywhere in between.
   2) Each shell has a **fixed energy**.
   3) When an electron moves between shells **electromagnetic radiation** is **emitted** or **absorbed**.
   4) Because the energy of shells is fixed, the radiation will have a **fixed frequency**.

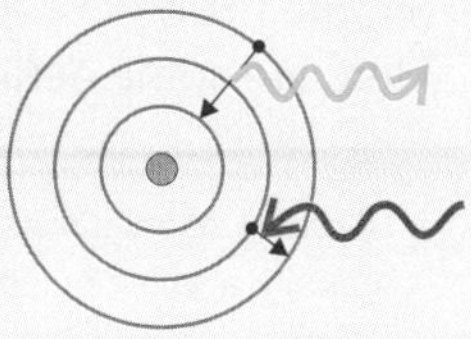

2) The frequencies of radiation emitted and absorbed by atoms were already known from experiments. The Bohr model fitted these observations — it looked good.

3) The Bohr model also explained why some elements (the noble gases) are **inert**. He said that the shells of an atom can only hold **fixed numbers of electrons**, and that an element's reactivity is due to its electrons. When an atom has **full shells** of electrons it is **stable** and does not react.

There's **More Than One** Model of Atomic Structure in Use Today

1) We now know that the Bohr model is **not perfect** — but it's still widely used to describe atoms because it's simple and explains many **observations** from experiments, like bonding and ionisation energy trends.
2) The most accurate model we have today involves complicated quantum mechanics. Basically, you can never **know** where an electron is or which direction it's going in at any moment, but you can say **how likely** it is to be at any particular point in the atom. Oh, and electrons can act as **waves** as well as particles (but you don't need to worry about the details).
3) This model might be **more accurate**, but it's a lot harder to get your head round and visualise. It **does** explain some observations that can't be accounted for by the Bohr model though. So scientists use whichever model is most relevant to whatever they're investigating.

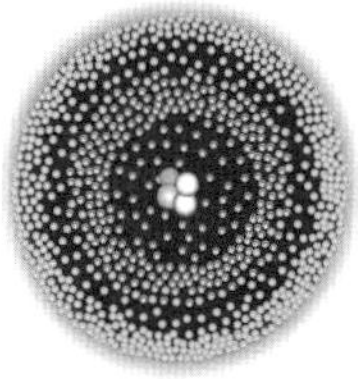

The quantum model of an atom with two shells of electrons. The denser the dots, the more likely an electron is to be there.

Practice Questions

Q1 What particle did J J Thompson discover?

Q2 Describe the model of the atom that was adopted because of Thompson's work.

Q3 Who developed the 'nuclear' model of the atom? What evidence did they have for it?

Q4 What are the names of the two particles in the nucleus of an atom?

Exam Question

Q1 Scientific theories are constantly being revised in the light of new evidence. New theories are accepted because they have been successfully tested by experiments or because they help to explain certain observations.

a) Niels Bohr thought that the model of the atom proposed by Ernest Rutherford did not describe the electrons in an atom correctly. Why did he think this and how was his model of the atom different from Rutherford's? [2 marks]

b) What happens when electrons in an atom move from one shell to another? [1 mark]

c) How did the Bohr model explain the lack of reactivity of the noble gases? [2 marks]

These models are tiny — even smaller than size zero, I reckon...

The process of developing a model to fit the evidence available, looking for more evidence to show if it's correct or not, then revising the model if necessary is really important. It happens with all new scientific ideas. Remember, scientific 'facts' are only accepted as true because no one's proved yet that they aren't. It might all be bunkum.

Relative Mass

Relative mass...What? Eh?...Read on...

Relative Masses are Masses of Atoms Compared to Carbon-12

The actual mass of an atom is **very, very tiny**. Don't worry about exactly how tiny for now, but it's far **too small** to weigh. So, the mass of one atom is compared to the mass of a different atom. This is its **relative mass**. Here are some definitions to learn.

The **relative atomic mass**, A_r, is the **average mass** of an atom of an element on a scale where an atom of **carbon-12** is 12.

Relative atomic mass is an average, so it's not usually a whole number. Relative isotopic mass is always a whole number (at AS level anyway). E.g. a natural sample of chlorine contains a mixture of ^{35}Cl (75%) and ^{37}Cl (25%), so the relative isotopic masses are 35 and 37. But its relative atomic mass is 35.5.

Relative isotopic mass is the mass of an atom of an **isotope** of an element on a scale where an atom of **carbon-12** is 12.

The **relative molecular mass** (or **relative formula mass**), M_r, is the average mass of a **molecule** or **formula unit** on a scale where an atom of **carbon-12** is 12.

To find the relative molecular mass, just add up the relative atomic mass values of all the atoms in the molecule, e.g. $M_r(C_2H_6O) = (2 \times 12) + (6 \times 1) + 16 = 46$.

Relative formula mass is used for compounds that are ionic (or giant covalent, such as SiO_2). To find the relative formula mass, just add up the relative atomic masses (A_r) of all the ions in the formula unit. (A_r of ion = A_r of atom. The electrons make no difference to the mass.) E.g. $M_r(CaF_2) = 40 + (2 \times 19) = 78$.

Relative Masses can be Measured Using a Mass Spectrometer

You can use a **mass spectrometer** to find out loads of stuff. It can tell you the **relative atomic mass**, **relative molecular mass**, **relative isotopic abundance**, **molecular structure** and your **horoscope** for the next fortnight.

There are **4** things that happen when a sample is squirted into a so-called **time-of-flight** mass spectrometer.

① **Vaporisation** — the sample is turned into **gas (vaporised)** using an electrical heater.

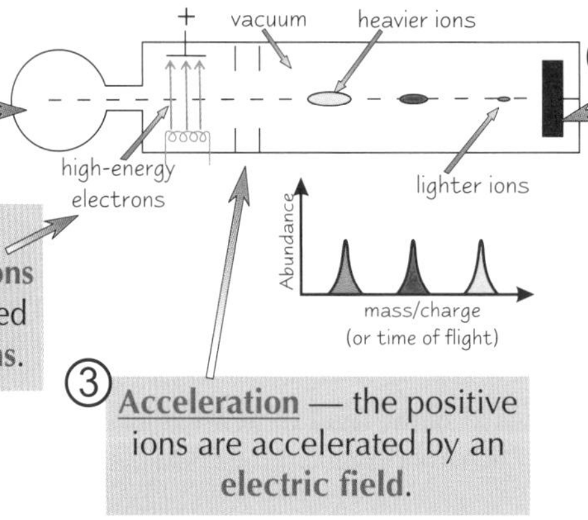

② **Ionisation** — the gas particles are bombarded with **high-energy electrons** to ionise them. Electrons are knocked off the particles, leaving **positive ions**.

③ **Acceleration** — the positive ions are accelerated by an **electric field**.

④ **Detection** — the time taken for the positive ions to reach the detector is measured. This depends on an ion's mass and charge — light, highly charged ions will reach the detector first, while heavier ions with a smaller charge will take longer.

For each sample analysed, a **mass spectrum** is produced.

A Mass Spectrum

The **y-axis** gives the **abundance of ions**, often as a percentage. For an element, the **height** of each peak gives the **relative isotopic abundance**, e.g. 75.5% are the ^{35}Cl isotope.

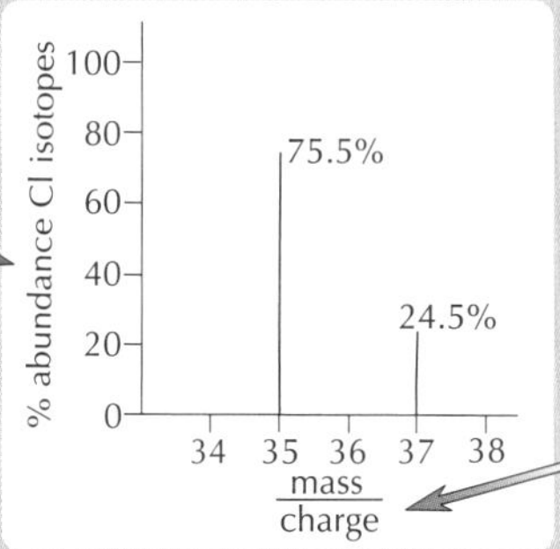

If the sample is an **element**, each line will represent a **different isotope** of the element.

The **x-axis** units are given as a '**mass/charge**' ratio. Since the charge on the ions is mostly **1+**, you can often assume the x-axis is simply the **relative mass**.

Relative Mass

A_r and Relative Isotopic Abundance can be Worked Out from a Mass Spectrum

You need to know how to calculate the **relative atomic mass** (A_r) of an element from the **mass spectrum**.

Here's how to calculate A_r for magnesium, using the mass spectrum below —

Step 1: For each peak, read the **% relative isotopic abundance** from the y-axis and the **relative isotopic mass** from the x-axis. **Multiply** them together to get the total mass for each isotope. $79 \times 24 = 1896$; $10 \times 25 = 250$; $11 \times 26 = 286$

Step 2: **Add** up these totals. $1896 + 250 + 286 = 2432$

Step 3: **Divide by 100** (since percentages were used). $A_r(\text{Mg}) = \dfrac{2432}{100} = 24.32 \approx \underline{\mathbf{24.3}}$

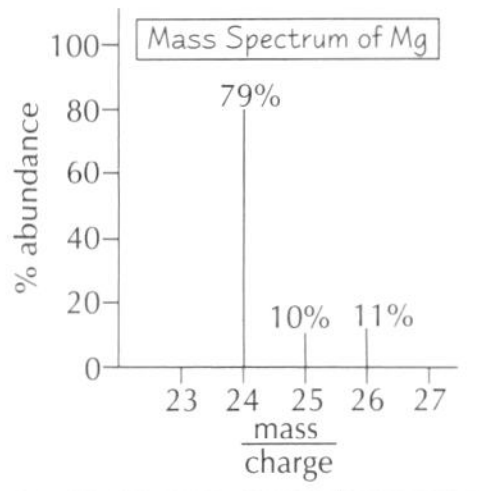

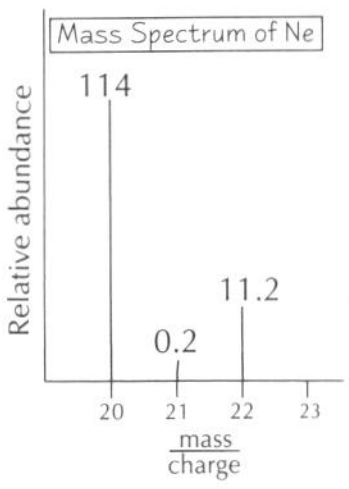

If the relative abundance is **not** given as a percentage, the total abundance may not add up to 100. In this case, don't panic. Just do steps 1 and 2 as above, but then divide by the **total relative abundance** instead of 100 — like this:

$$A_r(\text{Ne}) = \frac{(114 \times 20) + (0.2 \times 21) + (11.2 \times 22)}{114 + 0.2 + 11.2} \approx 20.18$$

You can also calculate the **% relative isotopic abundance** from this type of data. E.g., for **neon-20**:

$$\textbf{\% relative isotopic abundance} = \frac{\text{relative abundance}}{\text{total relative abundance}} \times 100\% = \frac{114}{114 + 0.2 + 11.2} \times 100\% \approx 90.91\%$$

Mass Spectrometry can be used to Find Out M_r

You can also get a mass spectrum for a **molecular sample**, such as ethanol (CH_3CH_2OH).

1) A **molecular ion**, $M^+_{(g)}$, is formed when the bombarding electrons remove 1 electron from the molecule. This gives the peak in the spectrum with the **highest mass** (furthest to the right, ignoring isotopes). The mass of M^+ gives $\mathbf{M_r}$ for the molecule, e.g. $CH_3CH_2OH^+$ has $M_r = 46$.

2) But it's not that simple — bombarding with electrons makes some molecules break up into fragments. These all show up on the mass spectrum, making a **fragmentation pattern**.

   For ethanol, the fragments you get include: CH_3^+ ($M_r = 15$), $CH_3CH_2^+$ ($M_r = 29$) and CH_2OH^+ ($M_r = 31$).

   Fragmentation patterns are actually pretty cool because you can use them to identify **molecules** and even their **structure**.

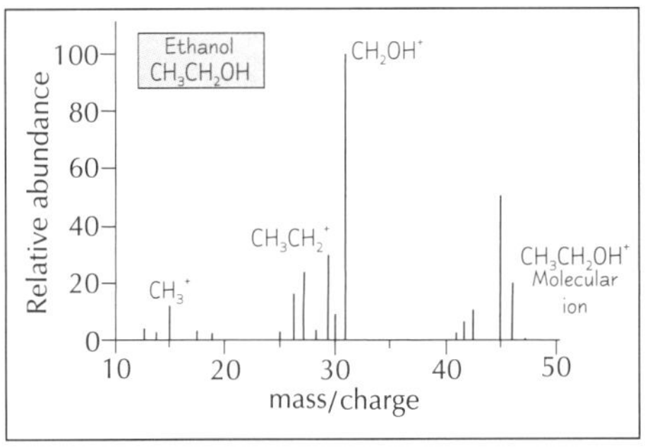

Practice Questions

Q1 Explain what relative atomic mass (A_r) and relative isotopic mass mean.

Q2 Explain the difference between relative molecular mass and relative formula mass.

Q3 Describe how a time-of-flight mass spectrometer works.

Exam Questions

Q1 Copper exists in two main isotopic forms, ^{63}Cu and ^{65}Cu.

a) Calculate the relative atomic mass of copper using the information from the mass spectrum. [2 marks]

b) Explain why the relative atomic mass of copper is not a whole number. [2 marks]

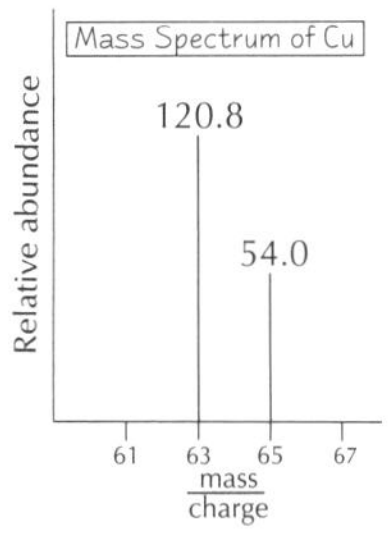

Q2 The percentage make-up of naturally occurring potassium is 93.11% ^{39}K, 0.12% ^{40}K and 6.77% ^{41}K.

a) What method is used to determine the mass and abundance of each isotope? [1 mark]

b) Use the information to determine the relative atomic mass of potassium. [2 marks]

You can't pick your relatives — you just have to learn them...

Working out M_r is dead easy — and using a calculator makes it even easier. It'll really help if you know the mass numbers for the first 20 elements or so, or you'll spend half your time looking back at the Periodic Table. I hope you've done the Practice and Exam Questions, cos they pretty much cover the rest of the stuff, and if you can get them right, you've nailed it.

Nuclear Radiation

Most of chemistry is basically about electrons. But these two pages are about the nucleus — get it while you can.

Nuclear Radiation — Alpha, Beta and Gamma

If an atom is **unstable**, it will **break down** to **become** stable. The **instability** could be caused by having **too many neutrons**, **not enough neutrons**, or just **too much energy** in the nucleus. The breaking down is called **radioactive decay**.

Alpha, **beta** or **gamma** radiation can be emitted. Learn the properties of these types of radiation.

	Alpha (α) Particles	Beta (β) Particles	Gamma (γ) Rays
What they are	Helium nuclei $^{4}_{2}He$	Fast-moving electrons $^{0}_{-1}e$	Very short wave electromagnetic waves
Penetrating power	Stopped by paper	Stopped by thin aluminium sheets	Stopped by very thick lead
Ionising ability	Strong	Moderate	Weak
Deflection in electric field	Slight	Large	Not deflected

Ionising particles **knock outer electrons** off atoms when they hit them — creating **ions**.

1) **Alpha** particles are **strongly positive** — so they can **remove electrons** from atoms. When an alpha particle hits an atom, it **transfers** some of its **energy** to the **atom**. The alpha particle **quickly ionises** lots of atoms and **loses** all its **energy**. That's why it has **low penetrating power**.
2) **Beta** particles have **lower charges** than alpha particles, but **higher speeds**. Beta particles can still **knock electrons** off atoms, but they hit atoms less frequently than alpha particles because they're smaller, so they have **better penetrating power**.

Nuclear Equations — Balance the Mass and Atomic Numbers

To find out what type of **radiation** or **element** is produced, balance the **top** and **bottom** numbers in the equation.

Example 1: What type of radiation is being lost?

$$^{14}_{6}C \rightarrow {}^{14}_{7}N + {}^{\square}_{\square}\square$$

14 – 14 = 0
6 – 7 = – 1
→ so radiation must be $^{0}_{-1}e$

Example 2: Which element is produced?

$$^{208}_{81}Tl \rightarrow {}^{\square}_{\square}\square + {}^{0}_{-1}e$$

208 – 0 = 208
81 – (–1) = 82 ← Atomic Number = Pb → $^{208}_{82}Pb$

Half-Life — The Time Taken for Half the Atoms in a Sample to Decay

1) Radioactive decay is **random** — this means it's impossible to know when a **single atom** will decay. But if you look at **large numbers** of atoms, then a pattern does become clear.
2) For radioactive atoms, the pattern is best described using the idea of **half-life**. The half-life is the average time taken for **half of the atoms** in a sample to decay. It has a **constant value** for any particular isotope.
3) For example, an isotope of radon has a half-life of about 4 days. This means that if you had 20 g of it now, in 4 days' time there will be only 10 g left. After 8 days there would be only 5 g, and after 12 days, 2.5 g, and so on.

Example: You have a sample containing 3 g of carbon-14 (half-life 5700 years).
How much carbon-14 would have been in the sample 22 800 years ago?
22 800 years is 4 half-lives, so there would have been 3 g × 2 × 2 × 2 × 2 = 48 g of carbon-14.

Radioactive Isotopes can be Used as Tracers

1) Because it's easy to **detect** radiation given out by **radioactive isotopes**, they're used as **tracers** — chemicals that can be tracked. This can be used to check how well parts of the body (or industrial equipment) are working.
2) Medical tracers can be given to a person, and as they move around the body their position can be **detected**. For example, radioactive iodine-131 is used to check how well a person's thyroid gland is functioning.
3) Only isotopes with suitable **half-lives** can be used as medical tracers — **not too long** and **not too short**:
   - a very long half-life is **dangerous** — the patient could be exposed to radiation for a long time,
   - a very short half-life is **inconvenient** — the tracers have to be prepared, administered, and then be allowed to make their way around the body, so a tracer with a half-life of a few seconds isn't going to be much good.

   And alpha emitters are no good — they'd cause damage by ionising atoms inside the body, and anyway, they wouldn't be detectable outside the body.

Iodine-131 has a half-life of 8 days.

One radioactive tracer too many.

Nuclear Radiation

Radioactive Isotopes Can be Used to Find Out **How Old Stuff Is**

1) Radioactive isotopes can be used to **determine** the **age** of **rocks** and **archaeological finds**.
2) **Radiocarbon dating** involves measuring how much of a particular isotope of **carbon** there is in **plant** or **animal** remains (including things made of wood, leather or bone — like arrowheads, axe handles, and so on).
3) The idea behind the technique is this...
   - All **living** things contain the **same percentage** of **carbon-14**:
     - When plants photosynthesise, they absorb carbon (in CO_2) from the atmosphere — including a small percentage of carbon-14.
     - As the carbon-14 atoms decay, they're replaced by more carbon-14 from the atmosphere.
     - Animals eat plants (or other animals that have eaten plants).
     - And the upshot is that all living things are constantly replenishing their levels of carbon-14 to match the atmosphere.
   - But as soon as they **die**, this percentage starts to **decrease** — because the carbon-14 atoms **decay**.
   - So the **less** carbon-14 in a sample of organic material, the **older** it must be.
4) You can then find the approximate **age** of the animal or plant (and therefore the arrowhead, axe handle...) with a calculation like the one on the previous page.

Nuclear Fusion — *Forming* ***Elements*** *in Stars*

Complete change of tack now... enough of breaking nuclei apart — this next bit is about putting nuclei **together**.

1) **Nuclear fusion** is when two small nuclei combine under high temperature to make one larger nucleus. It happens naturally all the time inside **stars**.
2) In stars, **hydrogen nuclei** combine to make **helium nuclei**, releasing **huge** amounts of **energy**. This is happening inside our Sun's core.

$$ {}^{2}_{1}H + {}^{1}_{1}H \rightarrow {}^{3}_{2}He + \gamma $$

3) When the hydrogen in a star's core runs out, the **temperature** and **pressure** of the core starts to rise. In a big enough star it'll get **hot** enough to fuse **heavier elements**, starting with helium.
4) In fact, large nuclei can **only** be made by stars (either inside them, or as a 'dead' star explodes as a supernova).

Practice Questions

Q1 Name the three types of nuclear radiation, and describe their penetrating powers and ionising abilities.

Q2 What is meant by half-life?

Q3 Describe how radioactive substances can be used as tracers. Describe the properties needed in a medical tracer.

Q4 Explain how radiocarbon dating works.

Q5 What is nuclear fusion? Where does it happen in nature?

Exam Questions

Q1 A radioactive isotope of the element polonium underwent two stages of radioactive decay. Complete the nuclear equations to identify the type of radiation produced in the first stage of decay and the final element produced.

$$ {}^{216}_{84}Po \rightarrow {}^{212}_{82}Pb + {}^{\square}_{\square}\square \qquad {}^{212}_{82}Pb \rightarrow {}^{\square}_{\square}\square + {}^{0}_{-1}e $$

[2 marks]

Q2 A radioactive isotope of sodium, ^{24}Na, decays by emitting a beta particle. It has a half-life of 15 hours.

a) Sodium's atomic number is 11. Give the atomic number, name and mass number of the isotope that is produced when ^{24}Na decays. [3 marks]

b) A sample of this isotope has a rate of decay of 800 counts per minute. How long will it take for the radiation levels to drop below 50 counts per minute? [2 marks]

Q3 Explain why isotopes which produce gamma radiation are used in medicine and not those that produce alpha particles. [2 marks]

How amazing is that — we're all made out of stardust...

Come on, admit it — the fact that you were made in a star (that's kinda true — the atoms inside you were put together in a star) is pretty mind-blowing. As for the stuff on radiation — make sure you have the properties of alpha, beta and gamma radiation nailed down firmly in your memory. It'll be fun, I promise... and I also promise you'll win the lottery.

The Mole and Equations

It'd be handy to be able to count out atoms — but they're way too tiny. You can't even see them, never mind get hold of them with tweezers. But not to worry — that's why moles were invented...

A **Mole** is Just a (Very Large) **Number of Particles**

1) **Amount of substance** is measured using a unit called the **mole** (**mol** for short) and given the symbol ***n***.
2) One mole is roughly **6.02×10^{23} particles** (**Avogadro's constant, L**).
3) It **doesn't matter** what the particles are.
   They can be atoms, molecules, penguins — **anything**.
4) Here's a nice simple formula for finding the number of moles from the number of atoms or molecules:

$$\text{Number of moles} = \frac{\text{Number of particles you have}}{\text{Number of particles in a mole}}$$

Example:
I have 1.5×10^{24} carbon atoms.
How many moles of carbon is this?

$$\text{Number of moles} = \frac{1.5 \times 10^{24}}{6.02 \times 10^{23}} = \textbf{2.5 moles}$$

Molar Mass is the Mass of **One Mole**

Molar mass, **M**, is the mass of **one mole** of something.

But the main thing to remember is:

Molar mass is just the same as the relative molecular mass
(or relative formula mass)

That's why the mole is such a ridiculous number of particles (6.02×10^{23}) — it's the number of particles for which the weight in g is the same as the relative molecular mass.

The only difference is you stick a 'g mol^{-1}' for 'grams per mole' on the end...

Example: Find the molar mass of $CaCO_3$.

Relative formula mass, M_r, of $CaCO_3$ = 40 + 12 + (3 × 16) = 100
So the molar mass, M, is **100 g mol^{-1}** — i.e. 1 mole of $CaCO_3$ weighs 100 g.

Here's another formula. This one's really important — you need it **all the time**:

$$\text{Number of moles} = \frac{\text{mass of substance}}{\text{molar mass}}$$

Example: How many moles of aluminium oxide are present in 5.1 g of Al_2O_3?

Molar mass of Al_2O_3 = (2 × 27) + (3 × 16)
= 102 g mol^{-1}

Number of moles of Al_2O_3 = $\frac{5.1}{102}$ = **0.05 moles**

Balanced Equations have **Equal Numbers** of each Atom on **Both Sides**

1) Balanced equations have the **same number** of each atom on **both** sides. They're... well... you know... balanced.
2) You can only add more atoms by adding **whole compounds**. You do this by putting a number **in front** of a compound or changing one that's already there. You **can't** mess with formulas — ever.

I'll show them who's unbalanced...

Example: Balance the equation $C_2H_6 + O_2 \rightarrow CO_2 + H_2O$.

$C_2H_6 + O_2 \rightarrow CO_2 + H_2O$

Left	Right
C = 2	C = 1
H = 6	H = 2
O = 2	O = 3

First work out **how many** of each atom you have on **each side**.

The right side needs 2 C's, so try **$2CO_2$**.
It also needs 6 H's, so try **$3H_2O$**.

$C_2H_6 + O_2 \rightarrow 2CO_2 + 3H_2O$

Left	Right
C = 2	C = 2
H = 6	H = 6
O = 2	O = 7

Nope, still not balanced.

The left side needs 7 O's, so try **$3\frac{1}{2}O_2$**.
This **balances** the equation. Phew.

$C_2H_6 + 3\frac{1}{2}O_2 \rightarrow 2CO_2 + 3H_2O$

Left	Right
C = 2	C = 2
H = 6	H = 6
O = 7	O = 7

Don't forget — you can use ½ to balance equations.

Always check your final equation balances.

The Mole and Equations

Balanced Equations can be Used to Work Out **Masses**

Example: Calculate the mass of iron oxide produced if 28 g of iron is burnt in air.

$$2Fe + \tfrac{3}{2}O_2 \rightarrow Fe_2O_3$$

The molar mass, M, of Fe is 56 g mol^{-1}, so the number of moles in 28 g of Fe = $\frac{\text{mass}}{M} = \frac{28}{56}$ = 0.5 moles

From the equation: 2 moles of Fe produces 1 mole of Fe_2O_3, so 0.5 moles of Fe produces 0.25 moles of Fe_2O_3.

M of Fe_2O_3 = (2 × 56) + (3 × 16) = 160 g mol^{-1}

Mass of Fe_2O_3 = no. of moles × M = 0.25 × 160 = **40 g**. And that's your answer.

Once you know the number of moles and the molar mass (M) of Fe_2O_3, it's easy to work out the mass.

State Symbols Give a Bit More Information about the Substances

State symbols are put after each compound in an equation. They tell you what **state of matter** things are in.

s = solid
l = liquid
g = gas
aq = aqueous (solution in water)

To show you what I mean, here's an example —

$$CaCO_{3\,(s)} + 2HCl_{(aq)} \rightarrow CaCl_{2\,(aq)} + H_2O_{(l)} + CO_{2\,(g)}$$

solid, aqueous, aqueous, liquid, gas

Practice Questions

Q1 What is the significance of Avogadro's constant?

Q2 Show that 5 moles of carbon dioxide has a mass of 220 g.

Q3 What is the state symbol for a solution in water of hydrochloric acid?

Exam Questions

Q1 Calculate the mass of ethene required to produce 258 g of chloroethane, C_2H_5Cl.

$C_2H_4 + HCl \rightarrow C_2H_5Cl$ [4 marks]

Q2 15 g of calcium carbonate is heated strongly so that it fully decomposes.

$CaCO_{3(s)} \rightarrow CaO_{(s)} + CO_{2(g)}$

Calculate the mass of calcium oxide produced. [3 marks]

Q3 Balance this equation: $KI + Pb(NO_3)_2 \rightarrow PbI_2 + 2KNO_3$ [1 mark]

Don't get in a state about equations...

You're probably completely fed up with all these equations, calculations, moles and whatnot... well hang in there — there's just one more double page of equations and the like to go. I've said it once, and I'll say it again — practise, practise, practise... it's the only road to salvation (by the way, where is salvation anyway?). Keep going... you're nearly there.

Empirical and Molecular Formulas

Here's another page piled high with numbers — it's all just glorified maths really.

Empirical and ***Molecular*** Formulas are ***Ratios***

You have to know what's what with empirical and molecular formulas, so here goes...

1) The **empirical formula** gives just the smallest whole number ratio of atoms in a compound.
2) The **molecular formula** gives the **actual** numbers of atoms in a molecule.
3) The molecular formula is made up of a whole **number** of empirical units.

Example: A molecule has an empirical formula of $C_4H_3O_2$, and a molecular mass of 166. Work out its molecular formula.

Compare the relative masses of the empirical and molecular formulas.

First find the **relative mass** of the atoms in the empirical formula:

$$(4 \times 12) + (3 \times 1) + (2 \times 16) = 48 + 3 + 32 = 83$$

But the **molecular mass** is 166,

so there are $\frac{166}{83} = 2$ empirical units in the molecule.

The molecular formula must be the **empirical formula × 2**,

so the molecular formula = $C_8H_6O_4$. So there you go.

Empirical Formulas are Calculated from ***Experiments***

You need to be able to work out empirical formulas from **experimental results** too.

Example: When a hydrocarbon is burnt in excess oxygen, 4.4 g of carbon dioxide and 1.8 g of water are made. What is the empirical formula of the hydrocarbon?

First work out how many moles of the products you have.

No. of moles of $CO_2 = \frac{\text{mass}}{M} = \frac{4.4}{12+(16\times 2)} = \frac{4.4}{44} = 0.1$ moles

1 mole of CO_2 contains 1 mole of carbon atoms, so you must have started with **0.1 moles of carbon atoms**.

No. of moles of $H_2O = \frac{1.8}{(2\times 1)+16} = \frac{1.8}{18} = 0.1$ moles

1 mole of H_2O contains 2 moles of hydrogen atoms (H), so you must have started with **0.2 moles of hydrogen atoms**.

Ratio C : H = 0.1 : 0.2 . Now you divide both numbers by the **smallest** — here it's 0.1.

So, the ratio C : H = 1 : 2. So the empirical formula must be CH_2.

This works because the only place the carbon in the carbon dioxide and the hydrogen in the water could have come from is the hydrocarbon.

As if that's not enough, you also need to know how to work out empirical formulas from the **percentages** of the different elements.

Example: A compound is found to have percentage composition 56.5% potassium, 8.7% carbon and 34.8% oxygen by mass. Calculate its empirical formula.

If you assume you've got 100 g of the compound, you can turn the % straight into mass, and then work out the number of moles as normal.

In **100 g** of compound there are:

Use $n = \frac{\text{mass}}{M}$

$\frac{56.5}{39} = 1.449$ moles of K $\frac{8.7}{12} = 0.725$ moles of C $\frac{34.8}{16} = 2.175$ moles of O

Divide each number of moles by the **smallest number** — in this case it's 0.725.

K: $\frac{1.449}{0.725} = 2.0$ C: $\frac{0.725}{0.725} = 1.0$ O: $\frac{2.175}{0.725} = 3.0$

The ratio of K : C : O = 2 : 1 : 3. So you know the empirical formula's got to be K_2CO_3.

Empirical and Molecular Formulas

Molecular Formulas are Calculated from Experimental Data Too

Once you know the empirical formula, you just need a bit more info and you can work out the **molecular formula** too.

Example:

When 4.6 g of an alcohol, with molar mass 46 g, is burnt in excess oxygen, it produces 8.8 g of carbon dioxide and 5.4 g of water.

Calculate the empirical formula for the alcohol and then its molecular formula.

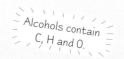

Alcohols contain C, H and O.

The carbon in the CO_2 and the hydrogen in the H_2O must have come from the alcohol — work out the number of moles of each of these.

No. of moles of $CO_2 = \frac{\text{mass}}{M} = \frac{8.8}{44} = 0.2$ moles

1 mole of CO_2 contains 1 mole of C. So, 0.2 moles of CO_2 contains **0.2 moles of C.**

No. of moles $H_2O = \frac{\text{mass}}{M} = \frac{5.4}{18} = 0.3$ moles

1 mole of H_2O contains 2 moles of H. So, 0.3 moles of H_2O contains **0.6 moles of H.**

Now work out the mass of carbon and hydrogen in the alcohol. The rest of the mass of the alcohol must be oxygen — so work out that too. Once you know the mass of O, you can work out how many moles there are of it.

Mass of C = no. of moles × M = 0.2 × 12 = 2.4 g

Mass of H = no. of moles × M = 0.6 × 1 = 0.6 g

Mass of O = 4.6 – (2.4 + 0.6) = 1.6 g

Number of moles O $= \frac{\text{mass}}{M} = \frac{1.6}{16} = 0.1$ moles

When you know the number of moles of each element, you've got the molar ratio. Divide each number by the smallest.

Molar ratio = C : H : O = 0.2 : 0.6 : 0.1 = 2 : 6 : 1

Empirical formula = C_2H_6O

Mass of empirical formula = (12 × 2) + (1 × 6) + 16 = 46 g

Compare the empirical and molecular masses.

In this example, the mass of the empirical formula equals the molecular mass, so the empirical and molecular formulas are the same.

Molecular formula = C_2H_6O

Practice Questions

Q1 Define 'empirical formula'.

Q2 What is the difference between a molecular formula and an empirical formula?

Exam Questions

Q1 Hydrocarbon X has a molecular mass of 78 g. It is found to have 92.3% carbon and 7.7% hydrogen by mass. Calculate the empirical and molecular formulae of X. [3 marks]

Q2 When 1.2 g of magnesium ribbon is heated in air, it burns to form a white powder, which has a mass of 2 g. What is the empirical formula of the powder? [2 marks]

Q3 When 19.8 g of an organic acid, A, is burnt in excess oxygen, 33 g of carbon dioxide and 10.8 g of water are produced. Calculate the empirical formula for A and hence its molecular formula, if $M_r(A) = 132$. [4 marks]

Hint: organic acids contain C, H and O.

The Empirical Strikes Back...

With this stuff, it's not enough to learn a few facts parrot-fashion, to regurgitate in the exam — you've gotta know how to use them. The only way to do that is to practise. Go through all the examples on these two pages again, this time working the answers out for yourself. Then test yourself on the practice exam questions. It'll help you sleep at night — honest.

Electron Shells and Atomic Spectra

Those little electrons prancing about like mini bunnies decide what'll react with what — it's what chemistry's all about.

Electrons in Atoms are in Fixed **Energy Levels**

1) Electrons move around the nucleus in **shells** (sometimes called **energy levels**).
Shells **further** from the nucleus have a greater energy level than shells closer to the nucleus.
2) Shells can only hold so many electrons:

Electron Shell	1st	2nd	3rd	4th
Maximum no. of electrons	2	8	18	32

There's more detail about this on page 56.

3) You need to be able to describe the electron structure of the first 36 atoms in the Periodic Table.
The **first 18** elements' electrons behave as you'd expect:
   - the first 2 electrons go into the 1st shell
   - the next 8 electrons go into the 2nd shell
   - the next 8 electrons go into the 3rd shell

   So, argon = 2, 8, 8; and sodium = 2, 8, 1

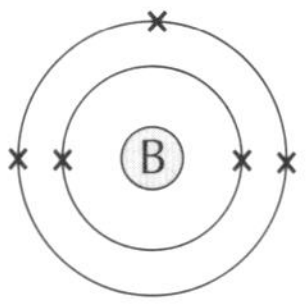

boron: 2, 3

4) Now it gets tricky. The 3rd and 4th shells overlap, so even though the 3rd shell isn't yet full, the next **two electrons** go in the **4th shell**.
So, potassium = 2, 8, 8, 1, and calcium = 2, 8, 8, 2.
That's the first 20 electrons taken care of.
5) Then it's back to **finish off the 3rd shell**, followed by the rest of the **4th** shell.
So, gallium = 2, 8, 18, 3, and krypton = 2, 8, 18, 8.

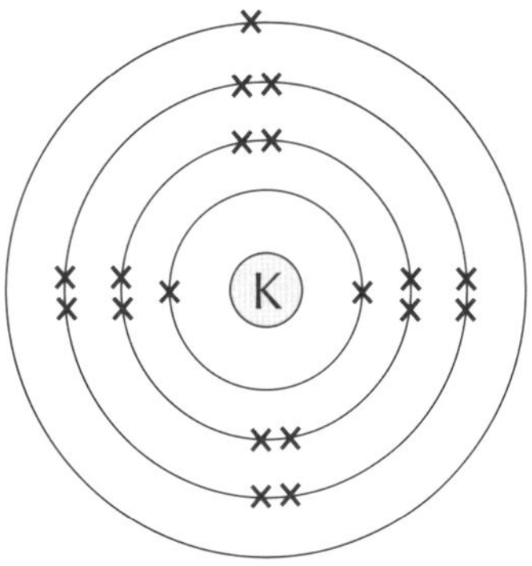

potassium: 2, 8, 8, 1

Electrons **Absorb or Release** Energy in **Fixed Amounts**

1) Atoms in their **ground state** have all their electrons at their **lowest** possible energy levels.
2) If an atom's electrons **take in energy** from their surroundings they can move to **higher energy levels**, further from the nucleus. At higher energy levels, electrons are said to be **excited**. (More excited than you right now, I'll bet.)
3) Electrons can also **release energy** by dropping down to a **lower energy level**.
4) The energy levels all have **certain fixed values** — they're **discrete**. Electrons can jump from one energy level to another by **absorbing or releasing** a fixed amount of energy.

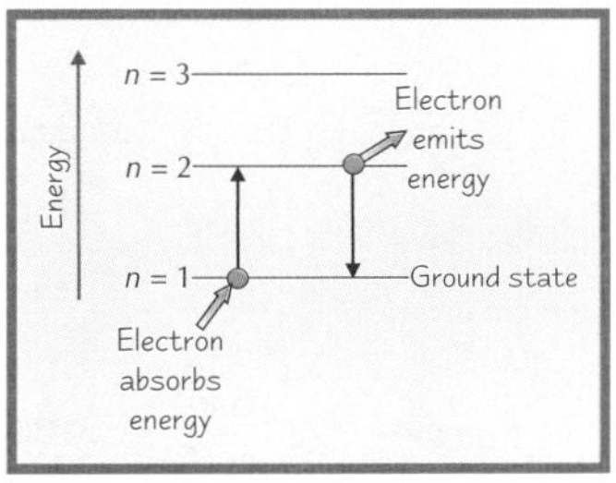

Absorption Spectra — Made Up of **Dark Lines**

1) Energy is related to **frequency** (see below). So when **electromagnetic radiation** is passed through a gaseous element, the electrons only absorb **certain frequencies**, corresponding to **differences between the energy levels**.
2) That means the radiation passing through has certain frequencies missing. A spectrum of this radiation is called an **atomic absorption spectrum**.
3) The missing frequencies show up as **dark bands** on a coloured background.

Absorption Spectrum

Emission Spectrum

Emission Spectra — Made Up of **Bright Lines**

1) When electrons **drop** to lower energy levels, they **give out** certain amounts of energy.
This produces lines in the spectrum too — but this time it's called an **emission spectrum**. For any particular element, the frequencies in an emission spectrum are the **same** as those missing in the absorption spectrum.
2) Each element has a **different** electron arrangement, so the frequencies of radiation absorbed and emitted are different. This means the **spectrum** for each element is unique.

Energy is Related to **Frequency**

When an electron moves to a higher or lower shell it **absorbs** or **emits** electromagnetic radiation with a certain frequency. The **amount of energy** absorbed or emitted is related to the **frequency** of the radiation by this equation:

$$\Delta E = h\nu$$

- ΔE: The difference in energy between two shells. The units are joules (J).
- ν: The Greek letter 'nu', the symbol for frequency. The units are hertz (Hz or s^{-1}).
- h: Just a number — Planck's constant. The units are joule seconds (Js).

Electron Shells and Atomic Spectra

Spectra are Made Up of **Sets of Lines**

1) You get lots of **sets of lines** in spectra — each set represents electrons moving to or from **a different energy level**. So, in an emission spectrum, you get one **set of lines** produced when electrons fall to the ***n* = 1** level, and another set produced when they fall to the ***n* = 2** level, and so on.
2) Spectra often seem to make as much sense as bar codes. But the emission spectrum of **hydrogen** is fairly simple because hydrogen only has **one** electron that can move. It has **three important sets of lines**:

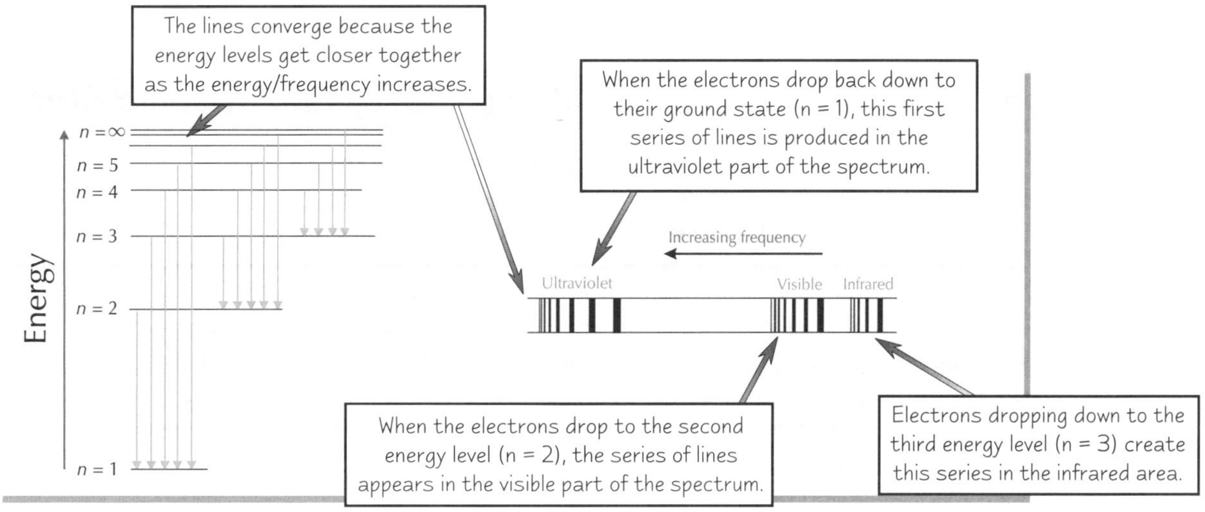

The lines converge because the energy levels get closer together as the energy/frequency increases.
When the electrons drop back down to their ground state (n = 1), this first series of lines is produced in the ultraviolet part of the spectrum.
n = ∞
n = 5
n = 4
n = 3
n = 2
n = 1
Energy
Increasing frequency
Ultraviolet
Visible
Infrared
When the electrons drop to the second energy level (n = 2), the series of lines appears in the visible part of the spectrum.
Electrons dropping down to the third energy level (n = 3) create this series in the infrared area.

Practice Questions

Q1 Write down the electronic structures of iron (atomic number 26) and bromine (atomic number 35).

Q2 Describe the differences between the absorption spectrum and the emission spectrum of an element.

Q3 Describe what the atomic emission spectrum of hydrogen shows.

Exam Questions

Q1 When an electron falls from the 3rd to the 2nd energy level of a hydrogen atom it emits visible light with a frequency of 4.57×10^{14} Hz. Plank's constant = 6.626×10^{-34} Js.

What is the difference in energy between the 3rd and 2nd energy levels of a hydrogen atom? [2 marks]

Q2 The diagram below shows part of an atomic absorption spectrum of a single element.
The dark lines in the spectrum are labelled A to E.

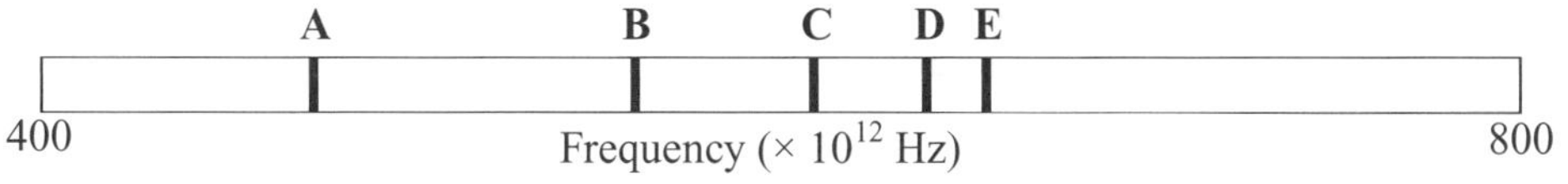

a) What happens in the atom when radiation is absorbed? [2 marks]
b) Which line in the spectrum represents the largest absorption of energy? [1 mark]
c) The same element is used to produce an atomic emission spectrum.
   (i) What would be different about this spectrum? [1 mark]
   (ii) What would be the same about the lines in the two spectra? [1 mark]
d) Explain why the lines get closer together from A to E. [1 mark]

Q3 The emission spectrum of the element sodium shows a set of lines in the visible part of the spectrum.
There is a strong line at a frequency 5.1×10^{14} Hz, which corresponds to the colour yellow.
What is the energy of the electron transition responsible for this line? (Planck's constant = 6.626×10^{-34} Js) [2 marks]

Spectra — weren't they the baddies in those James Bond films...

That business about the electron structure is a bit weird... I mean the bit about how electrons only partly fill up the third shell, then go into the fourth shell, then complete the third shell, and only then go back to finish off the fourth shell. I've always thought it's better to finish what you start, then you know where you are. Electrons... no common sense.

Ionic Bonding

Every atom's aim in life is to have a full outer shell of electrons. Once they've managed this, that's it — they're happy.

Compounds *are* ***Atoms*** *of Different Elements* ***Bonded*** *Together*

1) When different elements join or bond together, you get a **compound**.
2) There are two main types of bonding in compounds — **ionic** and **covalent**. You need to make sure you've got them **both** totally sussed.

E.g. When the elements hydrogen (H_2) and oxygen (O_2) combine, the compound water (H_2O) is formed.

Ionic Bonding *is when* ***Ions*** *are Stuck Together by* ***Electrostatic Attraction***

1) Ions are formed when electrons are **transferred** from one atom to another.
2) The simplest ions are single atoms which have either lost or gained 1, 2 or 3 electrons so that they've got a **full outer shell**. Here are some examples of ions:

A sodium atom (Na) **loses** 1 electron to form a sodium ion (Na^+)	$Na \rightarrow Na^+ + e^-$
A magnesium atom (Mg) **loses** 2 electrons to form a magnesium ion (Mg^{2+})	$Mg \rightarrow Mg^{2+} + 2e^-$
A chlorine atom (Cl) **gains** 1 electron to form a chloride ion (Cl^-)	$Cl + e^- \rightarrow Cl^-$
An oxygen atom (O) **gains** 2 electrons to form an oxide ion (O^{2-})	$O + 2e^- \rightarrow O^{2-}$

3) You **don't** have to remember what ion **each element** forms — nope, for a lot of them you just look at the Periodic Table. Elements in the same **group** all have the same number of **outer electrons**. So they have to **lose or gain** the same number to get the full outer shell that they're aiming for. And this means that they form ions with the **same charges**.
4) **Electrostatic attraction** holds positive and negative ions together — it's **very** strong. When atoms are held together like this, it's called **ionic bonding**.

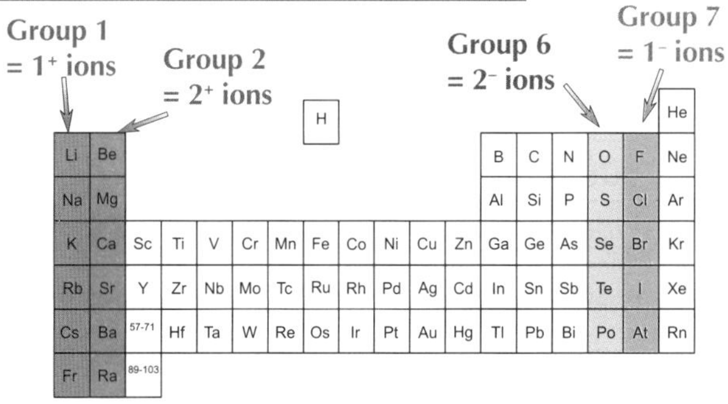

Sodium Chloride *and* ***Magnesium Oxide*** *are Ionic Compounds*

1) The formula of sodium chloride is **NaCl**. It just tells you that sodium chloride is made up of **Na^+ ions** and **Cl^- ions** (in a 1:1 ratio).
2) You can use '**dot-and-cross**' diagrams to show how ionic bonding works in sodium chloride —

Here, the dots represent the Na electrons and the crosses represent the Cl electrons (all electrons are really identical, but this is a good way of following their movement).

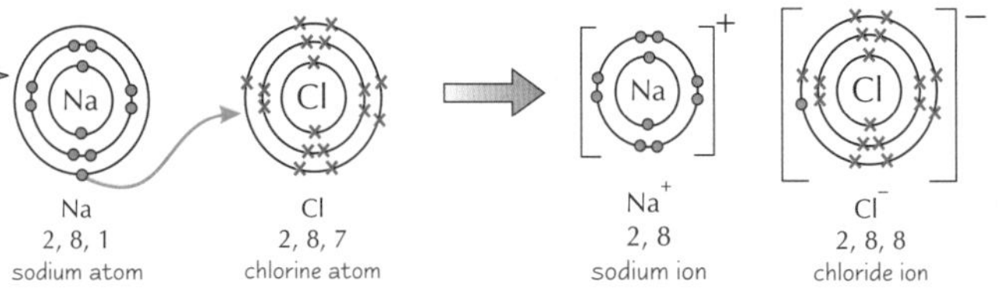

3) **Magnesium oxide**, MgO, is another good example:

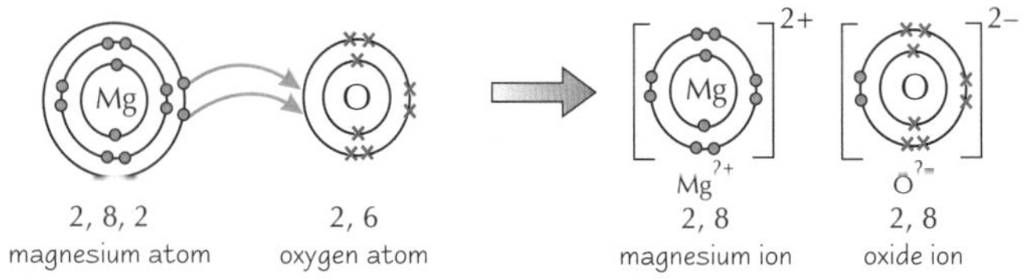

Dot (cross)

The positive charges in the compound **balance** the negative charges exactly — so the total overall charge is **zero**. This is a dead handy way of checking the formula.

- In **NaCl**, the single + charge on the Na^+ ion balances the single – charge on the Cl^- ion.
- In magnesium chloride, **$MgCl_2$**, the 2+ charge on the Mg^{2+} ion balances the two individual – charges on the two Cl^- ions.

Ionic Bonding

Sodium Chloride has a **Giant Ionic Lattice** Structure

1) Ionic crystals are giant lattices of ions. A **lattice** is just a **regular structure**.
2) The structure's called '**giant**' because it's made up of the same basic unit repeated over and over again.
3) In **sodium chloride**, the Na^+ and Cl^- ions are packed together. The sodium chloride lattice is **cube** shaped — different ionic compounds have different shaped structures, but they're all still giant lattices.

The Na^+ and Cl^- ions alternate.

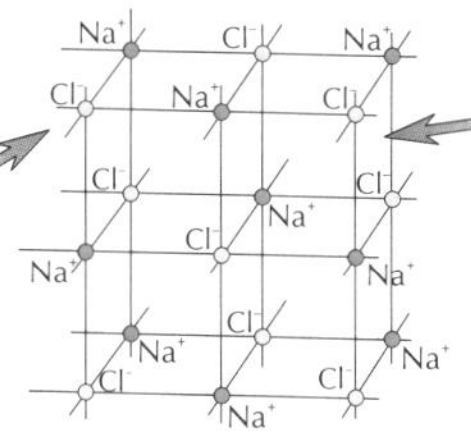

The lines show the ionic bonds between the ions.

Remember... dot-and-cross diagrams like on the previous page might make it look as if an ionic substance is made up of 1 or 2 positive ions bonded to 1 or 2 negative ions. But in fact, you get these giant ionic lattices...

The structure of ionic compounds decides their **physical properties**...

Ionic Structure *Explains the* ***Behaviour*** *of Ionic Compounds*

1) **Ionic compounds conduct electricity when they're molten or dissolved — but not when they're solid.**
   The ions in a liquid or a solution are free to move (and when they move, their charge moves with them). In a solid they're fixed in position by the strong ionic bonds.
2) **Ionic compounds have high melting points.**
   The giant ionic lattices are held together by strong electrostatic forces. It takes loads of energy to overcome these forces, so melting points are very high (801 °C for sodium chloride).
3) **Ionic compounds often dissolve in water.**
   Water molecules are polar — part of the molecule has a small negative charge, and the other bits have small positive charges (see p62). The water molecules pull the ions away from the lattice and cause it to dissolve.

Practice Questions

Q1 What's a compound?

Q2 Draw a 'dot-and-cross' diagram showing the bonding between magnesium and oxygen.

Q3 What type of force holds ionic substances together?

Q4 What happens when a current is passed through a dissolved ionic compound?

Exam Questions

Q1 a) Draw a labelled diagram to show the structure of sodium chloride. [3 marks]

b) What is the name of this type of structure? [1 mark]

c) Would you expect sodium chloride to have a high or a low melting point? Explain your answer. [4 marks]

Q2 a) Ions can be formed by electron transfer. Explain this and give an example for a positive and a negative ion. [3 marks]

b) Solid lead bromide does not conduct electricity, but molten lead bromide does. Explain this with reference to ionic bonding. [5 marks]

A black fly in your Chardonnay — isn't it ionic...

This stuff's easy marks in exams. Just make sure you can draw dot-and-cross diagrams showing the bonding in ionic compounds and you're sorted. Remember — atoms are lazy. It's easier to lose two electrons to get a full shell than it is to gain six, so that's what an atom's going to do. Practise drawing sodium chloride too, and don't stop till you're perfect.

Covalent Bonding

And now for covalent bonding — this is when atoms share electrons with one another so they've all got full outer shells.

Molecules are Groups of Atoms **Bonded** Together

Molecules are formed when **2 or more** atoms bond together, and are held together by **covalent bonds**.
It doesn't matter if the atoms are the **same** or **different**.

Chlorine gas (Cl_2), carbon monoxide (CO), water (H_2O) and ethanol (C_2H_5OH) are all molecules.

In covalent bonding, two atoms **share** electrons, so they've **both** got full outer shells of electrons. Both the positive nuclei are attracted **electrostatically** to the shared electrons.

E.g. two hydrogen atoms bond covalently to form a molecule of hydrogen.

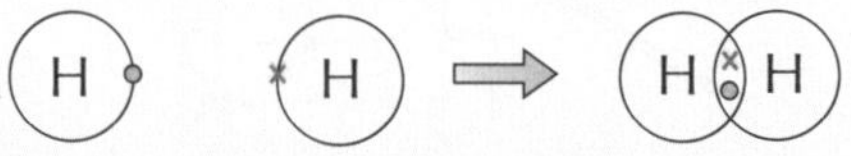

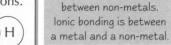

Covalent bonding happens between non-metals. Ionic bonding is between a metal and a non-metal.

Make sure you can **Draw** the **Bonding** in these Molecules

These diagrams don't show all the electrons in the molecules — just the ones in the **outer shells**:

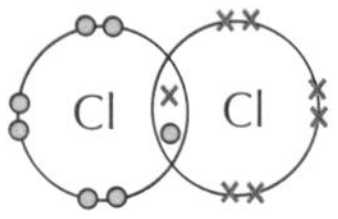

Chlorine, Cl_2

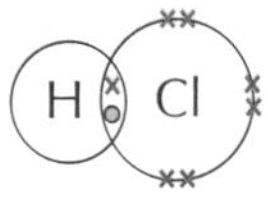

Hydrogen chloride, HCl

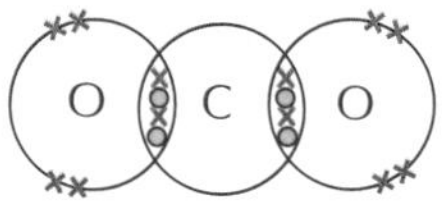

Carbon dioxide, CO_2

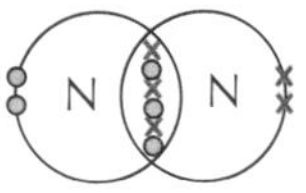

Nitrogen, N_2
(nitrogen's a triple-bonder.)

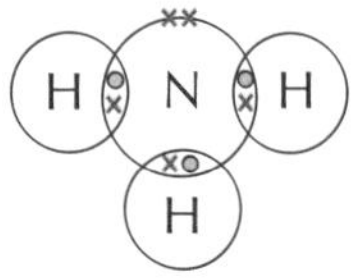

Ammonia, NH_3

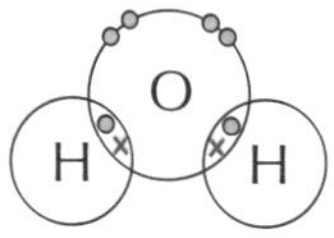

Water, H_2O

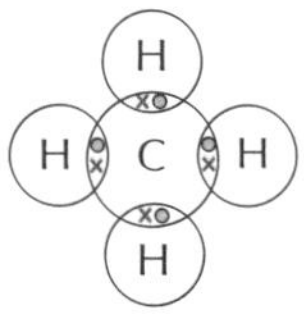

Methane, CH_4

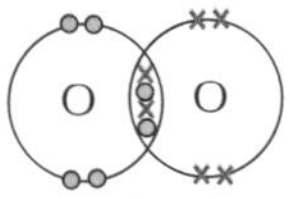

Oxygen, O_2

Dative Covalent Bonding is where **Both Electrons** come from **One Atom**

In the molecules above, atoms are acting in a bit of a "I'll lend you mine if you lend me yours" kind of way — each atom puts an electron (or two) into the bond, and in return, they get use of the electrons put in by another atom.

1) But there's another kind of covalent bond as well — a **dative** (or **coordinate**) covalent bond.
   This is where one atom donates **both electrons** to a bond.
2) The **ammonium ion** (NH_4^+) is formed by dative (or coordinate) covalent bonding — it's an example the examiners love. It forms when the nitrogen atom in an ammonia molecule **donates a pair of electrons** to a proton (H^+).

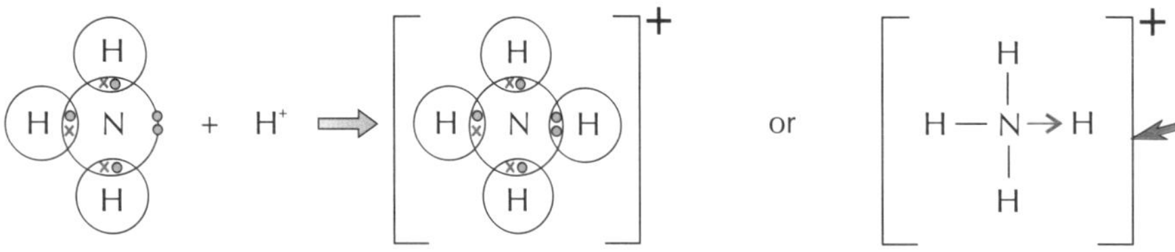

Dative covalent bonding is shown in diagrams by an arrow, pointing away from the 'donor' atom.

Molecular Substances Have Some **Typical Properties**

Substances made up of (reasonably small) **molecules** have some properties in common.

1) They usually have **fairly low** melting and boiling points — there's no giant structure that needs to be broken down.

   This is something that confuses loads of people — prepare to be enlightened...
   - To **melt** or **boil** a simple molecular compound, you only have to overcome the attractions **between** the molecules. These are pretty **weak** compared to ionic or covalent bonds — see page 64 for more info.
   - You **don't** need to overcome the much stronger covalent bonds that hold the atoms together in the molecules.

2) They **don't** conduct electricity, because there are **no charge carriers** that are free to move.
3) They're usually **insoluble** in water (or only very slightly soluble). The **polar** water molecules (see page 62) are more attracted to **each other** than the molecular substance, and so tend to leave it alone.

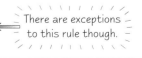

There are exceptions to this rule though.

Covalent Bonding

These **Bonding Models** Have Their **Limitations**

The **dot-and-cross models** of ionic and covalent bonding give the impression that electrons are either transferred (ionic bonding) or shared (covalent bonding). Like most things in life though it's not really quite as simple as that.

1) Most bonds aren't **purely ionic** or **purely covalent** but somewhere in between. This is down to **bond polarisation** (see page 62).
2) So, most compounds end up with a **mixture** of ionic and covalent properties.

Learn the Properties of **Ionic** and **Simple Molecular Substances**

So the **particles** that make up a substance, and the **forces** holding them together are what decide its physical properties. Here's a bit of a summary of the properties of ionic and covalent substances.

Bonding	Examples	Melting and boiling points	Typical state at STP	Does solid conduct electricity?	Does liquid conduct electricity?	Is it soluble in water?
Ionic	NaCl, $MgCl_2$	High	Solid	No (ions are held firmly in place)	Yes (ions are free to move)	Yes
Simple molecular (covalent)	CO_2, I_2, H_2O	Low (have to overcome van der Waals forces or hydrogen bonds, not covalent bonds)	Sometimes solid, usually liquid or gas (water is liquid because it has hydrogen bonds)	No	No	Depends on how polarised the molecule is

Practice Questions

Q1 What types of atoms form covalent bonds? Non-metals, metals or both?

Q2 Draw a dot-and-cross diagram to show the arrangement of the outer electrons in a molecule of hydrogen chloride.

Q3 Describe three typical physical properties of a molecular substance.

Q4 Describe a limitation of the covalent bonding model.

Exam Questions

Q1 a) Silicon is in the same group of the Periodic Table as carbon. Draw a dot-and-cross diagram (showing outer shell electrons only) to represent the bonding in the molecule silicon hydride (SiH_4). [2 marks]

b) Describe two **physical** properties that you would expect silicon hydride to exhibit. [2 marks]

Q2 Methane melts at –183 °C. Magnesium oxide melts at 2800 °C. Explain this difference in terms of bonding. [4 marks]

Q3 a) Draw a dot-and-cross diagram of the ammonia molecule (NH_3) showing the outer shell electrons only. [2 marks]

b) Draw a dot-and-cross diagram of the hydrogen chloride molecule (HCl) showing the outer shell electrons only. [2 marks]

c) Ammonia reacts with hydrogen chloride to form ammonium chloride. Draw a dot-and-cross diagram to show the bonding in ammonium chloride. [3 marks]

d) Predict whether ammonium chloride would be likely to be soluble or insoluble in water. Explain your answer. [2 marks]

Dative covalent bonds — an act of charity on an atomic scale...

More pretty diagrams to learn here folks — practise till you get every single dot and cross in the right place. It's totally amazing to think of these titchy little atoms sorting themselves out so they've got full outer shells of electrons. Remember — covalent bonding happens between two non-metals, whereas ionic bonding happens between a metal and a non-metal.

Giant Covalent and Metallic Structures

Just because something's held together with covalent bonds, that doesn't necessarily mean it's made up of small molecules. Not at all... some covalent substances form vast structures (well... vast compared to simple molecules).

Some **Covalently Bonded** Substances Have **Giant Structures**

1) **Covalent bonds** form when atoms **share** electrons with other atoms. Very often, this leads to the formation of small **molecules**, including CO_2, N_2 and the others on page 20.
2) But it can also lead to huge great **lattices** too — containing billions and billions of atoms.
3) These **giant** structures have a huge network of **covalently** bonded atoms.
4) **Carbon** and **silicon** can form these giant networks. This is because they can each form four strong, covalent bonds.

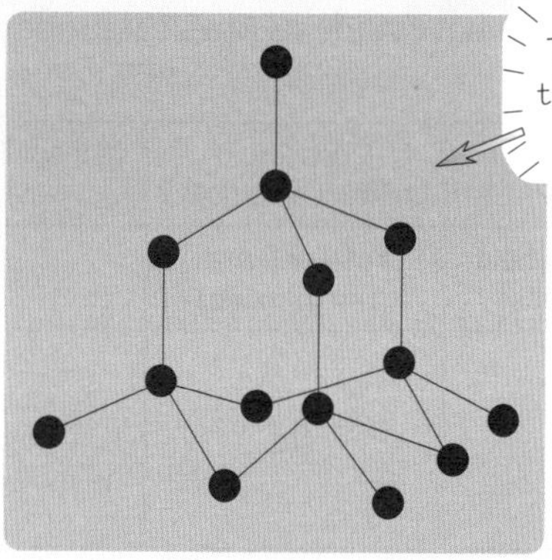

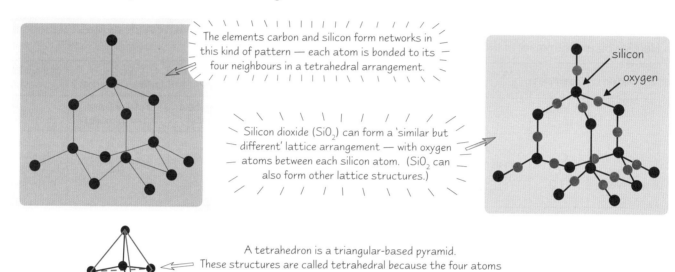

The elements carbon and silicon form networks in this kind of pattern — each atom is bonded to its four neighbours in a tetrahedral arrangement.

Silicon dioxide (SiO_2) can form a 'similar but different' lattice arrangement — with oxygen atoms between each silicon atom. (SiO_2 can also form other lattice structures.)

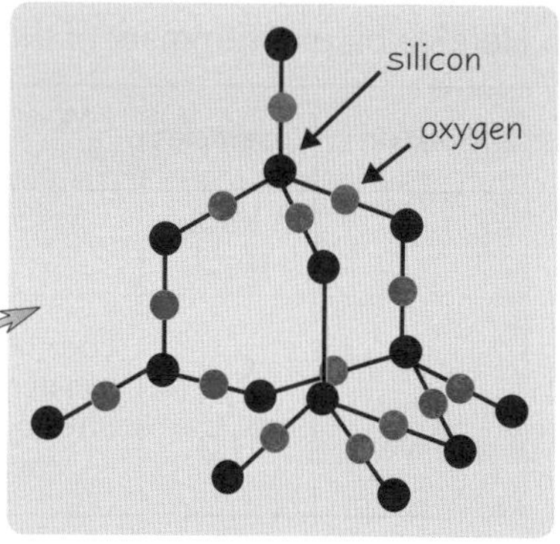

A tetrahedron is a triangular-based pyramid. These structures are called tetrahedral because the four atoms bonded to each carbon or silicon atom form a tetrahedron shape.

The **Properties** of Giant Structures Provide **Evidence** for **Covalent Bonding**

The forces holding individual particles together help determine a substance's **properties**. All of these **giant covalent structures** have some properties in common.

Because of the **strong covalent** bonds in giant molecular structures, they:
1) Have **very high melting points** — you need to break a lot of very strong bonds before the substance melts, which takes a lot of energy.
2) Are often extremely **hard** — again, this is because of the very strong bonds all through the lattice arrangement.
3) **Are good thermal conductors** — since vibrations travel easily through the stiff lattices.
4) Won't dissolve — the covalent bonds mean atoms are more attracted to their neighbours in the lattice than to solvent molecules. The fact that they are all **insoluble** in **polar solvents** like water shows that they **don't contain ions.**
5) **Can't conduct** electricity — since there are (in most giant lattice structures) no charged ions or free electrons (all the bonding electrons are held in localised electron bonds).

The exception to the "can't conduct electricity rule" here is graphite (a form of carbon). Carbon atoms form sheets, with each carbon atom sharing three of its outer shell electrons with three other carbon atoms. This leaves the fourth outer electron in each atom fairly free to move along the sheets, making graphite a conductor.

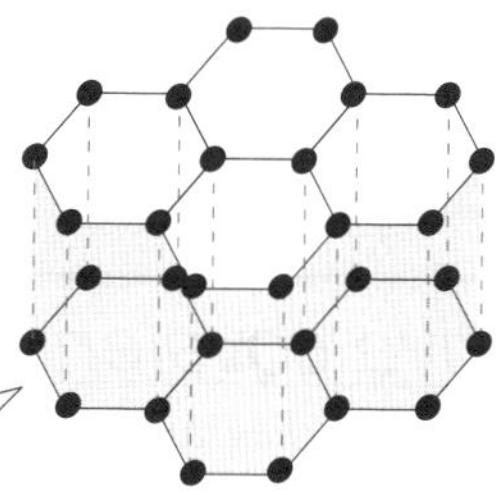

The individual sheets are held together by relatively weak forces.

Giant Covalent and Metallic Structures

Metals have Giant Structures Too

Metal elements exist as **giant metallic lattice structures**.

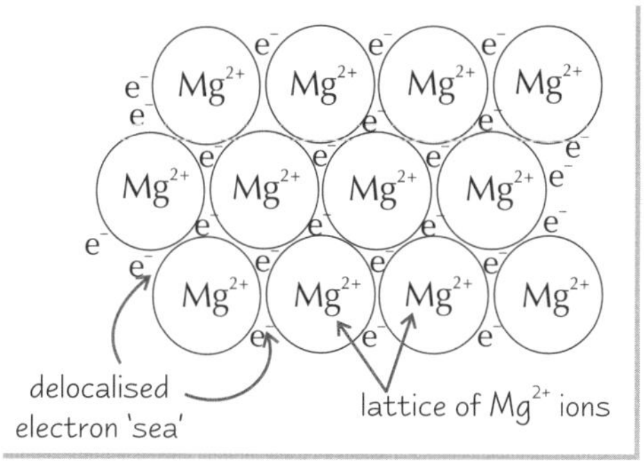

1) In metallic lattices, the electrons in the outermost shell of the metal atoms are **delocalised** — they're free to move. This leaves a **positive metal ion**, e.g. Na^+, Mg^{2+}, Al^{3+}.
2) The positive metal ions are **attracted** to the delocalised negative electrons. They form a lattice of closely packed positive ions in a **sea** of delocalised electrons — this is **metallic bonding**.
3) This model is a **simplification** that explains **most** properties of metals. In reality things aren't as straightforward. For example, the metal ions aren't static — they **vibrate** and their vibration **increases** with temperature, preventing the electrons moving freely through the metal lattice. (This is why the conductivity of a metal drops with increasing temperature.)

The **metallic bonding model** explains why metals do what they do —

1) The **melting points** of metals are generally **high** because of the strong metallic bonding, with the **number of delocalised electrons per atom** affecting the melting point. The **more** there are, the **stronger** the bonding will be and the **higher** the melting point. $\mathbf{Mg^{2+}}$ has **two** delocalised electrons per atom, so it's got a **higher melting point** than $\mathbf{Na^+}$, which only has **one**. The **size** of the metal ion and the **lattice structure** also affect the melting point.
2) As there are **no bonds** holding specific ions together, the metal ions can slide over each other when the structure is pulled, so metals can be **shaped** and are **ductile** (can be drawn into a wire).
3) The delocalised electrons can pass **kinetic energy** to each other, making metals **good thermal conductors**.
4) Metals are **good electrical conductors** because the **delocalised electrons** can carry a **current**.
5) Metals are **insoluble**, except in **liquid metals**, because of the **strength** of the metallic bonds.

Practice Questions

Q1 Are the melting points of giant covalent lattices high or low? Explain why?

Q2 Why won't giant covalent structures dissolve?

Q3 Explain how the model of metallic bonding accounts for:
(i) a metal's ability to conduct electricity, and (ii) the relatively high melting points of metals.

Exam Questions

Q1 a) Explain what is meant by metallic bonding. Draw a diagram to illustrate your explanation. [4 marks]
b) Explain why calcium has a higher melting point than potassium. [3 marks]

Q2 Carbon dioxide is a covalent compound that sublimes (turns directly from a solid to a gas) at –78 °C.
Silicon dioxide is a covalent compound that melts at 1610 °C. Explain these differences in terms of bonding. [5 marks]

Q3 Graphite is a giant covalent structure. However, unlike most giant covalent structures, it is able to conduct electricity. Explain why graphite is able to conduct electricity. [3 marks]

Q4 Electrical grade copper must be 99.99% pure. If sulfur and oxygen impurities react with the copper ions, its electrical conductivity is drastically reduced.
Use your knowledge of metallic and ionic bonding to explain this. [3 marks]

Q5 Carborundum (silicon carbide) has the formula SiC and is almost as hard as diamond.
a) What sort of structure would you expect carborundum to have as a solid? [1 mark]
b) Apart from hardness, give **two** other physical properties you would expect carborundum to have. [2 marks]

Tetrahedron — sounds like that monster from Greek mythology...

Examiners love giving you questions on these giant structures. Close the book and write down a list of the typical properties of a giant covalent lattice — then look back at the page and see what you missed. It might be less fun than ironing your underwear, but it's much more useful and the only way to make sure you sparkle in the exam.

Shapes of Molecules

Chemistry would be heaps more simple if all molecules were flat. But sadly they're not.

Molecular Shape *depends on* ***Electron Pairs*** *Around the* ***Central Atom***

Molecules and molecular ions come in loads of **different shapes**.

The shape depends on the **number of pairs** of electrons in the outer shell of the central atom.

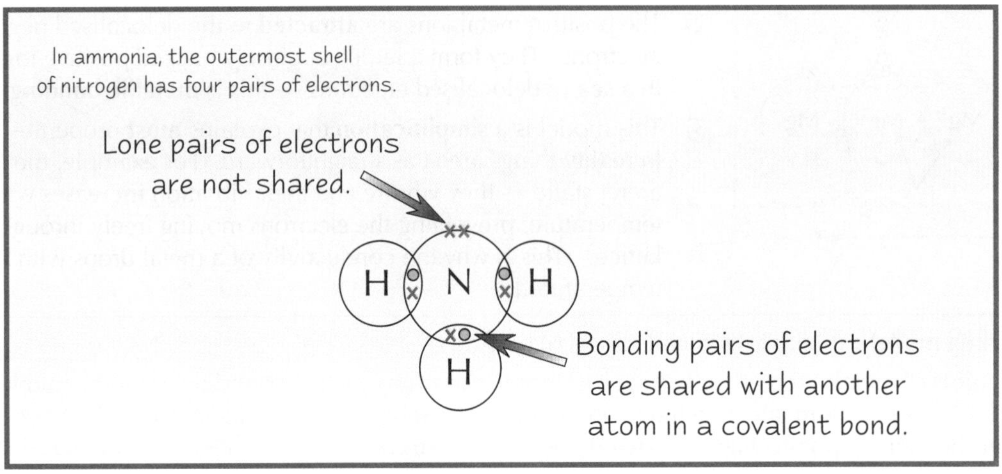
In ammonia, the outermost shell of nitrogen has four pairs of electrons.
Lone pairs of electrons are not shared.
H
N
H
H
Bonding pairs of electrons are shared with another atom in a covalent bond.

A lone pear

Electron Pairs ***Repel*** *Each Other*

1) Electrons are all **negatively charged**, so it's pretty obvious that electron pairs will **repel** each other as much as they can.
2) This sounds straightforward, but the **type** of the electron pair affects **how much** it repels other electron pairs. Lone pairs repel **more** than bonding pairs.
3) So, the **greatest** angles are between **lone pairs** of electrons, and bond angles between bonding pairs are often **reduced** because they are pushed together by lone-pair repulsion.

Lone-pair/lone-pair bond angles are the biggest. — *Lone-pair/bonding-pair bond angles are the second biggest.* — *Bonding-pair/bonding-pair bond angles are the smallest.*

4) This is known by the long-winded name '**electron-pair repulsion principle**'.

The central atoms in these molecules all have **four pairs** of electrons in their outer shells, but they're all **different shapes**.

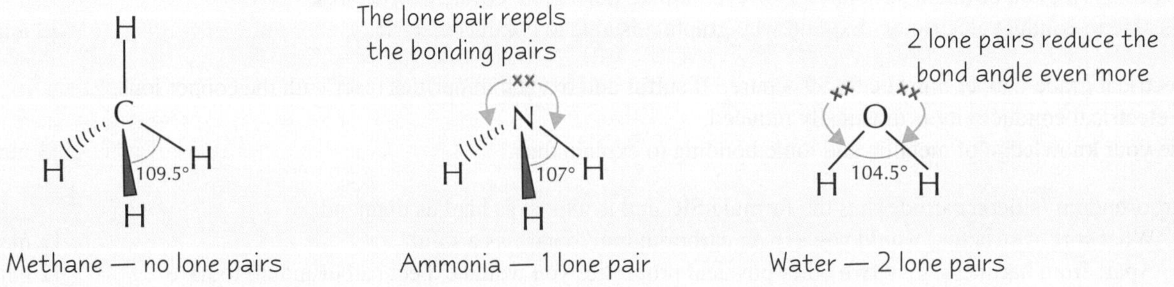
The lone pair repels the bonding pairs
2 lone pairs reduce the bond angle even more
C
H
H
H
H
109.5°
N
H
H
H
107°
O
H
H
104.5°
Methane — no lone pairs
Ammonia — 1 lone pair
Water — 2 lone pairs

Shapes of Molecules

Practise **Drawing** these Molecules

You can use the ideas from the previous page to draw **all sorts** of molecules — learn these rules...

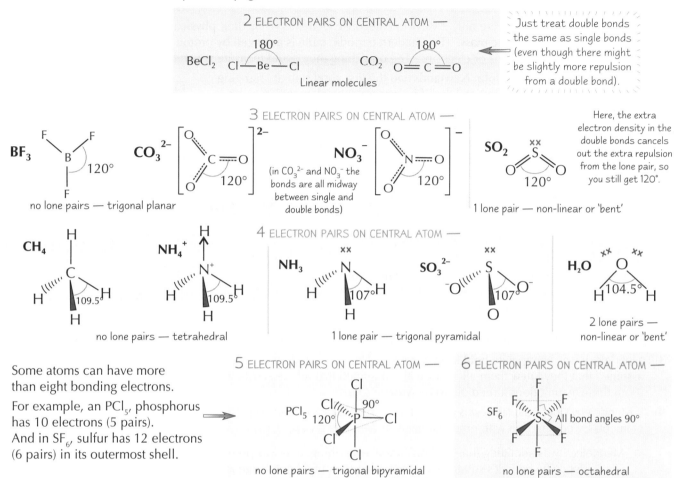

2 ELECTRON PAIRS ON CENTRAL ATOM —

Linear molecules

Just treat double bonds the same as single bonds (even though there might be slightly more repulsion from a double bond).

3 ELECTRON PAIRS ON CENTRAL ATOM —

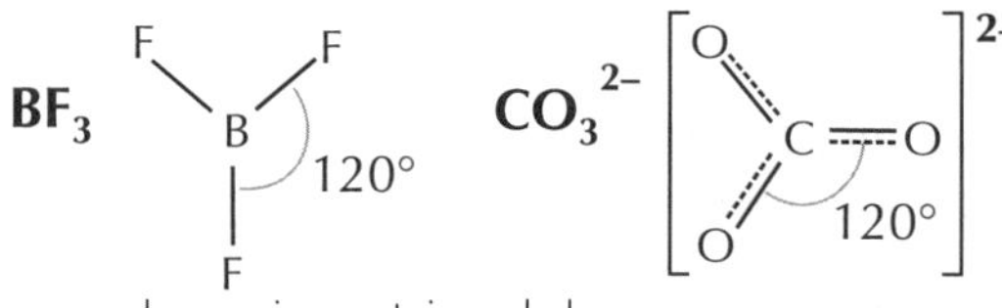

no lone pairs — trigonal planar

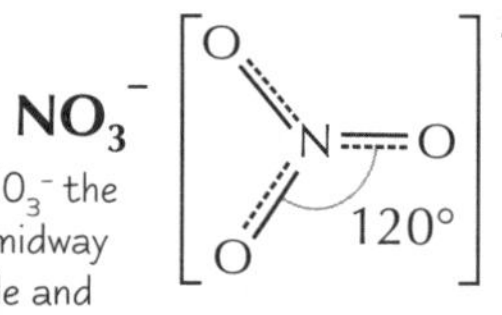

(in CO_3^{2-} and NO_3^- the bonds are all midway between single and double bonds)

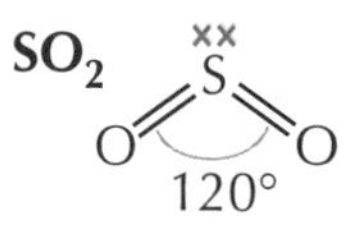

1 lone pair — non-linear or 'bent'

Here, the extra electron density in the double bonds cancels out the extra repulsion from the lone pair, so you still get 120°.

4 ELECTRON PAIRS ON CENTRAL ATOM —

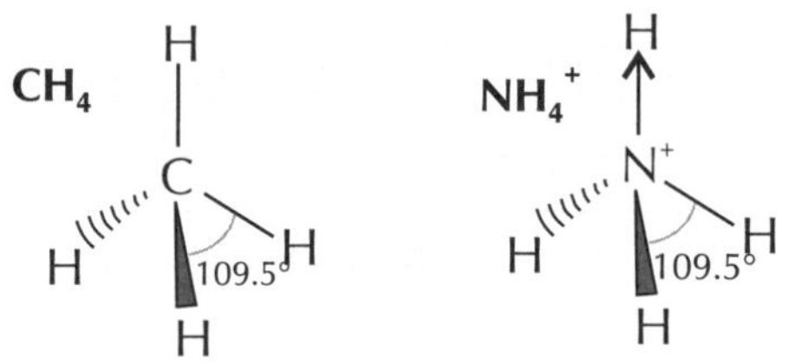

no lone pairs — tetrahedral

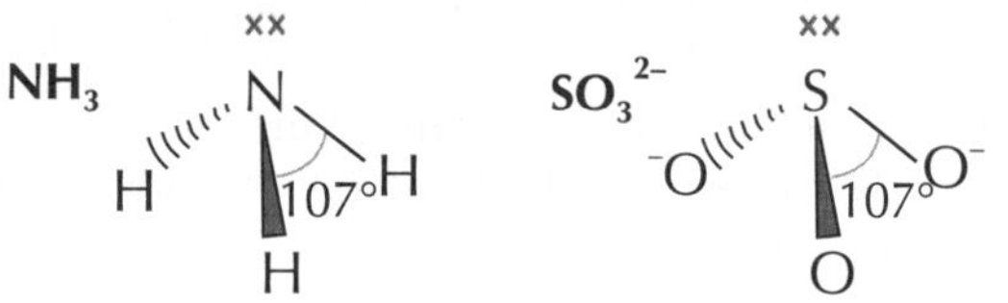

1 lone pair — trigonal pyramidal

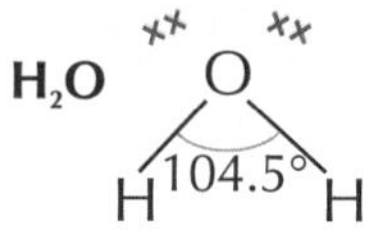

2 lone pairs — non-linear or 'bent'

Some atoms can have more than eight bonding electrons.

For example, an PCl_5, phosphorus has 10 electrons (5 pairs).
And in SF_6, sulfur has 12 electrons (6 pairs) in its outermost shell.

5 ELECTRON PAIRS ON CENTRAL ATOM —

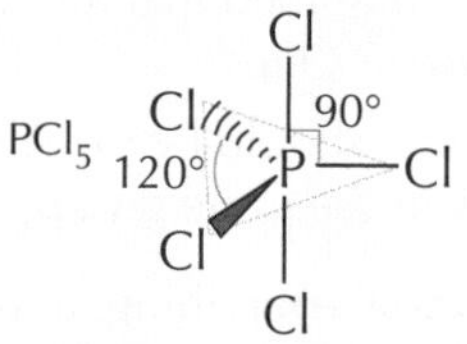

no lone pairs — trigonal bipyramidal

6 ELECTRON PAIRS ON CENTRAL ATOM —

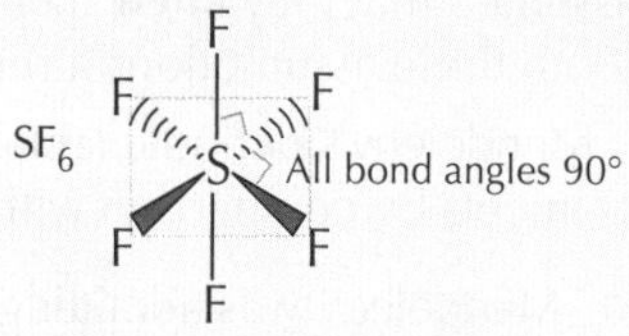

no lone pairs — octahedral

Practice Questions

Q1 What is a lone pair of electrons?

Q2 Write down the order of the strength of repulsion between different kinds of electron pair.

Q3 What shape is a water molecule?

Q4 Name a linear molecule.

Q5 Draw a tetrahedral molecule.

Exam Question

Q1 Nitrogen and boron can form the chlorides NCl_3 and BCl_3.

a) Draw 'dot-and-cross' diagrams to show the bonding in NCl_3 and BCl_3. [2 marks]

b) Draw the shapes of the molecules NCl_3 and BCl_3.
Show the approximate values of the bond angles on the diagrams and name each shape. [6 marks]

c) Explain why the shapes of NCl_3 and BCl_3 are different. [3 marks]

These molecules ain't square...

In the exam, those evil examiners might try to throw you by asking you to predict the shape of an unfamiliar molecule. Don't panic — it'll be just like one you do know, e.g. PH_3 is the same shape as NH_3. Make sure you can draw every single molecule on this page. Yep, that's right — from memory. And you need to know what the shapes are called too.

The Periodic Table

As far as Chemistry topics go, the Periodic Table is a bit of a biggie. So much so that they even want you to know the history of it. So make yourself comfortable and I'll tell you a story that began... oh, about 200 years ago...

*In the **1800s**, They Could only Group Elements by **Atomic Mass***

1) In the early 1800s, there were only 2 ways to categorise elements — by their **physical and chemical properties** and by their **relative atomic mass**. (The modern periodic table is arranged by proton number, but back then, they knew nothing about protons or electrons. The only thing they could measure was relative atomic mass.)
2) An English chemist called **John Newlands** had the first good stab at arranging the elements in 1863. He noticed that if he arranged the elements in order of **mass**, similar elements appeared at regular intervals — every **eighth element** was similar. He called this the **law of octaves**, and he listed some known elements in rows of seven so that the similar elements lined up in columns.

Li	Be	B	C	N	O	F
Na	Mg	Al	Si	P	S	Cl

3) Newlands presented his ideas to other scientists — but they **weren't convinced**. The problem was, the pattern **broke down** on the third row, with many transition metals like Fe, Cu and Zn messing it up completely.

Dmitri Mendeleev** Created the **First Accepted Version

1) In 1869, Russian chemist **Dmitri Mendeleev** produced a much better table which wasn't far off the one we have today.
2) Unlike everyone else, Mendeleev **left some gaps** in the table where the next element didn't seem to fit. By putting in gaps, he could keep elements with similar chemical properties in the same group. Mendeleev also **rearranged** some elements from their atomic mass order so that they fitted.

	Group 1	Group 2	Group 3	Group 4	Group 5	Group 6	Group 7
Period 1	H						
Period 2	Li	Be	B	C	N	O	F
Period 3	Na	Mg	Al	Si	P	S	Cl
Period 4	K / Cu	Ca / Zn	* / *	Ti / *	V / As	Cr / Se	Mn / Br
Period 5	Rb / Ag	Sr / Cd	Y / In	Zr / Sn	Nb / Sb	Mo / Te	* / I

3) Mendeleev was being quite **bold** leaving gaps — Newlands and others who'd tried arranging the elements had assumed that they **knew** them all. They'd also assumed that all the substances they were arranging **were elements**. (Both these assumptions turned out to be wrong. Oops.)
4) If Mendeleev's periodic table was correct then it should be possible to **predict** the properties of the missing elements by comparison with other elements in the same group.

Mendeleev was admitting that he didn't know everything, and was presenting his 'best guess' based on the evidence he had. It's still the case today that scientific knowledge is **tentative** — we know that our understanding of many areas of science is **incomplete** and might have to change quite radically in the future.

5) When elements were **later discovered** (e.g. germanium, scandium and gallium) with properties that matched Mendeleev's predictions, it showed that clever old Mendeleev had got it right.

*The **Modern Periodic Table** arranges Elements by **Proton Number***

	Group 1	Group 2											Group 3	Group 4	Group 5	Group 6	Group 7	Group 0
								1 H Hydrogen 1										4 He 2
2	7 Li 3	9 Be 4											11 B 5	12 C 6	14 N 7	16 O 8	19 F 9	20 Ne 10
3	23 Na 11	24 Mg 12											27 Al 13	28 Si 14	31 P 15	32 S 16	35.5 Cl 17	40 Ar 18
4	39 K 19	40 Ca 20	45 Sc 21	48 Ti 22	51 V 23	52 Cr 24	55 Mn	56 Fe 26	59 Co 27	59 Ni 28	64 Cu 29	65 Zn 30	70 Ga 31	73 Ge 32	75 As 33	79 Se 34	80 Br 35	84 Kr 36
5	86 Rb 37	88 Sr 38	89 Y 39	91 Zr 40	93 Nb 41	96 Mo 42	99 Tc 43	101 Ru 44	103 Rh 45	106 Pd 46	108 Ag 47	112 Cd 48	115 In 49	119 Sn 50	122 Sb 51	128 Te 52	127 I 53	131 Xe 54
6	133 Cs 55	137 Ba 56	57-71 Lanthanides	179 Hf 72	181 Ta 73	184 W 74	186 Re 75	190 Os 76	192 Ir 77	195 Pt 78	197 Au 79	201 Hg 80	204 Tl 81	207 Pb 82	209 Bi 83	210 Po 84	210 At 85	222 Rn 86
7	223 Fr 87	226 Ra 88	89-103 Actinides															

1) The modern Periodic Table is arranged according to **atomic (proton) number**.
2) The **noble gases** (Group 0) have also been added. (They were discovered in the 1890s.)

1) The modern Periodic Table is arranged into **periods** (rows) and **groups** (columns).
2) All the elements **within a period** have the same number of **electron shells**
   — the elements of Period 1 (hydrogen and helium) both have 1 electron shell.
   — the elements in Period 2 have 2 electron shells. And so on down the table...
3) All the elements **within a group** have the same number of **electrons in their outer shell**. This means they have similar physical and chemical properties. The group number tells you the number of electrons in the outer shell, e.g. Group 1 elements have 1 electron in their outer shell, Group 4 elements have 4 electrons, and so on...
4) Properties often **change gradually** as you go down each group. For example, the metals in Group 1 become **more reactive** as you go down the group, whereas the Group 7 elements become gradually **less reactive**.

The Periodic Table

Periodic Trends are Patterns in the Periodic Table

Periods 2 and 3 show similar trends in their melting and boiling points. These trends are linked to changes in **structure** and **bond strength**.

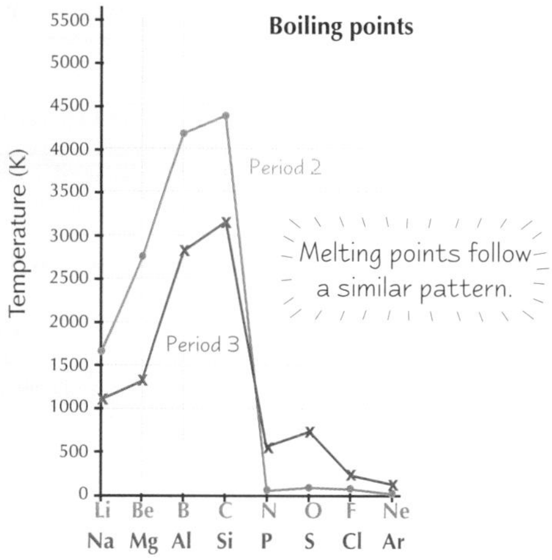

1) For the **metals** (Li and Be, Na, Mg and Al), melting and boiling points **increase** across the period because the **metal-metal bonds** get stronger. The bonds get stronger because the metal ions have an increasing number of **delocalised electrons** and a decreasing **radius**. This leads to a higher **charge density**, which attracts the ions together more strongly.
   The ionic radius decreases because the electrons are pulled in closer as the number of protons in the nucleus increases.
2) The elements with **giant covalent** structures have **strong covalent bonds** linking all their atoms together. **A lot** of energy is needed to break these bonds. So, for example, carbon (as graphite or diamond) and silicon have the **highest** melting and boiling points in their periods.
   (The carbon data in the graph opposite is for graphite — diamond has an even higher boiling point. But neither of them actually melts or boils at atmospheric pressure, they sublime from solid to gas.)
3) Next come the **simple molecular substances** (N_2, O_2 and F_2, P_4, S_8 and Cl_2). Their melting and boiling points depend upon the strength of the **intermolecular forces** (see page 64) between their molecules. Intermolecular forces are weak and easily broken so these elements have **low** melting and boiling points.
4) More atoms in a molecule mean stronger intermolecular forces. For example, in Period 3 sulfur is the **biggest molecule** (S_8), so it's got higher melting and boiling points than phosphorus or chlorine.
5) The noble gases (neon and argon) have the **lowest** melting and boiling points because they exist as **individual atoms** (they're monatomic) resulting in **very weak** intermolecular forces.

Practice Questions

Q1 In what ways is Newlands' "periodic table" not as good as Mendeleev's?

Q2 In what order did Mendeleev originally set out the elements?

Q3 In what order are the elements set out in the modern Periodic Table?

Q4 What is the name given to the columns in the Periodic Table?

Q5 What is the name given to the rows in the Periodic Table? *(Err, hello — easy questions alert.)*

Q6 Describe and explain the trends in boiling point of the elements in the first two periods.

Exam Questions

Q1 Use your knowledge of the Periodic Table and bonding to explain the following physical properties:
   a) Aluminium is a good electrical conductor with a fairly high melting point. [3 marks]
   b) Sulfur is a very poor electrical conductor with a relatively low melting point. [3 marks]

Q2 The table on the right shows the elements in Period 3 of the Periodic Table.
   Choose an element from the table that matches each of the following descriptions:

Na	Mg	Al	Si	P	S	Cl	Ar

   a) A diatomic molecule. [1 mark]
   b) A giant covalent structure. [1 mark]
   c) The metal with the highest melting point. [1 mark]
   d) A simple molecular substance that is a solid at room temperature. [1 mark]

*Periodic — probably the best table in the world...**

Dropped History for AS Chemistry, did you... Ha, bet you're regretting that now, aren't you. If so, you'll enjoy the free History lesson that you get here with the Periodic Table. Make sure you learn all the key details and particularly how to spell Mendeleev. This stuff's not here for fun — it's here because you're gonna get questions on it.

**Excluding Dinner and the Round, of course.*

Group 2

Given what you know about the Periodic Table, you'd expect all Group 2 elements to behave similarly. And they do. So get ready to learn about the elements magnesium, calcium, strontium and barium.

Group 2 Elements React with **Water** to Produce **Hydroxides**

When Group 2 elements react, they form ions with a charge of **2+**. This is because Group 2 atoms contain **2 electrons** in their outer shell.

$M \rightarrow M^{2+} + 2e^-$

E.g. $\mathbf{Ca} \rightarrow \mathbf{Ca^{2+}} + 2e^-$

Here, M stands for any Group 2 metal.

The Group 2 metals react with water to give a **metal hydroxide and hydrogen**.

$$M_{(s)} + 2H_2O_{(l)} \rightarrow M(OH)_{2\,(aq)} + H_{2\,(g)}$$

e.g. $$Ca_{(s)} + 2H_2O_{(l)} \rightarrow Ca(OH)_{2\,(aq)} + H_{2\,(g)}$$

They get **increasingly** reactive down the group because the outermost electrons are further from the nucleus, and so more easily lost.

Be	doesn't react
Mg	VERY slowly
Ca	steadily
Sr	fairly quickly
Ba	rapidly

Group 2 Oxides and Hydroxides are **Bases**

They form Alkaline Solutions in Water...

1) The **oxides** of the Group 2 metals react readily with **water** to form **metal hydroxides**, which dissolve. The **hydroxide ions, OH^-**, make these solutions **strongly alkaline**.
2) Magnesium oxide is an exception — it only reacts slowly and the hydroxide isn't very soluble.
3) The oxides form **more strongly alkaline** solutions as you go down the group. This is because the hydroxides get more soluble.

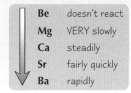

$$CaO_{(s)} + H_2O_{(l)} \rightarrow Ca^{2+}_{(aq)} + 2OH^-_{(aq)}$$

Calcium hydroxide solution has a pH of about 12.

...And They Neutralise Acids

Because they're **bases**, both the oxides and hydroxides **neutralise** dilute acids, forming solutions of the corresponding salts.

$$MgO_{(s)} + 2HCl_{(aq)} \rightarrow H_2O_{(l)} + MgCl_{2\,(aq)}$$

$$Mg(OH)_{2\,(s)} + 2HCl_{(aq)} \rightarrow 2H_2O_{(l)} + MgCl_{2\,(aq)}$$

Solubility Trends Depend on the **Compound Anion**

Generally, compounds of Group 2 elements that contain **singly charged** negative ions (e.g. OH^-) **increase** in solubility down the group, whereas compounds that contain **doubly charged** negative ions (e.g. CO_3^{2-} and SO_4^{2-}) **decrease** in solubility down the group.

Group 2 element	hydroxide (OH^-)	carbonate (CO_3^{2-})
magnesium	least soluble ↓	most soluble ↑
calcium		
strontium		
barium	most soluble	least soluble

Compounds like magnesium hydroxide which have **very low** solubilities are said to be **sparingly soluble**.

Group 2

Thermal Stability of Carbonates Changes Down the Group

Thermal decomposition is when a substance **breaks down** (decomposes) when **heated**.
Group 2 carbonates decompose to form the oxide and carbon dioxide.

$$MCO_{3\,(s)} \rightarrow MO_{(s)} + CO_{2\,(g)}$$

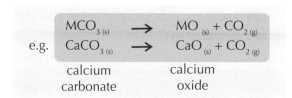

e.g. $$CaCO_{3\,(s)} \rightarrow CaO_{(s)} + CO_{2\,(g)}$$

calcium carbonate → calcium oxide

The more **thermally stable** a substance is, the **more heat** it will take to break it down.
The thermal stability of **Group 2 carbonates** changes as you go down Group 2.

Thermal stability increases down the group
Carbonate ions are **large anions** and can be made **unstable** by the presence of a **cation** (such as a Group 2 metal ion). The cation draws the electrons on the carbonate ion towards itself (it **polarises** it). This distorts the carbonate ion. The greater the distortion, the less stable the carbonate ion.
Large cations cause **less distortion** than small cations (they have a lower charge density). So the further down the group, the larger the cations, the less distortion caused and the **more stable** the carbonate anion. Phew... that was hard.

Anions are negatively charged ions, cations are positively charged ions.

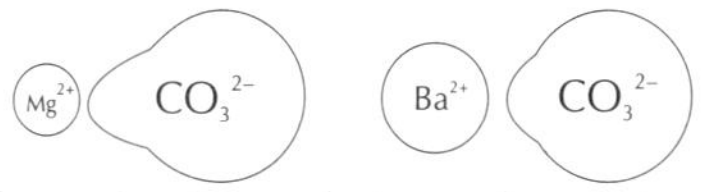

Magnesium ions polarise carbonate ions more than barium ions do, meaning magnesium carbonate is less stable.

Practice Questions

Q1 Which is the least reactive metal in Group 2?

Q2 Why does reactivity with water increase down Group 2?

Q3 Describe two reactions of a Group 2 oxide that show it to be a base.

Q4 How is the solubility of magnesium hydroxide often described?

Q5 Which is less soluble, barium hydroxide or magnesium hydroxide?

Q6 Write a general equation for the thermal decomposition of a Group 2 carbonate.
Use M to represent the Group 2 metal.

Exam Questions

Q1 a) The diagram on the right represents cations of the elements barium and calcium (not to scale).
Which of the two ions has the highest charge density? [1 mark]

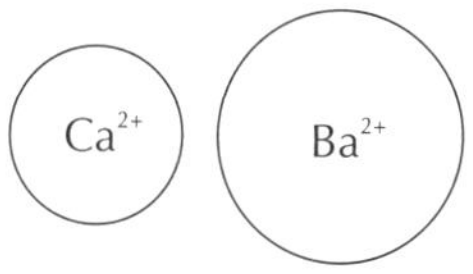

b) Write a balanced equation for the thermal decomposition of calcium carbonate including state symbols. [2 marks]

c) Barium and calcium both form carbonates.
Explain why barium carbonate is more thermally stable than calcium carbonate. [3 marks]

Q2 a) Write a balanced equation for the reaction of magnesium hydroxide with dilute hydrochloric acid. [2 marks]

b) Write a balanced equation for the reaction of calcium oxide with water. [2 marks]

c) Explain why calcium hydroxide is a stronger alkali than magnesium hydroxide. [2 marks]

I'm not gonna make it. You've gotta get me out of here, Doc...

We're deep in the dense jungle of Inorganic Chemistry now. Those carefree days of atomic structure are well behind us. It's now an endurance test and you've just got to keep going. By now, all the facts are probably blurring into one, all the compounds looking the same. It's tough, but you've got to stay awake, stay focused and keep learning. That's all you can do.

Gas Volumes and Entropy

These are good pages... okay there are a few calculations, but I like the pages anyway. I think it's because there's one of those "ooh... that's a bit weird" facts in the first bit. Surprised me when I first heard it, anyway.

All Gases Take Up the **Same Volume** under the Same Conditions

If temperature and pressure stay the same, **one mole** of **any** gas always has the **same volume**. *(Why is that, I always wonder.)*
At **room temperature and pressure** (r.t.p.), this happens to be **24 dm³**, (r.t.p. is 298 K (25 °C) and 101.3 kPa).

Here are two formulas for working out the number of moles in a volume of gas.
Don't forget — **ONLY** use them at r.t.p..

$$\textbf{Number of moles} = \frac{\textbf{Volume in dm}^3}{\textbf{24}} \quad \textbf{OR} \quad \textbf{Number of moles} = \frac{\textbf{Volume in cm}^3}{\textbf{24 000}}$$

Example: How many moles are there in 6 dm³ of oxygen gas at r.t.p.?

Number of moles = $\frac{6}{24}$ = **0.25 moles of oxygen molecules**

Example: Calculate the number of molecules in 18 dm³ of carbon dioxide gas at r.t.p..

First work out the number of **moles**: Number of moles = $\frac{18}{24}$ = **0.75 moles of CO_2 molecules**

Then use **Avogadro's constant** (p12) to work out the number of **molecules**:

Number of molecules = 0.75 × 6.02×10^{23} = **4.52×10^{23} molecules of CO_2**

That's not all... **Balanced Equations** can be used to **Work Out Gas Volumes**

It's pretty handy to be able to work out **how much gas** a reaction will produce.
It'll help you choose **large enough apparatus** for the job in hand... or else there might be a rather large bang.

Example: What volume of gas is produced when 15 g of sodium is reacted with excess water at r.t.p.?

$$2Na_{(s)} + 2H_2O_{(l)} \rightarrow 2NaOH_{(aq)} + H_{2(g)}$$

Excess water means you know all the sodium will react.

M of Na = 23 g, so number of moles in 15 g of Na = $\frac{15}{23}$ = 0.65 moles

From the equation, 2 moles of Na produces 1 mole of H_2,
so you know 0.65 moles Na produces $\frac{0.65}{2}$ = 0.325 moles H_2.

So the volume of H_2 = 0.325 × 24 = **7.8 dm³**

The reaction happens at room temperature and pressure, so you know 1 mole takes up 24 dm³.

Example: 29 g of butane (C_4H_{10}) undergoes complete combustion.
Find the volume of carbon dioxide produced at r.t.p..

M of butane = (12 × 4) + (1 × 10) = 58 g, so 29 g of butane is 0.5 moles.

The equation for the complete combustion of butane is: $2C_4H_{10(g)} + 13O_{2(g)} \rightarrow 8CO_{2(g)} + 10H_2O_{(g)}$.

From the equation, 2 moles of butane produces 8 moles of CO_2,
so 0.5 moles of butane must produce 2 moles of CO_2.

So the volume of CO_2 produced is 2 × 24 = **48 dm³**

Gas Volumes and Entropy

Entropy Tells you How Much **Disorder** there is

To explain **entropy** we need to go back to the good old **solid-liquid-gas** particle explanation thingies...

1) So... in **solids**, everything's nice and orderly. The particles don't move about freely — they just wobble about a fixed point. This means it's pretty easy to **predict** where a particle's going to be.
2) In **liquids**, the particles are still close together, but they can move about freely. So it's not quite so orderly and it's harder to **predict** the position of a particle.
3) In **gases**, the particles are very far apart, whizzing around wherever they like. There's **no order** — in fact, it's absolutely **random**. The position of a particle is totally **unpredictable**.

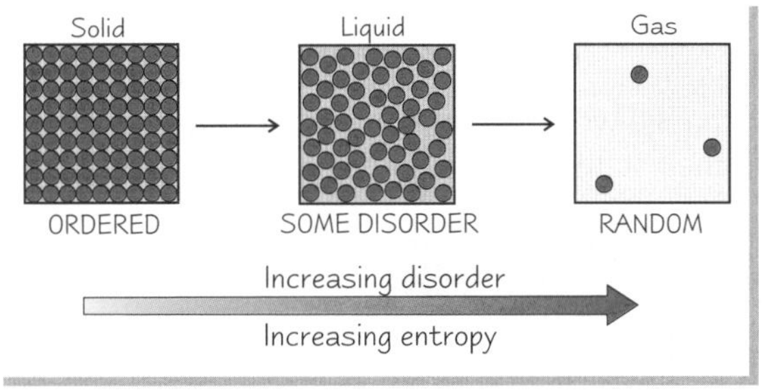

Looks like someone else has been reading this stuff...

Entropy is a measure of the **number of ways** the particles can be **arranged** — but it's basically just a measure of disorder. Now get this: substances **like** disorder. Particles will naturally move to give a substance the **maximum possible entropy**...

– Gases diffuse to fill all the available space because there are more ways of arranging particles in a bigger space.
– When something dissolves, the **solute** particles spread out in the **solvent**, and entropy increases.

Increasing the **number of particles** increases the entropy — a greater number of particles can be **arranged in more ways**. Also, a **mixture** of two different types of particle has more entropy than the same number of one type of particle.

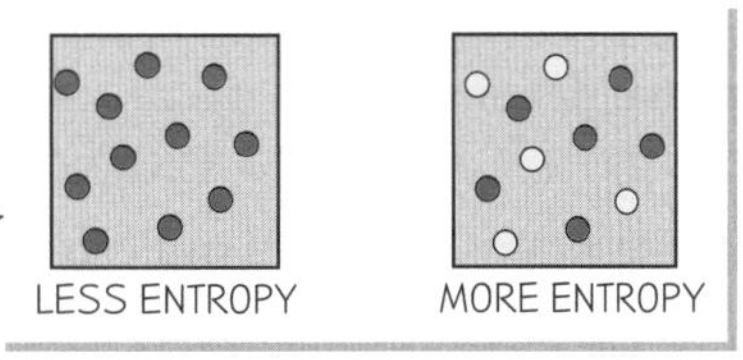

Practice Questions

Q1 Under what conditions does 1 mole of gas have a volume of 24 dm^3?

Q2 Write down the formula you'd use to find out how many moles there are in 100 dm^3 of a gas at r.t.p.?

Q3 Explain why dissolving sodium chloride crystals in water results in an increase in entropy.

Q4 In terms of entropy, why do gases diffuse to fill all the available space?

Exam Questions

Q1 State and explain how you would expect entropy to change in the following reaction

$$2Na(s) + 2H_2O(l) \rightarrow 2NaOH(aq) + H_2(g)$$ [3 marks]

Q2 10 g of calcium carbonate reacts with excess dilute hydrochloric acid at r.t.p. to produce calcium chloride, water and carbon dioxide.

a) Write a balanced equation for the reaction. [1 mark]

b) What volume of carbon dioxide is given off? [3 marks]

Q3 The equation below shows the decomposition of calcium carbonate.

$$CaCO_3(s) \rightarrow CaO(s) + CO_2(g)$$

Explain why the products in this reaction have a greater entropy than the reactants. [2 marks]

Now find the volume of hot air produced by two politicians in a room at r.t.p....

Do you find that thing about one mole of any gas taking up the same volume a bit surprising, or is it just me... Anyway, whether you find it surprising or not, make sure you can do all the calculations — there aren't many of them, so no excuses. The stuff about entropy is easy — remember that substances actually prefer disorder and you should be okay.

Enthalpy Changes

Enthalpy... not as complicated or fancy as the name makes it sound.

Chemical Reactions Have **Enthalpy Changes**

1) When chemical reactions happen, some bonds are **broken** and some bonds are **made**. More often than not, this'll cause a **change in energy**. The souped-up chemistry term for energy is **enthalpy**.

> **Enthalpy change**, ΔH (delta H), is the heat energy transferred in a reaction at **constant pressure**. The units of ΔH are **kJ mol^{-1}**.

2) You can find enthalpy changes either by **experiment** (p36) or in **textbooks**. Enthalpy changes you find in textbooks are usually **standard** enthalpy changes — enthalpy changes under **standard conditions** (**298 K** and **100 kPa**).

This is important because changes in enthalpy are affected by temperature and pressure — using standard conditions means that everyone knows exactly what the enthalpy change is describing.

3) You write $\Delta H^{\ominus}$ to show that measurements of enthalpy change were made under **standard conditions**, and that the elements were in their **standard states** (i.e. their states at a pressure of 100 kPa).

Reactions can be either **Exothermic** or **Endothermic**

Exothermic reactions **give out** energy. ΔH is **negative**. In exothermic reactions, the temperature often goes **up**.

Oxidation is exothermic. Here are two examples:

- The **combustion** of a fuel like methane ⟹ $CH_{4(g)} + 2O_{2(g)} \longrightarrow CO_{2(g)} + 2H_2O_{(l)}$ $\Delta H_r^{\ominus} = -890$ kJ mol^{-1} **exothermic**
- The oxidation of **carbohydrates**, such as glucose, $C_6H_{12}O_6$, in respiration.

The symbol $\Delta H_r^{\ominus}$ is explained on page 34.

Endothermic reactions **absorb** energy. ΔH is **positive**. In these reactions, the temperature often **falls**.

- The **thermal decomposition** of calcium carbonate is endothermic.

$$CaCO_{3(s)} \longrightarrow CaO_{(s)} + CO_{2(g)} \quad \Delta H_r^{\ominus} = +178 \text{ kJ mol}^{-1} \textbf{ endothermic}$$

- The main reactions of **photosynthesis** are also endothermic — sunlight supplies the energy.

Enthalpy Changes Can Be Calculated using **Average Bond Enthalpies**

1) You **need** energy to break bonds, so bond breaking is an **endothermic** process (ΔH is **positive**).
2) Energy is **released** when bonds are formed, so this is an **exothermic** process (ΔH is **negative**).
3) The **enthalpy change** for a reaction is the **overall effect** of these two changes. If you need **more** energy to **break** bonds than is released when bonds are made, ΔH is **positive**. If it's **less**, ΔH is **negative**.

> Enthalpy Change of Reaction = Total Energy Absorbed to Break Bonds − Total Energy Released in Making Bonds

4) **Bond enthalpy** is the **energy needed** to **break** a bond, or the **energy given out** when a bond **forms**. Stronger bonds have higher bond enthalpies.
5) Average bond enthalpies are published in textbooks to help calculate **enthalpy changes** of **reactions**. They're pretty straightforward to use...

Bond enthalpies always involve bond breaking in gaseous compounds. This makes comparisons fair.

Example: Calculate the overall enthalpy change for this reaction:
$N_2 + 3H_2 \rightarrow 2NH_3$
Use the average bond enthalpy values in the table.

Bond	Average Bond Enthalpy
N≡N	945 kJ mol^{-1}
H–H	436 kJ mol^{-1}
N–H	391 kJ mol^{-1}

Bonds broken: 1 × N≡N bond broken = 1 × 945 = 945 kJ mol^{-1}
3 × H–H bonds broken = 3 × 436 = 1308 kJ mol^{-1}

Total Energy Absorbed = 945 + 1308 = **2253 kJ mol^{-1}**

Bonds formed: 6 × N–H bonds formed = 6 × 391 = 2346 kJ mol^{-1}

Total Energy Released = **2346 kJ mol^{-1}**

Now you just subtract 'total energy released' from 'total energy absorbed':

Enthalpy Change of Reaction = 2253 − 2346 = **−93 kJ mol^{-1}**

If you can't remember which value to subtract from which, just take the smaller number from the bigger one then add the sign at the end — positive if 'bonds broken' was the bigger number (endothermic), negative if 'bonds formed' was bigger (exothermic).

Enthalpy Changes

Average Bond Enthalpies are not Exact

Water (H_2O) has got **two O–H bonds**. You'd think it'd take the same amount of energy to break them both... but it **doesn't**.

The **first** bond, $H–OH_{(g)}$: $E(H–OH) = +492 \text{ kJ mol}^{-1}$
The **second** bond, $H–O_{(g)}$: $E(H–O) = +428 \text{ kJ mol}^{-1}$

So, the **average** bond enthalpy is $\frac{492 + 428}{2}$ = **+460 kJ mol⁻¹**.

OH is a bit easier to break apart because of the extra electron repulsion.

The data book says the bond enthalpy for O–H is +463 kJ mol^{-1}. It's a bit different because it's the average for a much bigger range of molecules, not just water. For example, it includes the O-H bond in alcohols and carboxylic acids too.

Bond Enthalpy is Related to the Length of a Bond

1) In covalent molecules, the **positive nuclei** are attracted to the shared electrons.
2) But there isn't just an **attraction** between the nuclei and the shared electrons. The two **positively charged nuclei** also **repel** each other, as do the **electrons**.
3) The distance between the **two nuclei** is the distance where the **attractive** and **repulsive** forces balance each other. This distance is the **bond length**.
4) The **stronger** the attraction between the atoms, the higher the **bond enthalpy** and the **shorter** the bond length. It makes sense really. If there's more attraction, the nuclei will pull **closer** together.

A C=C bond has a **greater bond enthalpy** and is **shorter** than a C–C bond. Four electrons are shared in C=C and only two in C–C, so the **electron density** between the two carbon atoms is greater.
C≡C has an even **higher** bond enthalphy and is **shorter** than C=C — six electrons are shared here.

Bond	C–C	C=C	C≡C
Average Bond Dissociation Enthalpy (kJ mol^{-1})	+347	+612	+838
Bond length (nm)	0.154	0.134	0.120

Practice Questions

Q1 Is energy taken in or released when bonds are broken?

Q2 What state must compounds be in when bond enthalpies are measured?

Q3 Which is shorter, a single C–C bond or a double C=C bond?

Q4 Why might the figure in a textbook for a bond dissociation enthalpy not be the exact enthalpy change for that type of bond in a particular compound?

Exam Question

Q1

Bond	Compound	Bond length (nm)	Bond enthalpy (kJ mol^{-1})
C–O	alcohols	0.143	336
C=O	ketones	0.122	749

Explain why the bond energy of C=O in ketones is greater than the C–O bond energy in alcohols and the bond length of C=O is less than that of C–O. [6 marks]

If you can't stand the enthalpy, get out of the chemistry class...

Reactions are like pulling your Lego spaceship apart and building something new. Sometimes the bits get stuck together and you need to use loads of energy to pull 'em apart. Okay, so energy's not really released when you stick them together, but you can't have everything — and it wasn't that bad an analogy up till now. Ah, well... you best get on and learn this stuff.

Hess's Law

Now then... there's enthalpy change and there's enthalpy change.

There are Different Types of ΔH Depending On the **Reaction**

1) **Standard enthalpy change of reaction**, $\Delta H_r^\ominus$, is the enthalpy change when the reaction occurs in the **molar quantities** shown in the **chemical equation**, under standard conditions in their standard states.
2) **Standard enthalpy change of formation**, $\Delta H_f^\ominus$, is the enthalpy change when **1 mole** of a **compound** is formed from its **elements** in their standard states under standard conditions, e.g. $2C_{(s)} + 3H_{2(g)} + \frac{1}{2}O_{2(g)} \longrightarrow C_2H_5OH_{(l)}$
3) **Standard enthalpy change of combustion**, $\Delta H_c^\ominus$, is the enthalpy change when **1 mole** of a substance is completely **burned in oxygen** under standard conditions.

You use these different types of enthalpy change in calculations involving Hess's Law...

Hess's Law — the Total Enthalpy Change is **Independent** of the Route Taken

Hess's Law says that:

The **total enthalpy change** of a reaction is always **the same**, no matter **which route** is taken.

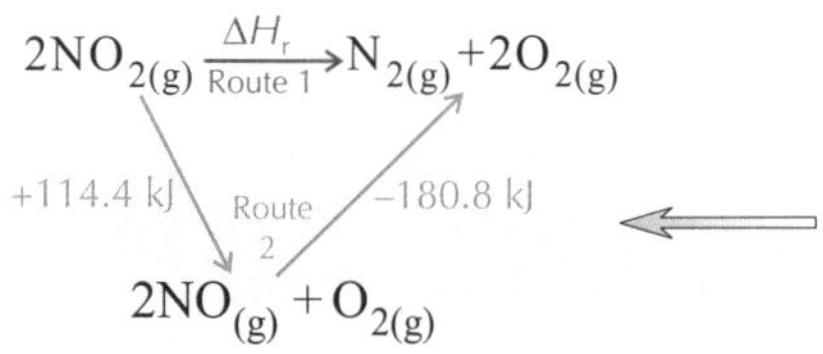

This law is handy for working out enthalpy changes that you **can't find directly** by doing an experiment.
Here's an example:
The **total enthalpy change** for route 1 is the **same as for route 2**.
So, $\Delta H_r = +114.4 + (-180.8) = -66.4$ kJ mol^{-1}.

Enthalpy Changes Can be Worked Out From **Enthalpies of Formation...**

Enthalpy changes of **formation** are useful for calculating enthalpy changes you can't find directly. You need to know $\Delta H_f^\ominus$ for **all** the reactants and products that are **compounds** (you can usually just look these up in textbooks). You also need to remember that the value of $\Delta H_f^\ominus$ for elements is **zero**.

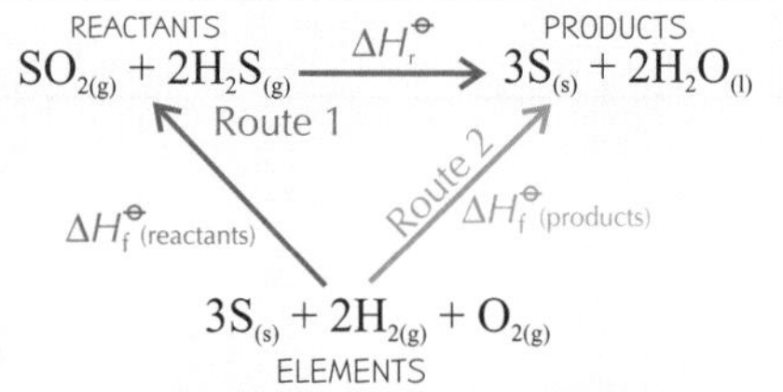

$\Delta H_f^\ominus[SO_{2(g)}] = -297$ kJ mol^{-1}

$\Delta H_f^\ominus[H_2S_{(g)}] = -20.2$ kJ mol^{-1}

$\Delta H_f^\ominus[H_2O_{(l)}] = -286$ kJ mol^{-1}

<u>Here's how to calculate $\Delta H_r^\ominus$ for the reaction shown...</u>

Using **Hess's Law**: Route 1 = Route 2

$\Delta H_r^\ominus$ + the sum of $\Delta H_f^\ominus$ (reactants) = the sum of $\Delta H_f^\ominus$ (products)

So, **$\Delta H_r^\ominus$ = the sum of $\Delta H_f^\ominus$ (products) – the sum of $\Delta H_f^\ominus$ (reactants)**

To find $\Delta H_r^\ominus$ of this reaction: $SO_{2(g)} + 2H_2S_{(g)} \rightarrow 3S_{(s)} + 2H_2O_{(l)}$
Just plug the numbers into the equation above:

$\Delta H_r^\ominus = [0 + (-286 \times 2)] - [-297 + (-20.2 \times 2)] = \mathbf{-234.6}$ **kJ mol^{-1}**

$\Delta H_f^\ominus$ of sulfur is zero — it's an element.

There's 2 moles of H_2O and 2 moles of H_2S.

...or From **Enthalpies of Combustion**

You can use a similar method to find **enthalpy changes of formation** from enthalpy changes of combustion.

<u>Here's how to calculate $\Delta H_f^\ominus$ of **ethanol**...</u>

Using Hess's Law: Route 1 = Route 2

$\Delta H_f^\ominus$[ethanol] + $\Delta H_c^\ominus$[ethanol] = $2\Delta H_c^\ominus$[C] + $3\Delta H_c^\ominus[H_2]$

$\Delta H_f^\ominus$[ethanol] + (−1367) = (2 × −394) + (3 × −286)

$\Delta H_f^\ominus$[ethanol] = −788 + −858 – (−1367) = **−279 kJ mol^{-1}**.

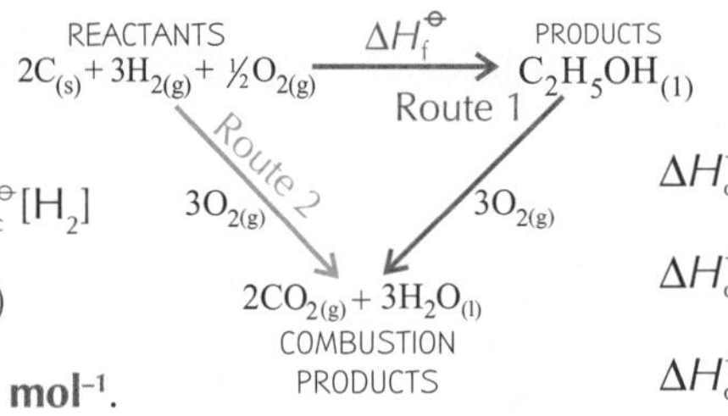

$\Delta H_c^\ominus[C_{(s)}] = -394$ kJ mol^{-1}

$\Delta H_c^\ominus[H_{2(g)}] = -286$ kJ mol^{-1}

$\Delta H_c^\ominus[\text{ethanol}_{(l)}] = -1367$ kJ mol^{-1}

Hess's Law

Reaction Enthalpies can be Calculated using Bond Enthalpies

There's not much you can't do with **Hess's Law**.*
You're still finding the enthalpy change for a **reaction**, but using **bond enthalpies** this time.

Example: Find the enthalpy change when the gases hydrogen and chlorine react to form 1 mole of hydrogen chloride gas.

Average bond enthalpies:
H – H: –436 kJ mol^{-1}
Cl – Cl: –243 kJ mol^{-1}
H – Cl: –431 kJ mol^{-1}

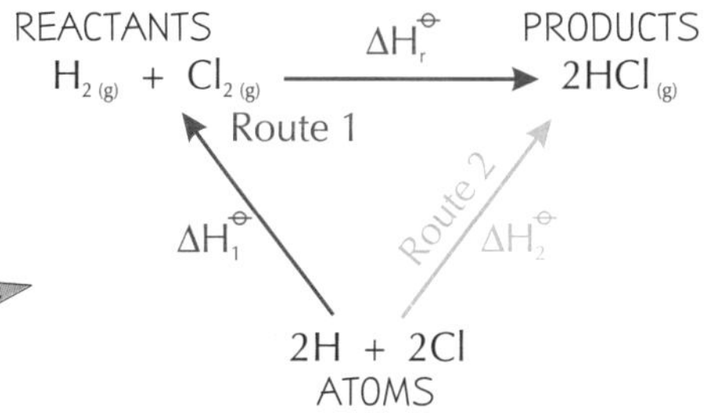

Here's your **Hess cycle** for the process.
And the calculation is nothing surprising...

Route 1 = Route 2
So $\Delta H_1 + \Delta H_r = \Delta H_2$, or alternatively: $\Delta H_r = \Delta H_2 - \Delta H_1$
Now you can put in the numbers: $\Delta H_r = (2 \times -431) - (-436 + -243) = -183$ kJ
But from the equation you can see that this would be the enthalpy change if 2 moles of HCl are formed. So the actual answer you need is –183 ÷ 2 = **–91.5 kJ**.

*For those few things, you need duct tape instead.

Practice Questions

Q1 Define: a) the standard enthalpy change of formation, b) the standard enthalpy change of combustion.
Q2 What does Hess's Law state?
Q3 What is the standard enthalpy change of formation of any element?

Exam Questions

Q1 If the standard enthalpy change of formation of $Al_2O_{3(s)}$ is –1676 kJ mol^{-1} and the standard enthalpy change of formation of $MgO_{(s)}$ is –602 kJ mol^{-1}, calculate the enthalpy change of the following reaction.

$$Al_2O_{3(s)} + 3Mg_{(s)} \rightarrow 2Al_{(s)} + 3MgO_{(s)}$$ [3 marks]

Q2 a) Write a balanced equation, including state symbols, for the complete combustion of propane gas. [3 marks]

b) Using the values of $\Delta H_f^\ominus$ given in the table, draw a Hess cycle to determine the standard enthalpy of combustion of propane. Hence calculate a value for $\Delta H_c^\ominus$ [propane]. [4 marks]

Substance	$\Delta H_f^\ominus$ in kJ/mol
C_3H_8(g)	–104.5
H_2O(l)	–286
CO_2(g)	–394

Q3 The equation below shows the fermentation of glucose.

$$C_6H_{12}O_{6\,(s)} \rightarrow 2C_2H_5OH_{(l)} + 2CO_{2\,(g)}$$

Calculate the enthalpy change for the reaction.
Use the Hess cycle and the standard enthalpies of combustion below in your calculations.

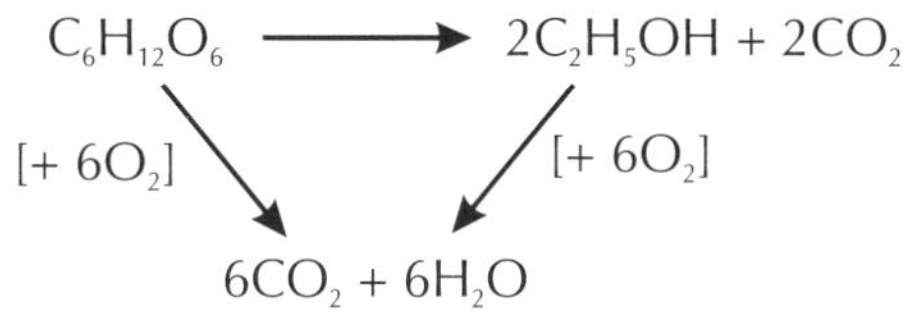

$\Delta H_c^\ominus$(glucose) = –2820 kJ mol^{-1}
$\Delta H_c^\ominus$(ethanol) = –1367 kJ mol^{-1} [3 marks]

To understand this lot, you're gonna need a bar of chocolate. Or two...

To get your head around those Hess diagrams, you're going to have to do more than skim them. It'll also help if you know the definitions for those standard enthalpy thingumabobs. If I were you, you know what I'd do... I'd read those Hess Cycle examples again and make sure you understand how the elements/compounds at each corner were chosen to be there.

Measuring Enthalpy Changes

You can find some enthalpy changes by doing an experiment and then a calculation...

You can find out ***Enthalpy Changes*** *using* ***Calorimetry***

In **calorimetry** you find how much heat is given out by a reaction by measuring the **temperature change** of some water.

1) To find the enthalpy of **combustion** of a **flammable liquid**, you burn it — using apparatus like this...
2) As the fuel burns, it heats the water. You can work out the **heat absorbed** by the water if you know the **mass of water**, the **temperature change of the water** (ΔT), and the **specific heat capacity of water** (= 4.18 J g^{-1} K^{-1}) — see below for the details.
3) Ideally, all the heat given out by the fuel as it burns would be **absorbed** by the water — allowing you to work out the enthalpy change of combustion (see below). In practice, you **always** lose some heat (as you heat the apparatus and the surroundings).

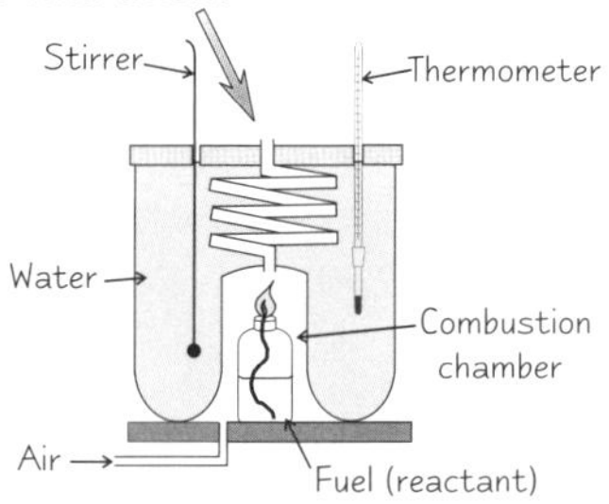

Calorimetry can also be used to calculate an enthalpy change for a reaction that happens **in solution**, such as **neutralisation** or **displacement**.

1) To find the enthalpy change in a neutralisation reaction, add a **known volume** of acid to an **insulated container** and measure the **temperature**.
2) Then add a **known volume** of alkali, and record the **temperature rise**. (Stir the solution to make sure the solution is evenly heated.)
3) You can work out the heat needed to **raise the temperature** of the solution formed using the formula below — this **equals** the **heat given out** by the **reaction**.
4) You can usually assume that all solutions (reactants and product) have the **same density as water**. This means you can use **volume** (rather than mass) in your calculations (as 1 cm^3 of water has a mass of 1 g). You can also usually assume that the specific heat capacity of the **solution** formed is the **same** as that for **water**.

The specific heat capacity of water is the amount of heat energy it takes to raise the temperature of 1 g of water by 1 K.

Calculate ***Enthalpy Changes*** *Using the* ***Equation q = mcΔT***

It seems there's a snazzy equation for everything these days, and enthalpy change is no exception:

$q = mc\Delta T$ where, q = heat lost or gained (in joules). This is the same as the enthalpy change if the pressure is constant.
m = mass of water in the calorimeter, or solution in the insulated container (in grams)
c = specific heat capacity of water (4.18 J $g^{-1}K^{-1}$)
ΔT = the change in temperature of the water or solution

Example:

In a laboratory experiment, 1.16 g of an organic liquid fuel was completely burned in oxygen.
The heat formed during this combustion raised the temperature of 100 g of water from 295.3 K to 357.8 K.
Calculate the standard enthalpy of combustion, $\Delta H_c^\ominus$, of the fuel. Its M_r is 58.

Remember — *m* is the mass of water, NOT the mass of fuel.

1. First off, you need to calculate the **amount of heat** given out by the fuel using ***q = mcΔT***.

$q = mc\Delta T$

$q = 100 \times 4.18 \times (357.8 - 295.3) = 26\,125 \text{ J} = 26.125 \text{ kJ}$

Change the amount of heat from J to kJ.

2. The standard enthalpy of combustion involves 1 mole of fuel. So next you need to find out **how many moles** of fuel produced this heat. It's back to the old $n = \frac{\text{mass}}{\text{M}}$ equation.

$$n = \frac{1.16}{58} = 0.02 \text{ moles of fuel}$$

3. So, the heat produced by 1 mole of fuel = $\frac{-26.125}{0.02}$

≈ **-1306 kJ mol^{-1}**. This is the standard enthalpy change of combustion.

It's negative because combustion is an exothermic reaction.

The actual $\Delta H_c^\ominus$ of this compound is -1615 kJ mol^{-1} — loads of heat has been **lost** and not measured (see next page).

Measuring Enthalpy Changes

Experimental Results *Always* Include *Errors*

You need know about **errors** in experiments — there are **two kinds**, and you always get **both** when you do an experiment.

1) **Systematic errors** are repeated **every time** you carry out the experiment, and always affect your result in the **same way** (e.g. they always make your answer bigger than it should be, or always make it smaller than it should be).
   They're due to the **experimental set-up**, or **limitations of the equipment**.
   For example, a balance that always reads 0.2 g less than the true value will result in systematic errors.
2) Here are some examples of **systematic errors** in calorimetry experiments...

Experimental problems with calorimetry generally...

- Some heat will be **absorbed** by the **container**, rather than going towards heating up the **water**.
- Some heat is always **lost to the surroundings** during the experiment (however well you **insulate** the container).

Experimental problems with flammable-liquid calorimetry...

- Some combustion may be **incomplete** — which will mean **less energy** will be given out.
- Some of the flammable liquid may escape by **evaporation** (it's usually quite **volatile**).

3) **Random errors** are... random — there's no pattern to them. And they **always** happen.
   The best way to deal with these is to **repeat** your experiment, and take the **average** of all your readings (see below).

Accuracy and *Reliability* are *NOT* the Same

Ideally you want both of these.

1) **Accuracy** and **reliability** are not the same thing. **Accuracy** means 'how close to the true value' your results are. **Reliability** means 'how reproducible' your results are.
2) **Repeating** an experiment shows whether your results are **reliable**. If you repeat an experiment and find the average (the mean), the effect of **random errors** is reduced — **positive** random errors and **negative** random errors should mostly **cancel out**. The more times you repeat an experiment, the more reliable your mean is.
3) But reliable results **aren't** necessarily more **accurate**. Repeating an experiment doesn't do anything to eliminate **systematic** errors.

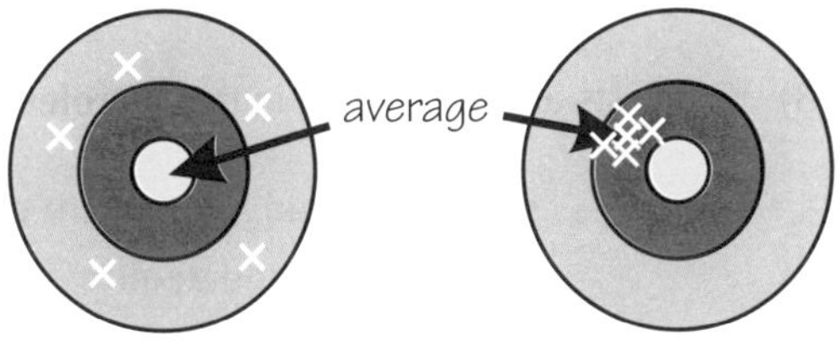

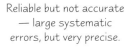

Accurate but not reliable — large random errors, but centred around the bullseye. The average is spot on.

Reliable but not accurate — large systematic errors, but very precise.

Practice Questions

Q1 Briefly describe an experiment that could be carried out to find the enthalpy change of a reaction.

Q2 Why is the enthalpy change determined in a laboratory likely to be lower than the value shown in a data book?

Q3 What equation is used to calculate the enthalpy change in a calorimetry experiment?

Exam Questions

Q1 The initial temperature of 25 cm^3 of 1.0 mol dm^{-3} hydrochloric acid in a polystyrene cup was measured as 19 °C.
This acid was exactly neutralised by 25 cm^3 of 1.0 mol dm^{-3} sodium hydroxide solution.
The maximum temperature of the resulting solution was measured as 25.5 °C.
Calculate the molar enthalpy change of neutralisation for the hydrochloric acid. (You may assume the neutral solution formed has a specific heat capacity of 4.18 J K^{-1} g^{-1}, and a density of 1.0 g cm^{-3}.) [7 marks]

Q2 A 50 cm^3 sample of 0.2 M copper(II) sulfate solution placed in a polystyrene beaker gave a temperature increase of 2.6 K when excess zinc powder was added and stirred. (Ignore the increase in volume due to the zinc.)

a) Calculate the enthalpy change when 1 mole of zinc reacts. Assume the solution's specific heat capacity is 4.18 J $g^{-1}K^{-1}$.
   The equation for the reaction is: $Zn_{(s)} + CuSO_{4(aq)} \rightarrow Cu_{(s)} + ZnSO_{4(aq)}$ [6 marks]

b) Describe one source of systematic error, and the effect this will have on the experimental results. [2 marks]

It can bz hard to noticz whzn you'rz making systzmatic zrrors...

Errors always happen — that's a fact of life. But that doesn't mean you can just turn your mind off to them. Sometimes you might be able to see what your systematic errors are, and do something about them. As for random errors... well, not being slapdash about things, plus repeating your experiments, can help reduce those. It's all quite "How Science Works-y", this.

Catalysts

You've met catalysts before at GCSE... so what's that look for...

Catalysts Increase the Rate of Reactions

You can use **catalysts** to make chemical reactions happen **faster**. Learn this definition:

A catalyst **speeds up** a chemical reaction, but can be recovered **chemically unchanged** at the end of the reaction.

Learn this definition of **catalysis** as well while you're at it...

Catalysis means **speeding up** a chemical reaction by using a catalyst.

1) Catalysts are **great**. They **don't** get used up in reactions, so you only need a **tiny bit** of catalyst to catalyse a **huge** amount of stuff. Many **do** take part in reactions, but they're **remade** at the end.
2) Catalysts are **very fussy** about which reactions they catalyse. Many will **only** work on a single reaction.

An example of a catalyst is **iron**. It's used in the **Haber process** to make ammonia.

$$N_{2(g)} + 3H_{2(g)} \xrightleftharpoons{Fe_{(s)}} 2NH_{3(g)}$$

3) Catalysts are used **loads** in the **petroleum industry**.

This'll make more sense when you read pages 46 and 47.

- Long chain alkanes are **cracked** into shorter, more useful molecules using **zeolite** catalysts.
- **Platinum** and **zeolite** catalysts are used in the **isomerisation** of straight chain alkanes.
- Catalysts made out of **platinum** and another metal are used in **reforming**. Reforming's where alkanes are converted to **cycloalkanes** and then to **arenes** (see page 47).

Heterogeneous Catalysts are in Different States from the Reactants

Heterogeneous catalysts are in a **different physical state** from the reactants.
So, if the catalyst is **solid**, the reactants will have to be **gases** or **liquids**. Here are two examples —

When **iron**'s used as a **catalyst** in the **Haber process** (see above), it's a **heterogeneous** catalyst. Iron's a **solid** and the reactants are hydrogen **gas** and nitrogen **gas**.

Take it from me... heterogeneous catalysts are more fun than going snowboarding dressed as a bishop.

Platinum is used as a **heterogeneous catalyst** in **catalytic converters**.
Catalytic converters sit quietly in a car **exhaust** and stop some **pollutants** from coming out.
Without catalytic converters, cars spew out **lots** of bad stuff, like **carbon monoxide** (which is poisonous), **oxides of nitrogen** and **unburnt hydrocarbons**. When the sun shines on nitrogen oxides and hydrocarbons, **low-level** (or ground level) **ozone** is produced.
This **isn't** good ozone, like the stuff in the sky, but can combine with other pollutants to form **smog** (which makes you **cough** and **choke**, and generally doesn't do you much good).
Catalytic converters **get rid** of them by changing them to **harmless gases**, like **water vapour** and **nitrogen**, or to **less harmful** ones like **carbon dioxide**.

Catalysts

Reactions Happen **On** Heterogeneous Catalysts

Solid heterogeneous catalysts can provide a **surface** for a reaction to take place on.

Here's how it works —

1) **Reactant molecules** arrive at the **surface** and **bond** with the solid catalyst. This is called **adsorption**.
2) The bonds between the **reactant's** atoms are **weakened** and **break up**. This forms **radicals**. These radicals then **get together** and make **new molecules**.
3) The new molecules are then detached from the catalyst. This is called **desorption**.

This example shows you how a catalytic converter changes the harmful gases **nitrogen monoxide, NO**, and **carbon monoxide, CO**, to **nitrogen** and **carbon dioxide**.

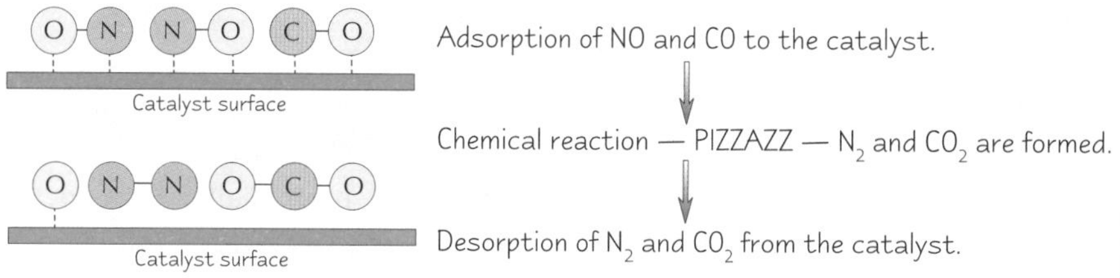
O
N
N
O
C
O
Catalyst surface
Catalyst surface
Adsorption of NO and CO to the catalyst.
Chemical reaction — PIZZAZZ — N_2 and CO_2 are formed.
Desorption of N_2 and CO_2 from the catalyst.

Remember — the adsorption **mustn't** be **too strong** or it won't **let go** of the atoms. **BUT** — it needs to be **strong enough** to **weaken** the bonds between the reactant molecules so that the new molecules can form.

Catalysts Can Be **Poisoned**

Catalysts can be **poisoned** so they don't work any more. For instance:

1) **Carbon monoxide**, CO, poisons the solid **iron catalyst** used in the **Haber process**.
2) **Lead** poisons **catalytic converters**, which are used to remove pollutants from car exhausts. This **was** a problem when lead was added to petrol, but it's OK now there's **unleaded petrol**.

Heterogeneous catalysts often get poisoned because the **poison** clings to the catalyst's surface **more strongly** than the reactant does. So, the catalyst is **prevented** from getting involved in the reaction it's meant to be **speeding up**.

Practice Questions

Q1 Explain what a catalyst is.

Q2 Give two examples of catalysts.

Q3 What is a heterogeneous catalyst? Explain how a heterogeneous catalyst works.

Exam Question

Q1 The following reaction represents an important stage in the industrial manufacture of sulfuric acid.

$$2SO_2(g) + O_2(g) \rightarrow 2SO_3(g)$$

a) The catalyst used is $V_2O_5(s)$. Explain why this is considered a heterogeneous catalyst here. [1 mark]

b) How could you show experimentally that $V_2O_5(s)$ is a catalyst and not a reactant? [1 mark]

c) Platinum catalysts are more efficient than vanadium catalysts but are seldom used because they are susceptible to poisoning by arsenic. Suggest an explanation for how the poisoning happens. [2 marks]

Adsorption — one of those words you'll only ever use in chemistry...

Heterogeneous catalysts (remember... hetero- = 'different') aren't too bad. I think of molecules as atoms holding on to each other using both hands. But then when they have to hang on to the catalyst as well, that leaves only one hand free to hold on to their atom pals — a weaker bond. Okay, as analogies go, it's pretty stupid... but it helped me remember.

Organic Groups

Organic chemistry is concerned with chemicals built around carbon chains. You might think this restriction would limit the amount that could be said. But no... there's a surprising amount to say about carbon chains. Whoop-di-doo.

Alkanes are **Saturated Hydrocarbons**

1) Alkanes have the **general formula C_nH_{2n+2}**. They only contain **carbon** and **hydrogen** atoms, so they're **hydrocarbons**.
2) Every carbon atom in an alkane has **four single bonds** with other atoms. It's **impossible** for carbon to make more than four bonds, so alkanes are **saturated**. Here are a few examples of alkanes:

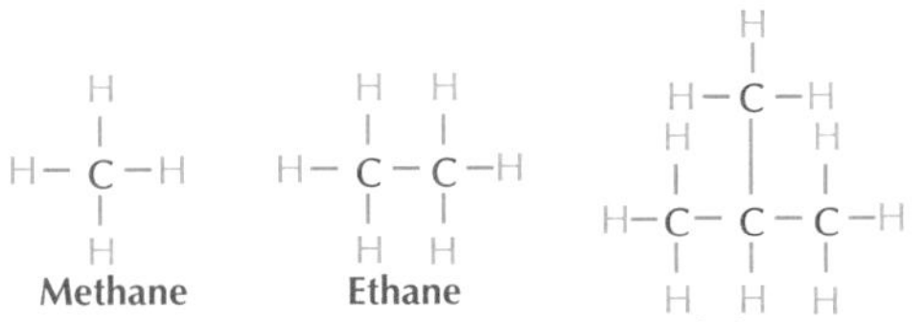

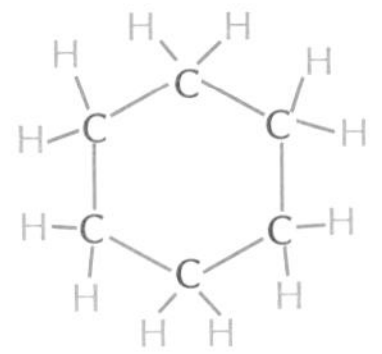

Cyclohexane C_6H_{12}

cycloalkanes have two fewer hydrogens than straight-chain alkanes

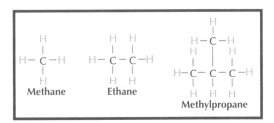

3) You get **cycloalkanes** (or cyclic alkanes) too. They have a ring of carbon atoms with two hydrogens attached to each carbon.
4) Cycloalkanes have a **different general formula** from that of normal alkanes (**C_nH_{2n}**), but they are still **saturated**.

Alkanes, alkenes, alchohols and ethers are examples of homologous series — families of compounds with a particular characteristic.

Alkenes are **Unsaturated Hydrocarbons**

1) Alkenes have the **general formula C_nH_{2n}**.
They're just made of carbon and hydrogen atoms, so they're also **hydrocarbons**.
2) Alkene molecules **all** have at least one **C=C double covalent bond**. Molecules with C=C double bonds are **unsaturated** because they can make more bonds with extra atoms in **addition** reactions.

Here are a few pretty diagrams of **alkenes**:

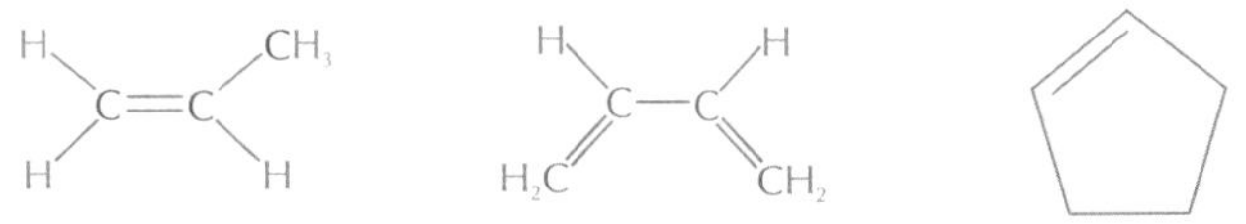

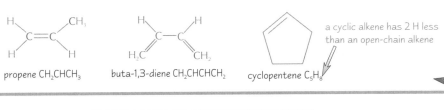

propene CH_2CHCH_3 buta-1,3-diene $CH_2CHCHCH_2$ cyclopentene C_5H_8

a cyclic alkene has 2 H less than an open-chain alkene

See the next page for more about how compounds are named.

Cyclopentene and benzene are shown using skeletal formulas — see p42.

Benzene has a Ring of **Delocalised Electrons**

1) **Benzene** (C_6H_6) is like a **cyclic alkene** with 6 carbons and 3 double bonds.
2) It's more **stable** (less reactive) than you'd expect though, because the double bond electrons are **delocalised** around the carbon ring (they're not attached to any particular carbon atom). That's why its symbol has a **circle** in it.

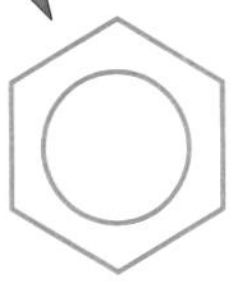

benzene

Compounds with **benzene ring structures** are called **arenes**, or **aromatic compounds**.
All other organic compounds (e.g. alkanes and alkenes) are called **aliphatic compounds**.

Alcohols and **Ethers** Contain **Oxygen**

1) The alcohol homologous series has the **general formula $C_nH_{2n+1}OH$**.
2) This –OH is called a **hydroxyl group** — it can be attached to any carbon atom in the chain.

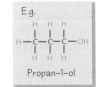

E.g.

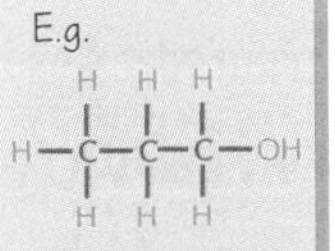

Propan-1-ol

E.g.

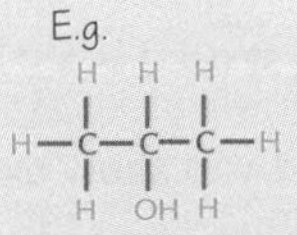

Propan-2-ol

3) **Ethers** have an **oxygen atom** interrupting the carbon chain.
4) Ethers and alcohols can be **isomers** of each other (see p42), but they're different homologous series.

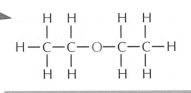

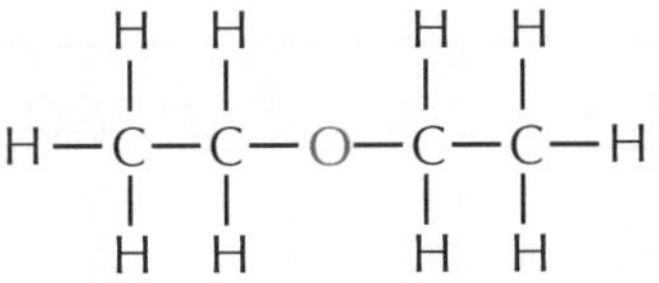

Organic Groups

Nomenclature is a Fancy Word for the **Naming** of Organic Compounds

You can name any organic compound using these **rules** of nomenclature.

1) Count the carbon atoms in the **longest continuous chain** — this gives you the stem:

Number of carbons	1	2	3	4	5	6	7	8	9	10
Stem	meth-	eth-	prop-	but-	pent-	hex-	hept-	oct-	non-	dec-

2) The **main functional group** (see next page) of the molecule usually gives you the end of the name (the **suffix**) — see the table on the right.

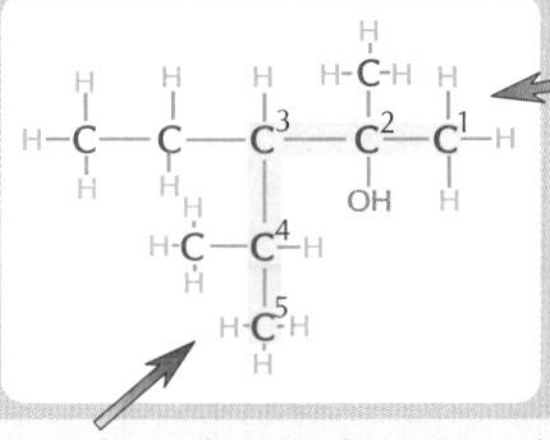

The longest chain is **5** carbons, so the stem is **pent-**

Don't forget — the longest carbon chain may be bent.

The main functional group is **-OH**, so the compound's name is going to be based on "**pentanol**".

3) Number the carbons in the **longest** carbon chain so that the carbon with the main functional group attached has the lowest possible number.
If there's more than one longest chain, pick the one with the **most side-chains**.
4) Write the carbon number that the functional group is on **before the suffix**.
Here, the –OH is on carbon-2, so it's pentan-2-ol.
5) Any side-chains or less important functional groups are added as prefixes at the start of the name. Put them in **alphabetical** order, with the **number** of the carbon atom each is attached to.
6) If there's more than one **identical** side-chain or functional group, use **di-** (2), **tri-** (3) or **tetra-** (4) before that part of the name — but ignore this when working out the alphabetical order.

There's an ethyl group on carbon-3, and methyl groups on carbon-2 and carbon-4, so it's **3-ethyl-2,4-dimethylpentan-2-ol**

For Unit 1, you only have to be able to name alkanes and alcohols. Phew...

Homologous series	Prefix or Suffix	Example
alkanes	-ane	Propane $CH_3CH_2CH_3$
side-chains in branched alkanes	alkyl- (-yl)	methylpropane $CH_3CH(CH_3)CH_3$
alkenes	-ene	propene $CH_3CH{=}CH_2$
haloalkanes/ halogenoalkanes	chloro- bromo- iodo-	chlorethane CH_3CH_2Cl
alcohols	-ol	ethanol CH_3CH_2OH
aldehydes	-al	ethanal CH_3CHO
ketones	-one	propanone CH_3COCH_3
cycloalkanes	cyclo- -ane	cyclohexane C_6H_{12}
arenes	benzene	ethylbenzene $C_6H_5C_2H_5$
carboxylic acids	-oic acid	ethanoic acid CH_3COOH
ethers	alkoxy-	methoxypropane $CH_3OCH_2CH_2CH_3$

Practice Questions

Q1 Describe the main features of alkanes, alkenes, alcohols and ethers.

Q2 What is a benzene ring? Draw its symbol.
Explain why it is drawn like this, rather than with alternate single and double bonds.

Q3 In what order should prefixes be listed in the name of an organic compound?

Exam Questions

Q1 There are a number of different molecules with the molecular formula C_5H_{10}.
Draw hydrocarbons with this formula that match the following descriptions:

a) a cycloalkane, [2 marks]

b) a branched alkene, [2 marks]

c) an unbranched alkene. [2 marks]

Q2 The following homologous series each include a compound with the formula C_3H_8O.
Draw the structure of the compound C_3H_8O in each homologous series.

a) ethers, [1 mark]

b) alcohols. [1 mark]

It's as easy as 1,2,3-trichloropentan-2-ol...

The best thing to do now is find some random organic compounds and work out their names using the rules. Then have a bash at it the other way around — read the name and draw the compound. It might seem a wee bit tedious now, but come the exam, you'll be thanking me. Doing the exam questions will give you some good practice too.

Isomerism

Isomers have the same molecular formula, but different arrangements of atoms.

*There are **Loads of Ways** of **Representing** Organic Compounds*

TYPE OF FORMULA	WHAT IT SHOWS YOU	FORMULA FOR BUTAN-1-OL
General formula	A formula that can describe **any member** of a family of compounds.	$C_nH_{2n+1}OH$ (for all alcohols)
Molecular formula	The **actual** number of atoms of each element in a molecule.	$C_4H_{10}O$
Structural formula	Shows the atoms **carbon by carbon**, with the attached hydrogens and functional groups.	$CH_3CH_2CH_2CH_2OH$
Displayed formula	Shows how all the atoms are **arranged**, and all the bonds between them.	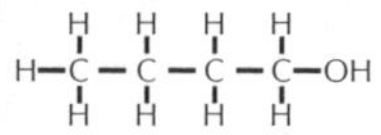
Skeletal formula	Shows the **bonds** of the carbon skeleton **only**, with any functional groups. The hydrogen and carbon atoms aren't shown. This is handy for drawing large complicated structures, like cyclic hydrocarbons.	

A functional group is a reactive part of a molecule — it gives it many of its chemical properties.

***Structural Isomers** have different **Structural Arrangements** of Atoms*

In structural isomers, the atoms are **connected** in different ways. But they still have the **same molecular formula**. There are **three** different types of structural isomer:

1 DIFFERENT CARBON SKELETON

The **carbon skeleton** can be arranged differently — for example, as a **straight chain**, or **branched** in different ways.

These isomers have **similar chemical properties** — but their **physical properties**, like boiling point, will be **different** because of the change in shape of the molecule.

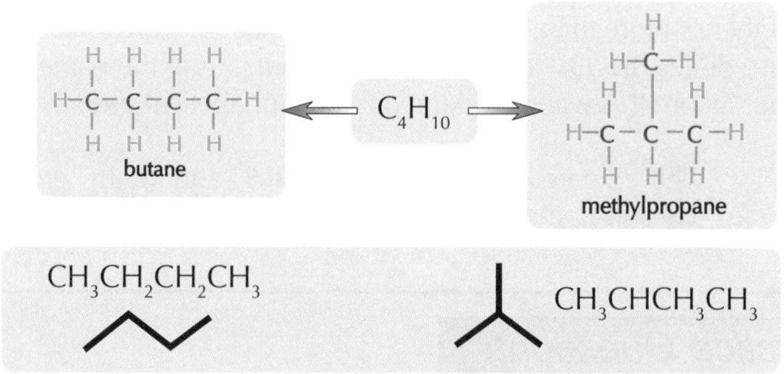

2 FUNCTIONAL GROUP IN DIFFERENT PLACE

The **skeleton** and the **functional group** could be the same, only with the functional group attached to a **different carbon atom**.

These also have **different physical properties**, and the **chemical properties** might be **different** too.

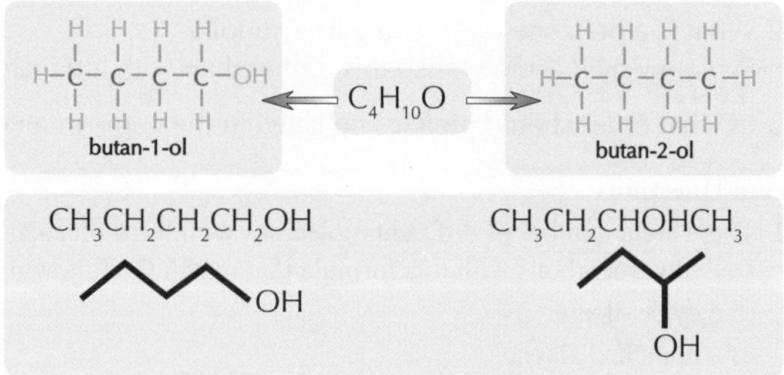

3 DIFFERENT FUNCTIONAL GROUPS

The same atoms can be arranged into **different functional groups**.

These have very **different physical** and **chemical** properties.

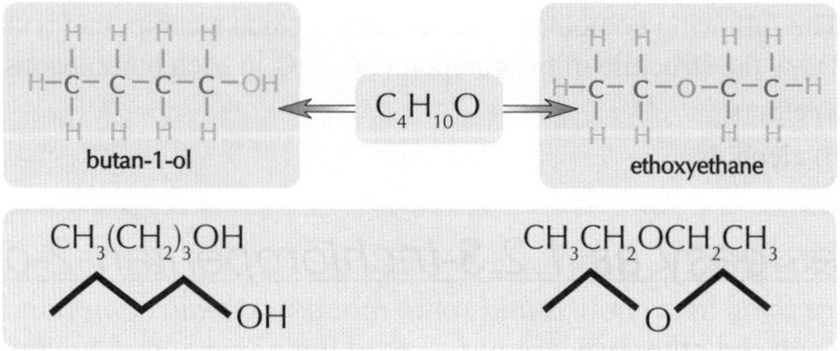

Isomerism

*Don't be Fooled — What Looks Like an Isomer Might **Not** Be*

Atoms can rotate as much as they like around single **C–C bonds**. Remember this when you work out structural isomers — sometimes what looks like an isomer, isn't.

For example, **propanol** can only be put together in two different ways...

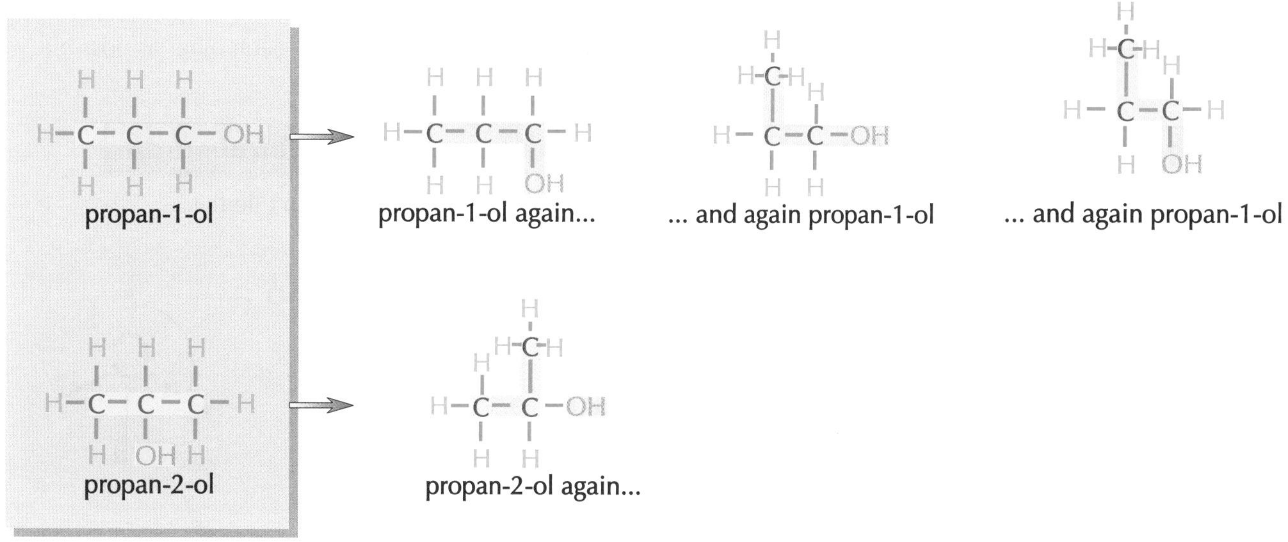

Practice Questions

Q1 Describe the differences between a structural formula, a displayed formula and a skeletal formula.

Q2 What are structural isomers?

Q3 Describe the three different types of structural isomer.

Q4 Explain why propene (C_3H_6) has no isomers.

Exam Questions

Q1 Draw the displayed formula of each of the four isomers of $C_4H_{10}O$ which contain an alcohol functional group. Give the name of each compound. [8 marks]

Q2 Draw the displayed and skeletal formulas of a compound that matches each of the descriptions below:
a) a cyclic alkane with the formula C_6H_{12}, [2 marks]
b) a branched alkene with the formula C_4H_8. [2 marks]

Q3 Name the following molecules:

a)

[1 mark]

b)

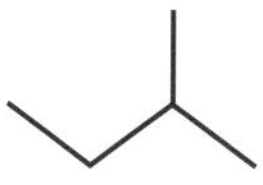

[1 mark]

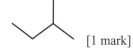

Human structural isomers...

Shapes of Organic Molecules

You've seen some of these ideas before, but this time we're talking organic molecules...

Electron Repulsion Helps Explain the Shapes of Molecules

1) You've seen before that the **shape** of a molecule depends on the electrons in the **outer shells** of the atoms involved.
2) In a nutshell...
   - Electron pairs **repel** each other.
   - So molecules take the shape that allows all the pairs of electrons to get as **far** from each other as possible.

Look at page 24 for a reminder about how electron pairs repel each other.

Single-Bonded Carbon Atoms Have Their Bonds Arranged Like a Tetrahedron

1) When a carbon atom makes four single bonds (as in alkanes), the molecule doesn't lie flat. Instead the atoms around each carbon form **3D tetrahedral shapes**.

A tetrahedron is a triangular-based pyramid.

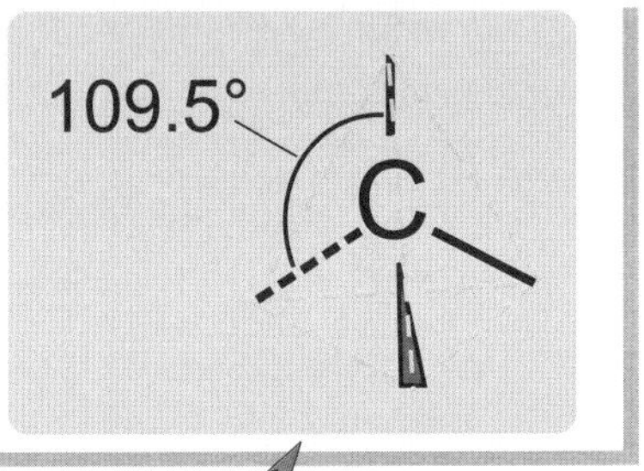

2) The angle between any two of the covalent bonds is **109.5°**. At this angle, the bonds (i.e. the electron pairs) are as **far apart** from each other as possible.

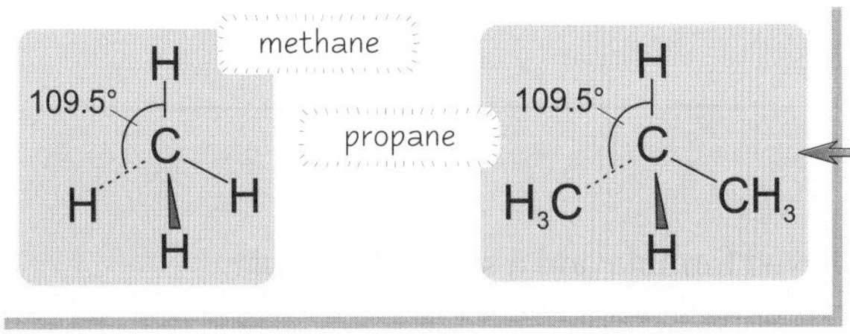

3) To show this a bit more clearly, **wedges** are used to represent bonds 'coming out of the page' and **dotted lines** represent bonds 'going into the page'.

4) This **tetrahedral** shape around each carbon atom means that single-bonded carbon chains containing 3 or more carbon atoms form a 'wiggly line' — **3D models** show this pretty well (see next page).

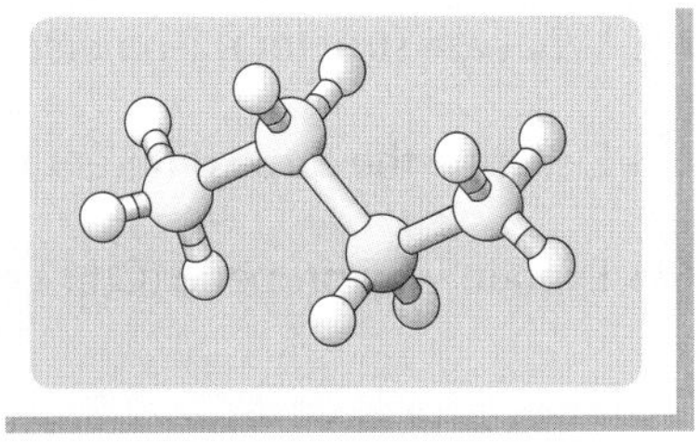

Atoms Round a Double-Bonded Carbon form an Equilateral Triangle

When there's a **double-bond** involved, the situation is different.

1) The C=C double bond and the atoms bonded to these carbons are **planar** (flat).

The bond angles are all 120°.

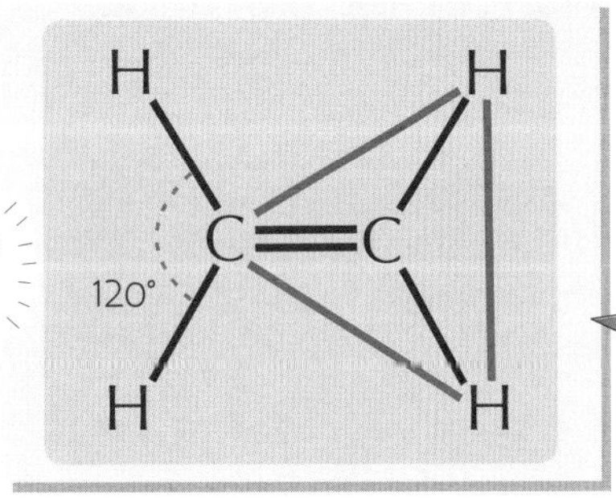

2) Each double-bond carbon and the atoms attached to it are said to be **trigonal planar** — the attached atoms are at the corners of an imaginary **equilateral triangle**.

3) Only the **double-bonded** carbon atoms in a molecule (plus the atoms attached to them) lie in a plane.
   For example, ethene, C_2H_4, is completely planar.
   But in propene, C_3H_6, only the >C=C< unit is planar.

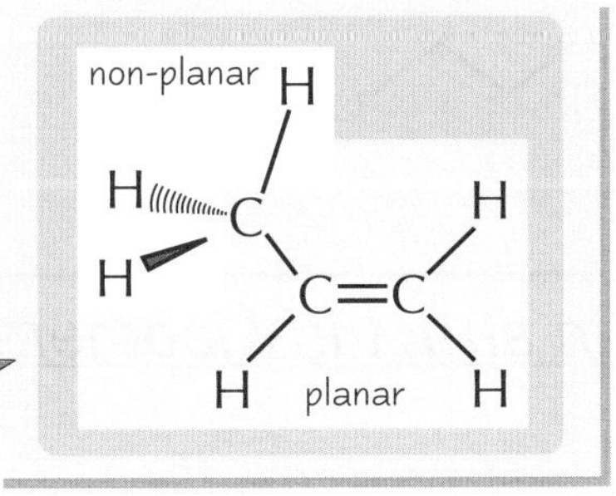

Shapes of Organic Molecules

Models Make it **Easier** to Understand the **Shapes** of Molecules

You can use a **molecular modelling** kit to get a better idea of molecular shape.

1) A **space-filling model** shows the shape of the atoms including the electron orbitals, but you can't easily see the bonding between atoms.
2) A **ball-and-stick model** shows the bonds between the atoms more clearly — you can see that atoms can **rotate freely** around **C–C** single bonds.

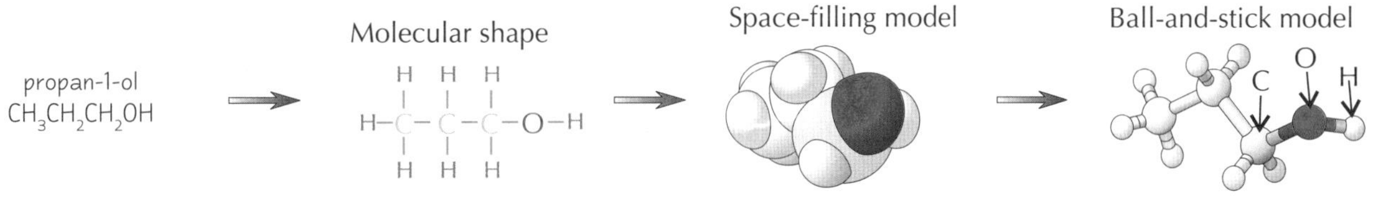

You can make molecules with double-bonds using these kits too.
Kinda pretty...

These kits also model how C=C double bonds have restricted rotation — see p104.

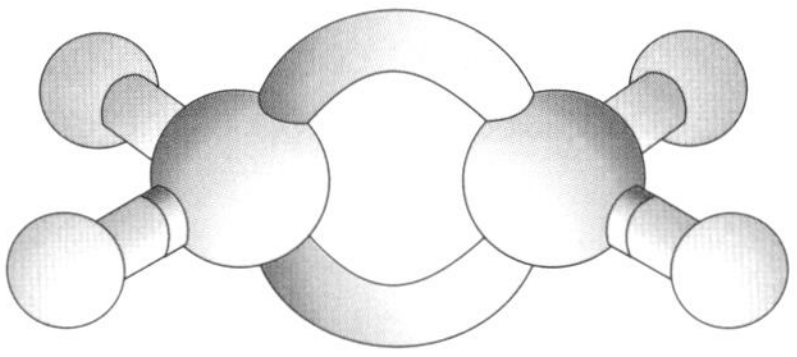

Practice Questions

Q1 Explain what determines the basic shape of a molecule.

Q2 Describe the shape of a molecule of: a) methane, b) butane.

Q3 How does the arrangement of atoms around a carbon atom with only single bonds differ from the arrangement of atoms around a carbon atom that forms a double bond?

Exam Questions

Q1 a) Use wedges and dotted lines to show the three-dimensional structure of propene.
Mark two different bond angles on your diagram. Label each of these angles with its size. [3 marks]

b) On the right is the displayed formula of propa-1,2-diene.
Mark two different bond angles on your diagram.
Label each of these angles with its size. [2 marks]

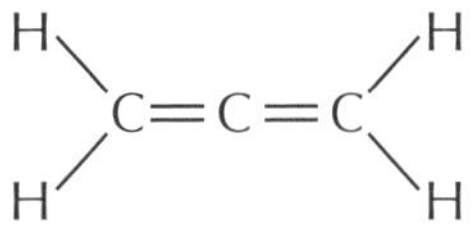

Q2 a) Write the molecular formula for methanol. [1 mark]

b) (i) Use wedges and dotted lines to show the three-dimensional structure of methanol. [1 mark]

(ii) On your diagram, mark one tetrahedral bond angle. [1 mark]

Q3 a) Use wedges and dotted lines to show the three-dimensional structure of methylpropane. [2 marks]

b) Explain why the molecule exists as this shape. [2 marks]

Models aren't just pretty — they're clever too...

Getting your head around how atoms are arranged in organic molecules is tricky. Remember — double bond carbons and the atoms attached to them form a flat unit, whereas if there are only single bonds, the atoms will form 3-D tetrahedral shapes. It's no wonder that displayed formulas of organic molecules are usually drawn instead. It makes life a lot simpler.

Catalysts and Petroleum

Petroleum is just a fancy word for crude oil — the black, yukky stuff they get out of the ground using huge oil wells.

Crude Oil is a Mixture of Hydrocarbons

Hydrocarbons are compounds that contain only hydrogen and carbon.

1) Petroleum or crude oil is mostly **alkanes**. They range from **smallish alkanes**, like propane, to **massive alkanes** with more than 50 carbons.
2) Crude oil isn't very useful as it is, but you can **separate** it into more useful bits (or **fractions**) by **fractional distillation**.

- First, the crude oil is **vaporised** at about 350 °C.
- The vaporised crude oil goes into the **fractionating column** and rises up through the trays. The largest hydrocarbons don't **vaporise** at all, because their boiling points are too high — they just run to the bottom and form a gooey **residue**.
- As the crude oil vapour goes up the fractionating column, it gets **cooler**. Because of the different chain lengths, each fraction **condenses** at a different temperature. The fractions are **drawn off** at different levels in the column.
- The hydrocarbons with the **lowest boiling points** don't condense. They're drawn off as **gases** at the top of the column.

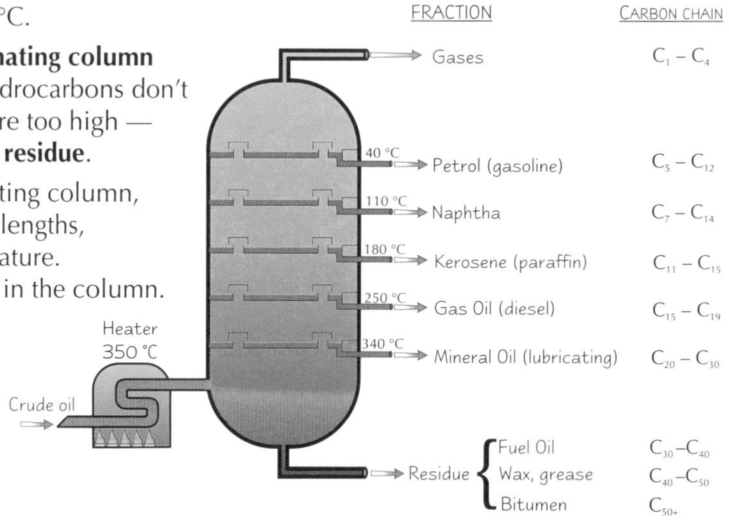

Heavy Fractions can be 'Cracked' to Make Smaller Molecules

1) People want loads of the **light** fractions like petrol and naphtha. They don't want so much of the **heavier** stuff like bitumen though.
2) To meet this demand, the less popular heavier fractions are **cracked**. Cracking involves **breaking** long-chain alkanes into **smaller** hydrocarbons (which can include alkenes). It involves breaking the **C–C bonds**.

You could crack **decane** like this —

$$\underset{\text{decane}}{C_{10}H_{22}} \rightarrow \underset{\text{ethene}}{C_2H_4} + \underset{\text{octane}}{C_8H_{18}}$$

There are **two types** of **cracking** you need to know about:

THERMAL CRACKING

- It takes place at **high temperature** (up to 1000 °C) and **high pressure** (up to 70 atm).
- It produces a lot of **alkenes**.
- These **alkenes** are used to make heaps of valuable products, like **polymers**. A good example is **poly(ethene)**, which is made from ethene (have a squiz at page 102 for more on polymers).

CATALYTIC CRACKING

- This makes mostly **motor fuels** and **aromatic** hydrocarbons (see page 40).
- It uses something called a **zeolite catalyst**, at a **slight pressure** and **high temperature** (about 450 °C).
- Using a catalyst **cuts costs**, because the reaction can be done at a **lower** temperature and pressure. The catalyst also **speeds** up the reaction, and time is money and all that.

Isomerisation creates Branched-Chain Isomers

See page 42 for more info on isomers.

Catalysts can do more than break down big molecules to make smaller ones, though.

1) For some uses (see the next page for an example), **branched-chain** isomers are more useful than the **straight-chain** ones.
2) **Isomerisation** is often carried out by heating a **straight-chain** alkane with a **platinum catalyst** stuck on inert aluminium oxide. The molecule is broken up and put back together as a **branched-chain isomer**.

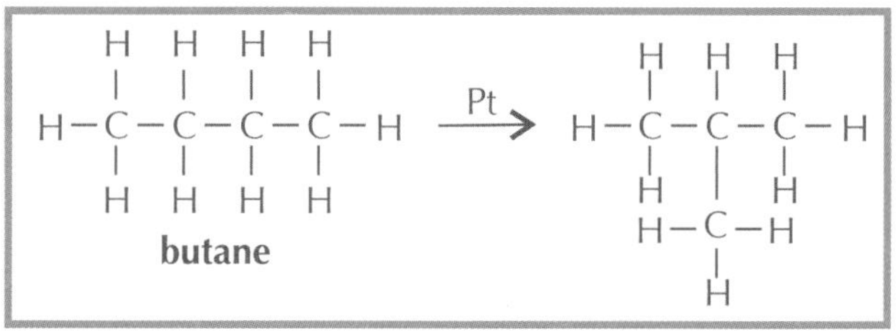

3) A form of **zeolite** (a mineral with minute tunnels and cavities) is then used as a **molecular sieve** to separate the isomers. The molecules which still have **straight chains** go through the zeolite 'sieve' and are **recycled**.

Catalysts and Petroleum

Alkanes can be **Reformed** into **Cycloalkanes** and **Arenes**

Reforming converts **alkanes** into **arenes** (aromatic hydrocarbons — see page 40).

It also needs a catalyst (e.g. platinum stuck on aluminium oxide again).

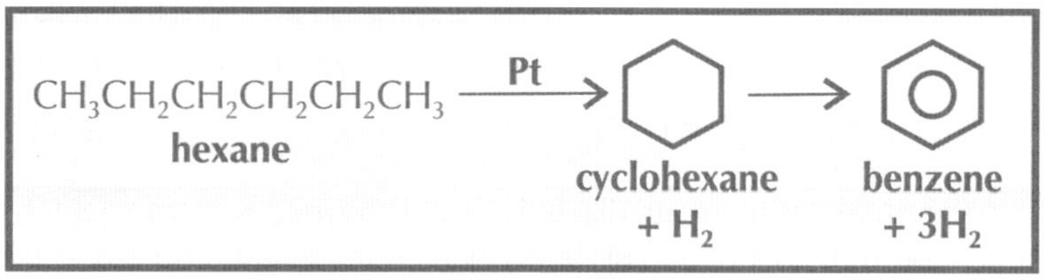

Hydrocarbons with a **High Octane Rating** Burn More **Smoothly**

And here's the explanation as to **why** you'd want fewer straight-chain alkanes in your fuel...

1) Here's a super-quick whizz through how a **petrol engine** works:
   The **fuel/air** mixture is squashed by a **piston** and **ignited** with a spark, creating an **explosion**. This drives the piston up again, turning the **crankshaft**. Four pistons work **one after the other**, so that the engine runs smoothly.
2) The problem is, **straight-chain alkanes** in petrol tend to **auto-ignite** — when the fuel/air mixture is compressed they explode without being ignited by the spark. This extra explosion causes '**knocking**' in the engine.
3) To get rid of knocking and make combustion more efficient, **shorter branched-chain alkanes**, **cycloalkanes** and **arenes** are included in petrols, creating a **high octane rating**.

The octane rating of a petrol tells you how likely it is to auto-ignite.

The higher the number, the less likely it is to auto-ignite.

It's based on a scale where 100% heptane has a rating of 0, and 100% 2,2,4-trimethylpentane has a rating of 100.

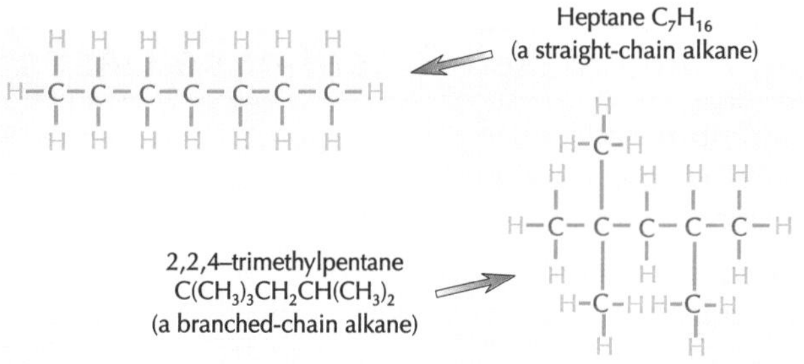

Practice Questions

Q1 Describe the process of fractional distillation.

Q2 What is cracking?

Q3 Describe the processes of: a) isomerisation, b) reforming.

Exam Question

Q1 Crude oil is a source of fuels and petrochemicals. It's vaporised and separated into fractions using fractional distillation.

a) Some heavier fractions are processed using cracking.
   (i) Give one economic reason why cracking is carried out. [2 marks]
   (ii) Write an equation for the thermal cracking of dodecane, $C_{12}H_{26}$. [1 mark]

b) Some hydrocarbons are processed using isomerisation or reforming, producing a petrol with a high octane rating.
   (i) What is meant by a petrol's octane rating? [2 marks]
   (ii) What types of compound are found in a petrol with a high octane rating? What effect do they have on the petrol's performance? [4 marks]
   (iii) Draw and name two isomers formed from pentane by isomerisation. Which isomer would increase the octane rating of a petrol the most? [5 marks]

Crude oil — not the kind of oil you could take home to meet your mother...

This ain't the most exciting page in the history of the known universe. Although in a galaxy far, far away there may be lots of pages on even more boring topics. But, that's neither here nor there, cos you've got to learn the stuff anyway. Get these processes straight in your brain and make sure you know why people bother to do them.

Fuels

If we didn't burn fuels to keep warm and power vehicles, we'd all wear lots of jumpers and use pogo sticks. Maybe.

Many **Organic** Compounds Burn to Give **Carbon Dioxide**, **Water** and **Heat**

1) When you burn an alkane in plenty of **oxygen**, you end up with **carbon dioxide** and **water** (in the form of steam).
   E.g. $CH_{4(g)} + 2O_{2(g)} \rightarrow CO_{2(g)} + 2H_2O_{(g)}$ $C_8H_{18(g)} + 12\frac{1}{2}O_{2(g)} \rightarrow 8CO_{2(g)} + 9H_2O_{(g)}$
2) The combustion of an alkane is an **exothermic** reaction, which is why alkanes make great **fuels** — burning just one mole of methane releases a humungous amount of energy.
3) **Alcohols** react in a similar way. When an alcohol burns, the products are also just **carbon dioxide** and **water**.
   E.g. $2CH_3OH_{(l)} + 3O_{2(g)} \rightarrow 2CO_{2(g)} + 4H_2O_{(g)}$ $C_2H_5OH_{(l)} + 3O_{2(g)} \rightarrow 2CO_{2(g)} + 3H_2O_{(g)}$
   These reactions are also very exothermic — meaning alcohols can be used as fuels too.

Carbon Monoxide is Formed if Alkanes Burn **Incompletely**

If there's not enough oxygen, hydrocarbons **combust incompletely**, and you get carbon monoxide gas instead of carbon dioxide. E.g. $CH_{4(g)} + 1\frac{1}{2}O_{2(g)} \rightarrow CO_{(g)} + 2H_2O_{(g)}$ $C_8H_{18(l)} + 8\frac{1}{2}O_{2(g)} \rightarrow 8CO_{(g)} + 9H_2O_{(g)}$

This is bad news because carbon monoxide gas is **poisonous**. Carbon monoxide molecules bind to the same sites on **haemoglobin molecules** in red blood cells as oxygen molecules. So **oxygen** can't be carried around the body.

Burning Fuels Makes **Greenhouse Gases**

Burning **carbon-based** fuels (e.g. in transport, power stations etc.) is one factor that's causing an increase in the amount of **carbon dioxide** in the atmosphere. This build-up of carbon dioxide is causing something called the '**enhanced greenhouse effect**'.

1) This **enhanced greenhouse effect** (see page 88 for more information) is causing the Earth to **warm up** slowly and is a **huge** problem. It's leading to effects such as the melting of the polar ice caps.
2) The Earth naturally radiates infrared radiation out into space. But greenhouse gases absorb some of this **infrared**, meaning the Earth becomes warmer.
3) **Controlling** this global warming isn't easy. It'll need a **sustained** effort from people in countries all around the world. Some ways for countries to reduce their CO_2 emissions are covered on the next page.

Greenhouse gases absorb infrared radiation emitted by the Earth

And if that's Not Bad Enough... **Burning Fuels** Produces Other **Pollutants** Too

UNBURNT HYDROCARBONS AND OXIDES OF NITROGEN (NO_x) CONTRIBUTE TO SMOG

1) Engines **don't burn** all the fuel molecules. Some of these come out as **unburnt hydrocarbons**.
2) **Oxides of nitrogen** (NO_x) are produced when the high pressure and temperature in a car engine cause the nitrogen and oxygen in the air to react together.
3) The hydrocarbons and nitrogen oxides react in the presence of sunlight to form **ground-level ozone** (O_3). This is a component of **photochemical smog**, which can irritate eyes, aggravate respiratory problems and even cause lung damage (ozone isn't nice stuff, unless it's high up in the atmosphere as part of the ozone layer — see p. 92).

SULFUR DIOXIDE LEADS TO ACID RAIN

1) **Acid rain** is caused by burning fossil fuels that contain **sulfur**. The sulfur burns to produce **sulfur dioxide** gas which then enters the atmosphere, dissolves in the moisture, and is converted into **sulfuric acid**.
   The same process occurs when nitrogen dioxide escapes into the atmosphere — nitric acid is produced.
2) Acid rain destroys trees and vegetation, as well as corroding buildings and statues and killing fish in lakes.

Any tiny particles of liquid suspended in the air (such as these acid droplets) are particulates. Solid particulates, such as carbon, are also produced. Particulates are bad because they can settle in people's lungs and cause trouble. They also contribute to cardiovascular problems (which can lead to heart attacks and strokes).

Fuels

Society Needs To **Decide** How to Handle All These **Problems**

Pollution is a serious problem. Some pollutants cause health problems for **individuals**, while others can cause problems on a much larger scale, affecting the whole **planet**.

1) **Transport**, **industry** and **power generation** are the biggest sources of air pollutants.
2) Sulfur dioxide is removed from power station flue gases using **calcium oxide**.
3) **Catalytic converters** reduce unburnt hydrocarbon, sulfur dioxide and nitrogen oxide emissions from **vehicles**. Also, oxygenates are now added to petrol to reduce carbon monoxide emissions — they help the fuel to combust fully.
4) But our **carbon dioxide** emissions remain pretty high — partly because most of our electricity comes from burning **fossil fuels**, and partly because the number of cars on the roads has steadily **increased**.
5) There are various things that could be done fairly **quickly** to reduce the problem of pollution. Some methods are easier to adopt than others though. For example...
   - Governments can change **laws** to reduce pollution. For example, in the UK **sulfur** and **nitrogen oxide** emissions from power stations have been **reduced** as **laws** about emissions have been tightened. Also, new vehicles are not allowed to pollute above a certain level, and the yearly MOT inspection includes an **emissions test**. Catalytic converters have been **compulsory** on new cars in the UK since 1992.
   - Governments can **tax** pollution more highly — e.g. raise taxes on fuel, or on highly polluting engines.
   - People can reduce the amount of pollution they produce by changing their **behaviour** — e.g. they could be encouraged to make **fewer** car or plane **journeys**, '**car share**' more frequently, and so on.

   But will people be **willing** to pay higher taxes, or change their behaviour in this way?
6) Other things will take **longer** to implement — e.g. develop **new fuels** that cause less pollution (see next page).
7) One thing is for sure... at some point in the future, we'll have to do things very differently. This is because of a different kind of problem...

Fossil Fuels are **Non-Renewable**

The various kinds of pollution produced by burning these fuels aren't the only problems. They're also becoming more and more scarce as we use more and more of them.

1) The three fossil fuels **coal**, **oil** and **natural gas** are major fuels. But, there's a finite amount of them and they're running out.
2) Oil will be the first to go — and as it gets really scarce, it'll become more **expensive**. It's not **sustainable** to keep using them willy-nilly.

(There's lots about sustainable energy sources on the next page).

"Bruce... bring some more fossils — the barbie's going out."

Practice Questions

Q1 Are the combustion reactions of alkanes endothermic or exothermic?

Q2 Write an equation for the combustion of ethanol.

Q3 Name two types of pollution caused by burning fossil fuels. Describe how this pollution could be reduced.

Exam Questions

Q1 a) Write a balanced equation for the complete combustion of octane. [2 marks]

b) Explain why burning an alkane in a limited supply of oxygen is potentially dangerous. [2 marks]

Q2 a) (i) Explain how the burning of fossil fuels can lead to photochemical smog. [4 marks]

(ii) State how the levels of the pollutants that lead to photochemical smog can be reduced. [1 mark]

b) Another problem caused by pollution is acid rain.
Name two pollutants which lead to acid rain, and explain how this problem can be reduced. [3 marks]

c) Describe two types of measure that governments can take to try to reduce pollution. [2 marks]

These pages are packed fuel with important facts...

We rely on fuels to provide the energy for our 21st century lifestyles — cars-a-plenty, power on tap, and so on. It's certainly convenient, but there are problems too — such as the greenhouse effect, plus the fact that we're going to run out of fossil fuels fairly soon-ish. Learn all the stuff and all the biz on these pages — even those fiddly technical details.

Fuels of the Future

It looks like we're going to need to do something different in the future to provide all the energy we need. There are various potential options, but they all have their pros and cons.

We Need to be Thinking About **Fuels** for the **Future**

1) In the **short term**, it makes sense to be as **economical** with our fuel use as we realistically can — to reduce **pollution** and its effects, and also to **eke out** our reserves of fossil fuels.
2) But in the **long term**, we're going to have to find more **sustainable** sources of energy. There are various possibilities. None of them is ideal in every way, but each might earn a place in the '**energy mix**' in the future.
3) Developing more sustainable energy sources is a task that will involve all kinds of **scientists** for a long time.

We Could Use More **Renewable** Fuels

'Renewable' means it won't run out.

1) Examples of renewable fuels include **wind**, **solar** or **wave** power.
2) As well as being **renewable**, these are also **carbon neutral**, so they don't add **greenhouse gases** (or any other pollution) into the atmosphere.
   However, CO_2 will still be given out during the manufacture of solar panels, wind turbines etc.
3) But there are objections, including:
   - they're not sufficiently **reliable** (it's not always windy or sunny, for example),
   - it takes an **awful lot** of wind turbines, solar panels or wave energy collectors to get even a fraction of the energy currently supplied by fossil fuels.

1) Fuels such as **biodiesel** or **bioethanol** are also renewable. These do produce CO_2 when they're burnt, but it's CO_2 that the plants they're made from **absorbed** while growing, so these **biofuels** are usually still classed as **carbon neutral**.
   But CO_2 is still given out while refining and transporting the fuel, as well as making the fertilisers and powering agricultural machinery used to grow and harvest the crops.
2) At the moment biofuels are still **expensive** to produce.
3) Also, the land used to grow crops for fuel can't be used to grow **food** — this could be a serious problem... **Developed** countries (like us) will create a huge demand as they try to find fossil fuel alternatives. Poorer **developing** countries (in South America, say) will use this as a way of **earning money**, and rush to convert farming land to produce 'crops for fuels'. This may mean they won't grow enough food to eat.

We Could Use More **Nuclear Power**

1) Nuclear **fission** (the process currently used to generate nuclear power) doesn't produce carbon dioxide or other kinds of air pollution.
2) But **mining** and **refining** the uranium ore, as well as building and finally decommissioning nuclear plants needs lots of energy (which means there probably will be CO_2 produced at some stage in the process).
3) Then there's the **radioactive waste** to deal with — not an easy problem to solve, because some of it stays radioactive for thousands of years (tens of thousands of years in some cases).
4) There are also public fears about the possibility of a nuclear **disaster**...

We Could Use More **Hydrogen**

1) Hydrogen gas can either be **burned** in a modified engine, or used in a **fuel cell**. (A **fuel cell** converts hydrogen and oxygen into **water**, and this chemical process produces **electricity**.) Either way, the big advantage is that **water** is the only waste product.
2) Hydrogen can be obtained from **seawater** — but it takes **energy** to extract it. This is why it's more accurate in some ways to think of hydrogen as an '**energy carrier**' rather than a true '**energy source**'.
3) The method used to extract the hydrogen determines how environmentally friendly the fuel is. If the energy used comes from a **renewable** source, say wind or solar, hydrogen fuel will be pretty much **carbon neutral** (except for the carbon emitted when making the solar panels, wind turbines etc.).
4) There are difficulties in **transporting** and **storing** hydrogen. It's highly **flammable**, and it has to be **liquified** due to the **low energy to volume ratio** of hydrogen gas. It will also mean building a whole new fuel supply **infrastructure** (chemical plants to produce the hydrogen fuel, a network of refuelling stations, pipelines...).

Fuels of the Future

Choosing an **Energy Strategy** — Lots of Decisions to Make

1) Demands for energy are **increasing** rapidly, as the world's **population** continues to grow and countries become **richer**. **Climate change** is a big problem too.
2) This means the UK has to make tough **decisions** about where to get its energy from.
3) To ensure its '**energy security**', the UK must make sure that it will be able to get enough **clean**, **affordable** energy, despite:
   - increasing **competition** from other countries for available supplies, which means **higher prices** (for example, as other countries become more industrial, they want more fuel),
   - supplies potentially being disrupted due to various **political** issues (such as unstable or unfriendly **governments**, or **terrorism**).
4) The UK government's plan to ensure energy security involves:
   - encouraging the public and industry to become more **energy efficient**,
   - continuing to make use of our **coal**, **oil** and **gas** reserves,
   - creating **financial incentives** to reduce CO_2 emissions,
   - using more **renewable** energy,
   - using more **nuclear** power.
5) The decisions could be different for different countries. For example, Brazil has few oil resources but it does have large amounts of **agricultural land** and a good **climate** — so they may concentrate more on growing crops in order to produce **biofuels**. (The majority of cars in Brazil already run on fuels containing bioethanol).

For example, **Carbon Capture and Storage** (**CCS**) technology may be able to reduce CO_2 emissions — this involves **burying** CO_2 before it reaches the atmosphere.

Financial incentives may make it more attractive for businesses to develop this kind of technology (e.g. they may have to **pay** for each tonne of carbon they emit).

Practice Questions

Q1 What is meant by a 'renewable' fuel?

Q2 Suggest why some people may claim that biofuels may cause more serious problems than they solve.

Q3 Describe some of the pros and cons of using nuclear power.

Q4 Explain why hydrogen from seawater is more of an 'energy carrier' than a true 'energy source'.

Q5 Describe some of the factors that have to be considered when making a policy to ensure 'energy security'.

Exam Questions

Q1 a) Describe the disadvantages associated with the continued large-scale use of fossil fuels as an energy source. [2 marks]

b) Describe the advantages **and** disadvantages of the following alternatives:

(i) wind power [3 marks]

(ii) nuclear power [2 marks]

(iii) hydrogen [3 marks]

Q2 In a classroom debate on the future of fuels, Martin argues that bioethanol is not a solution to the Earth's 'greenhouse effect' problem because "the combustion of bioethanol still produces carbon dioxide". However, Samantha maintains that bioethanol is "carbon neutral".

To what extent are Martin and Samantha's arguments right or wrong? [4 marks]

I'm all for energy security — get your hands off my pie...

It's a tricky one, this. There probably aren't many people around who'd be willing to give up energy being 'on tap' like it is here at the moment. And that means that countries everywhere are going to need to make sure they've got reliable supplies of (hopefully clean) energy. Mark my words... scientists are going to be working on this for a long time to come.

More Calculations

If you're not sure how to write a balanced equation, look back at page 12 before you go any further. If you're pretty confident you know how to do them, read on...

Balanced Equations can be used to Work out Masses

You've already seen this in Unit 1. But it's an important idea in Unit 2 as well...

Example: Calculate the mass of aluminium required to produce 2.04 g of aluminium oxide in this reaction: $2Al + \frac{3}{2}O_2 \rightarrow Al_2O_3$

No. of moles = $\frac{\text{Mass of substance}}{\text{Molar mass}}$

The molar mass, M, of Al_2O_3 = (2 × 27) + (3 × 16) = 102 g mol^{-1}, so 2.04 g of Al_2O_3 = $\frac{\text{mass}}{M} = \frac{2.04}{102}$ = 0.02 moles

From the equation: 1 mole of Al_2O_3 needs 2 moles of Al, so 0.02 moles of Al_2O_3 needs 0.04 moles of Al.

M of Al = 27 g mol^{-1}, so mass of Al needed is number of moles × M = 0.04 × 27 = **1.08 g.**

That's not all... Balanced Equations can be used to Work out Gas Volumes

In a similar way, equations can be used to work out **volumes** of **gases** (you saw this idea in Unit 1 too). Remember... 1 mole of **any** gas occupies a volume of **24 dm³** at room **temperature and pressure** (r.t.p.) — see p30.

Example: What volume of gas is produced when 207 g of K_2CO_3 is reacted with excess HCl at r.t.p.?

$$K_2CO_{3(s)} + 2HCl_{(aq)} \rightarrow 2KCl_{(aq)} + H_2O_{(l)} + CO_{2(g)}$$

Excess HCl means you know all the carbonate will react.

M of K_2CO_3 = (2 × 39) + 12 + (3 × 16) = 138 g mol^{-1}, so the number of moles in 207 g of K_2CO_3 = $\frac{207}{138}$ = 1.5 moles

From the equation, 1 mole of K_2CO_3 produces 1 mole of CO_2, so you know 1.5 moles of K_2CO_3 produces 1.5 moles of CO_2.

So the volume of CO_2 = 1.5 × 24 = **36 dm³**

The reaction happens at room temperature and pressure, so you know 1 mole takes up 24 dm³.

In Ionic Equations the Charges must Balance too

In **ionic equations**, only the **reacting particles** are included. You don't have to worry about the rest of the stuff. For example, **dichromate(VI) ions** ($Cr_2O_7^{2-}$) react according to the following ionic equation...

Example: Balance the ionic equation $Cr_2O_7^{2-} + H^+ + e^- \rightarrow Cr^{3+} + H_2O$.

$Cr_2O_7^{2-} + H^+ + e^- \rightarrow Cr^{3+} + H_2O$

Left	Right
Cr = 2	Cr = 1
O = 7	O = 1
H = 1	H = 2

First decide **how many** of each atom you have on **each side**.

The right side needs 2 Cr's, so try **$2Cr^{3+}$**. It also needs 7 O's, so try **$7H_2O$**.

$Cr_2O_7^{2-} + H^+ + e^- \rightarrow 2Cr^{3+} + 7H_2O$

Left	Right
Cr = 2	Cr = 2
O = 7	O = 7
H = 1	H = 14

It's not balanced yet.

The left side needs 14 H's, so try **$14H^+$**. Now the **charges** just need balancing.

$Cr_2O_7^{2-} + 14H^+ + e^- \rightarrow 2Cr^{3+} + 7H_2O$

Left	Right
Cr = 2	Cr = 2
O = 7	O = 7
H = 14	H = 14

Charges on left side	Charges on right side
(2–) + (14 × 1+) + (1–) = 11+	(2 × 3+) = 6+

The left side needs five **additional** electrons. So the balanced ionic equation is:

$$Cr_2O_7^{2-} + 14H^+ + 6e^- \rightarrow 2Cr^{3+} + 7H_2O$$

More Calculations

In a Solution the **Concentration** in Measured in **mol dm^{-3}**

1 dm³ = 1000 cm³ = 1 litre

1) The **concentration** of a solution is how many **moles** are dissolved per **1 dm³** of solution.
   The units are **mol dm^{-3}** (or M).
   Here's the formula to find the **number of moles**.

$$\text{Number of moles} = \frac{\text{Concentration} \times \text{Volume (in cm}^3\text{)}}{1000}$$

Example: What mass of sodium hydroxide needs to be dissolved to make 50 cm³ of 2 M solution?

$$\text{Number of moles} = \frac{2 \times 50}{1000} = 0.1 \text{ moles of NaOH}$$

Molar mass, M, of NaOH = 23 + 16 + 1 = 40 g

Mass = number of moles × M = 0.1 × 40 = **4 g**

2) A solution that has **more moles per dm³** than another is **more concentrated**.
   A solution that has **fewer moles per dm³** than another is **more dilute**.

Percentage Yield Is ***Never 100%***

1) The **theoretical yield** is the **mass of product** that **should** be formed. It assumes **no** chemicals are '**lost**' in a process. You can use the **masses of reactants** and a **balanced equation** to calculate the theoretical yield for a reaction.
2) For example, take the reaction used to make **hydrated ammonium iron(II) sulfate**. It's a complicated reaction, but the calculation is easy. Say you react **1.40 g** of **iron filings**, and everything else is in excess.

$$Fe_{(s)} + 2NH_{3\,(aq)} + 2H_2SO_{4\,(aq)} + 6H_2O_{(l)} \rightarrow (NH_4)_2Fe(SO_4)_2.6H_2O_{(s)} + H_{2\,(g)}$$

- Number of moles of **iron** (A_r = 56) reacted = mass ÷ molar mass = 1.40 ÷ 56 = **0.025 moles.**
  From the equation, 'moles of iron : moles of ammonium iron(II) sulfate' is 1 : 1, so 0.025 moles of product should form.
- Molar mass of $(NH_4)_2Fe(SO_4)_2.6H_2O_{(s)}$ = 392 g mol^{-1}, so **theoretical yield** = 0.025 × 392 = **9.8 g.**

3) The **actual** mass of product (the **actual yield**) will always be **less** than the theoretical yield. There are many reasons for this. For example, sometimes not all the 'starting' chemicals react fully. And some chemicals are always 'lost', e.g. some solution gets left on filter paper, or is lost during transfers between containers.
4) You can work out the **percentage yield** using this formula:
5) So if your actual yield of hydrated ammonium iron(II) sulfate crystals was **5.2 g**, then your **percentage yield** was:

$$\text{Percentage yield} = \frac{\text{Actual Yield}}{\text{Theoretical Yield}} \times 100\%$$

Percentage yield = (5.2 ÷ 9.8) × 100% = **53%**

Practice Questions

Q1 Write down the formula used to calculate the concentration of a solution.

Q2 Explain what is meant by percentage yield.

Exam Questions

Q1 Calculate the mass of propene required to produce 49.2 g of bromopropane: $C_3H_6 + HBr \rightarrow C_3H_7Br$ [4 marks]

Q2 10.5 g of magnesium carbonate is heated strongly so that it fully decomposes. $MgCO_{3(s)} \rightarrow MgO_{(s)} + CO_{2(g)}$
   a) Calculate the mass of magnesium oxide. [3 marks]
   b) Calculate the volume of gas produced. [3 marks]

Q3 A dry sample of barium sulfate was made as follows: $BaCl_{2(aq)} + H_2SO_{4(aq)} \rightarrow BaSO_{4(s)} + 2HCl_{(aq)}$
   a) If 25 cm³ of 1.0 mol/dm³ barium chloride solution was used, how many moles of barium chloride were available? [1 mark]
   b) What is the theoretical yield of barium sulfate if the other reactants are in excess? [3 marks]
   c) If 5.20 g of dry barium sulfate were recovered, what was the percentage yield of barium sulfate? [1 mark]

My mate Dave stared at some juice for an hour — it said concentrate...

If you've struggled with some of this maths-y stuff before, don't be put off — look at this as another chance to get your head round it. And if after reading these pages you're still struggling, have a cup of tea, relax your brain, and have another look in a couple of hours. Or tomorrow maybe. Some topics just take a few goes before they make any sense, that's all.

Titrations

*Titrations are used to find out the **concentrations** of acid or alkali solutions. They're also handy when you're making soluble salts of soluble bases.*

Titrations need to be done *Accurately*

1) **Titrations** allow you to find out **exactly** how much acid is needed to **neutralise** a quantity of alkali.
2) You measure out some **alkali** using a pipette and put it in a flask, along with some **indicator**, e.g. **phenolphthalein**.
3) First of all, do a rough titration to get an idea where the **end point** is (the point where the alkali is **exactly neutralised** and the indicator changes colour). Add the **acid** to the alkali using a **burette** — giving the flask a regular **swirl**.
4) Now do an **accurate** titration. Run the acid in to within 2 cm^3 of the end point, then add the acid **dropwise**. If you don't notice exactly when the solution changed colour you've **overshot** and your result won't be accurate.
5) **Record** the amount of acid used to **neutralise** the alkali. It's best to **repeat** this process a few times, making sure you get the same answer each time.

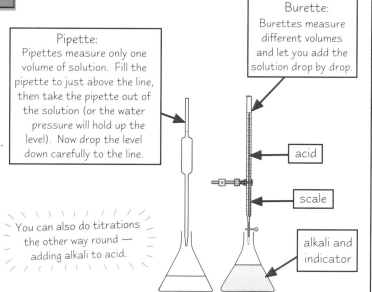

Pipette:
Pipettes measure only one volume of solution. Fill the pipette to just above the line, then take the pipette out of the solution (or the water pressure will hold up the level). Now drop the level down carefully to the line.

Burette:
Burettes measure different volumes and let you add the solution drop by drop.

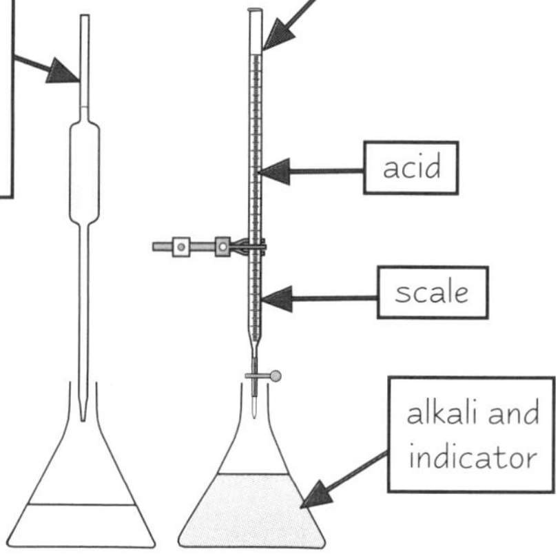

You can also do titrations the other way round — adding alkali to acid.

Indicators Show you when the Reaction's *Just Finished*

Indicators change **colour**, as if by magic. In titrations, indicators that change colour quickly over a **very small pH range** are used so you know **exactly** when the reaction has ended.

The main two indicators for **acid/alkali reactions** are —

methyl orange — turns **yellow** to **red** when adding acid to alkali.
phenolphthalein — turns **red** to **colourless** when adding acid to alkali.

Universal indicator is no good here — its colour change is too gradual.

Choppy seas made it difficult for Captain Blackbird to read the burette accurately.

You can Calculate *Molarities* from Titrations

Now for the calculations...

Example: 25 cm^3 of 0.5 M HCl was used to neutralise 35 cm^3 of NaOH solution. Calculate the concentration of the sodium hydroxide solution.

First write a **balanced equation** and decide **what you know** and what you **need to know**:

$$\mathrm{HCl + NaOH \rightarrow NaCl + H_2O}$$

HCl	NaOH
25cm³	**35cm³**
0.5 M	**?**

Now work out how many **moles of HCl** you have:

It's just the formula from page 53.

$$\text{Number of moles HCl} = \frac{\text{concentration} \times \text{volume (cm}^3)}{1000} = \frac{0.5 \times 25}{1000} = 0.0125 \text{ moles}$$

From the equation, you know 1 mole of HCl neutralises 1 mole of NaOH.
So 0.0125 moles of HCl must neutralise **0.0125** moles of NaOH.

Now it's a doddle to work out the **concentration of NaOH**.

$$\text{Concentration of NaOH}_{(aq)} = \frac{\text{moles of NaOH} \times 1000}{\text{volume (cm}^3)} = \frac{0.0125 \times 1000}{35} = \mathbf{0.36 \text{ mol dm}^{-3}}$$

If you're asked for the concentration in g dm^{-3}, you need to now use the formula from p12 — number of moles = mass ÷ M_r

Titrations

You use a Pretty Similar Method to Calculate Volumes for Reactions

This is usually used for **planning experiments**.

You need to use this formula again, but this time **rearrange** it to find the volume. →

$$\text{number of moles} = \frac{\text{concentration} \times \text{volume (cm}^3\text{)}}{1000}$$

Example: 20.4 cm³ of a 0.5 M solution of sodium carbonate reacts with 1.5 M nitric acid. Calculate the volume of nitric acid required to neutralise the sodium carbonate.

Like before, first write a **balanced equation** for the reaction and decide **what you know** and what you **want to know**:

$$Na_2CO_3 + 2HNO_3 \rightarrow 2NaNO_3 + H_2O + CO_2$$

Na_2CO_3	$2HNO_3$
20.4 cm³	**?**
0.5 M	**1.5 M**

Now work out how many **moles** of Na_2CO_3 you've got:

$$\text{No. of moles of } Na_2CO_3 = \frac{\text{concentration} \times \text{volume (cm}^3\text{)}}{1000} = \frac{0.5 \times 20.4}{1000} = 0.0102 \text{ moles}$$

1 mole of Na_2CO_3 neutralises 2 moles of HNO_3, so 0.0102 moles of Na_2CO_3 neutralises **0.0204 moles of HNO_3**.

Now you know the number of moles of HNO_3 and the concentration, you can work out the **volume**:

$$\text{Volume of } HNO_3 = \frac{\text{number of moles} \times 1000}{\text{concentration}} = \frac{0.0204 \times 1000}{1.5} = \mathbf{13.6\ cm^3}$$

Practice Questions

Q1 Describe the procedure for doing a titration.

Q2 What colour change would you expect to see if you added enough hydrochloric acid to a conical flask containing sodium hydroxide and methyl orange?

Exam Questions

Q1 Calculate the concentration of a solution of ethanoic acid, CH_3COOH, if 25.4 cm³ of it is neutralised by 14.6 cm³ of 0.5 M sodium hydroxide solution. $\mathbf{CH_3COOH + NaOH \rightarrow CH_3COONa + H_2O}$ [3 marks]

Q2 You are supplied with 0.75 g of calcium carbonate and a solution of 0.25 M sulfuric acid. What volume of acid will be needed to neutralise the calcium carbonate?
$\mathbf{CaCO_3 + H_2SO_4 \rightarrow CaSO_4 + H_2O + CO_2}$ [4 marks]

Burettes and pipettes — big glass things, just waiting to be dropped...

Titrations are annoyingly fiddly. But you do get to use big, impressive-looking equipment and feel like you're doing something important. It's really tempting to rush it and let half the acid gush into the alkali first. But it's totally not worth it, cos you'll just have to do it again. Yep, this is definitely one of those slow-and-steady-wins-the-race situations.

Electronic Structure

Electrons... they're what Chemistry is all about. But I admit that some of the details of how they behave are a bit fiddly.

Electron Shells are Made Up of Sub-Shells and Orbitals

1) In the currently accepted model of the atom, electrons have **fixed energies**. This helps to explain why electrons are **attracted** to the nucleus, but are not **drawn into it**.
2) The electrons move around the nucleus in certain regions of the atom called **shells** or **energy levels**. Each shell is given a number called the **principal quantum number**. The **further** a shell is from the nucleus, the **higher** its energy and the **larger** its principal quantum number.
3) But **experiments** show that not all the electrons in a shell have **exactly** the same energy. The **atomic model** explains this by dividing shells up into **sub-shells** that have **slightly different** energies.
4) The sub-shells consist of different numbers of **orbitals**, where an orbital is just the **bit of space** which an electron moves in. Each orbital can each hold up to **2 electrons**. If there are two electrons in an orbital, they spin in **opposite** directions — this is called **spin-pairing**.
5) Different types of sub-shell are labelled using the letters s, p, d and f. The **first** shell contains just an **s-orbital**, and so can hold just **two** electrons. The **second** shell contains an **s-orbital** and **three p-orbitals**, and so can hold up to **eight** electrons altogether.

This table shows the number of electrons that fit in each type of sub-shell.

Sub-shell	Number of orbitals	Maximum electrons
s	1	1 × 2 = 2
p	3	3 × 2 = 6
d	5	5 × 2 = 10
f	7	7 × 2 = 14

And this one shows the sub-shells and electrons in the first four energy levels.

Shell	Sub-shells	Total number of electrons	
1st	1*s*	2	= 2
2nd	2*s* 2*p*	2 + (3 × 2)	= 8
3rd	3*s* 3*p* 3*d*	2 + (3 × 2) + (5 × 2)	= 18
4th	4*s* 4*p* 4*d* 4*f*	2 + (3 × 2) + (5 × 2) + (7 × 2)	= 32

Work Out Electron Configurations by Filling the Lowest Energy Levels First

You can figure out most electronic configurations pretty easily, so long as you know a few simple rules.

1) Electrons fill up the **lowest** energy sub-shells first — the diagram below shows the order of filling.

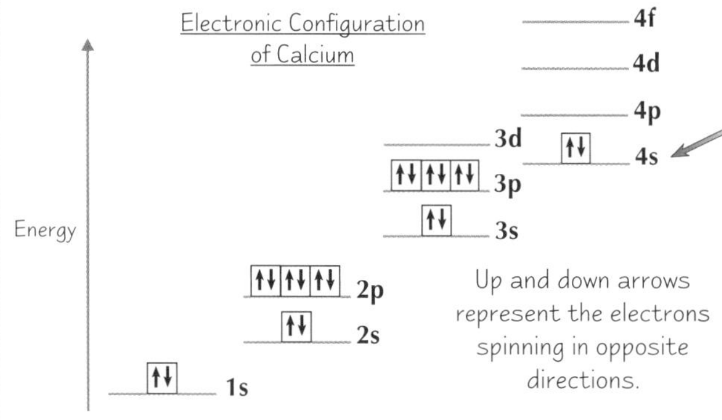

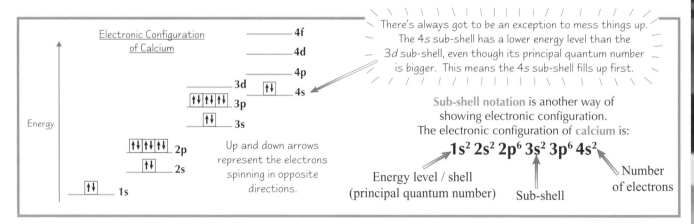

There's always got to be an exception to mess things up. The 4*s* sub-shell has a lower energy level than the 3*d* sub-shell, even though its principal quantum number is bigger. This means the 4*s* sub-shell fills up first.

Sub-shell notation is another way of showing electronic configuration. The electronic configuration of **calcium** is:

$$1s^2\ 2s^2\ 2p^6\ 3s^2\ 3p^6\ 4s^2$$

Energy level / shell (principal quantum number) — Sub-shell — Number of electrons

2) Electrons fill orbitals **singly** before they start sharing.

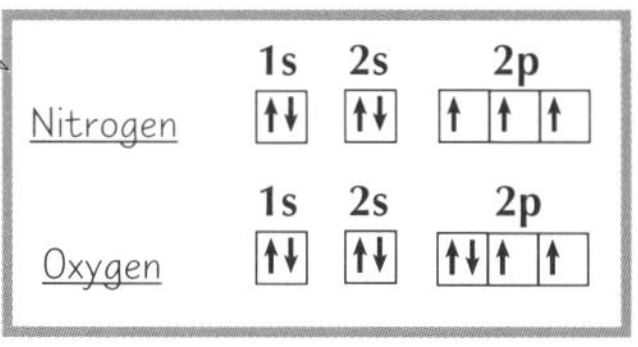

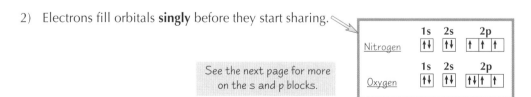

See the next page for more on the s and p blocks.

Watch out — **noble gas symbols**, like that of Argon (Ar), are sometimes used in electron configurations. For example, calcium ($1s^2\ 2s^2\ 2p^6\ 3s^2\ 3p^6\ 4s^2$) can be written as $[Ar]4s^2$, where $[Ar] = 1s^2\ 2s^2\ 2p^6\ 3s^2\ 3p^6$.

Electronic Structure

You can use the Periodic Table to work out *Electron Configurations*

The periodic table can be split into an **s block**, **d block** and **p block**.
Doing this shows you which sub-shells all the electrons go into.

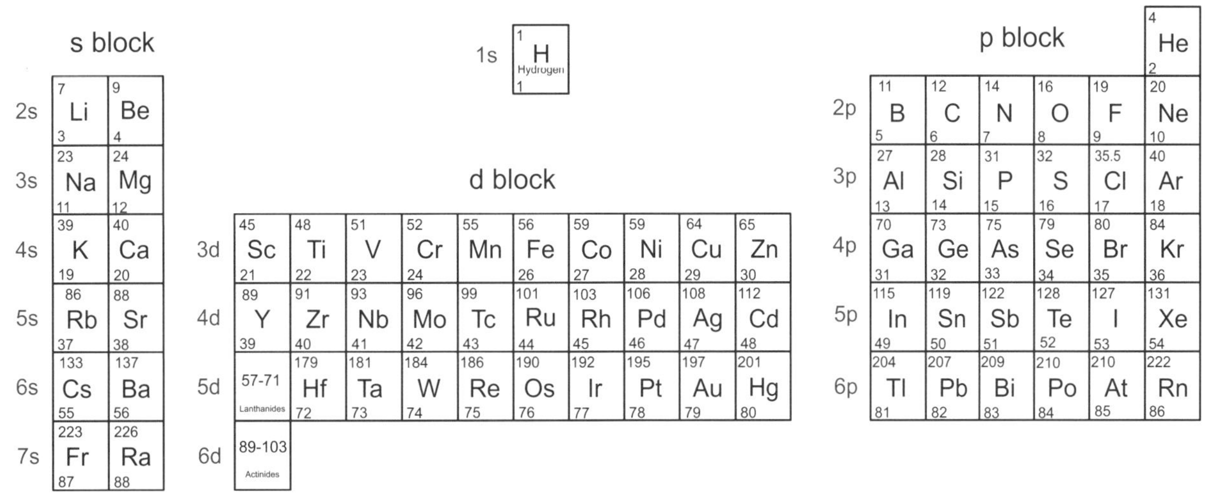

s block
d block
p block
1s 1 H Hydrogen 1
2s 7 Li 3 | 9 Be 4
3s 23 Na 11 | 24 Mg 12
4s 39 K 19 | 40 Ca 20
5s 86 Rb 37 | 88 Sr 38
6s 133 Cs 55 | 137 Ba 56
7s 223 Fr 87 | 226 Ra 88
3d 45 Sc 21 | 48 Ti 22 | 51 V 23 | 52 Cr 24 | 55 Mn | 56 Fe 26 | 59 Co 27 | 59 Ni 28 | 64 Cu 29 | 65 Zn 30
4d 89 Y 39 | 91 Zr 40 | 93 Nb 41 | 96 Mo 42 | 99 Tc 43 | 101 Ru 44 | 103 Rh 45 | 106 Pd 46 | 108 Ag 47 | 112 Cd 48
5d 57-71 Lanthanides | 179 Hf 72 | 181 Ta 73 | 184 W 74 | 186 Re 75 | 190 Os 76 | 192 Ir 77 | 195 Pt 78 | 197 Au 79 | 201 Hg 80
6d 89-103 Actinides
4 He 2
2p 11 B 5 | 12 C 6 | 14 N 7 | 16 O 8 | 19 F 9 | 20 Ne 10
3p 27 Al 13 | 28 Si 14 | 31 P 15 | 32 S 16 | 35.5 Cl 17 | 40 Ar 18
4p 70 Ga 31 | 73 Ge 32 | 75 As 33 | 79 Se 34 | 80 Br 35 | 84 Kr 36
5p 115 In 49 | 119 Sn 50 | 122 Sb 51 | 128 Te 52 | 127 I 53 | 131 Xe 54
6p 204 Tl 81 | 207 Pb 82 | 209 Bi 83 | 210 Po 84 | 210 At 85 | 222 Rn 86

1) The **s-block** elements have an outer shell electron configuration of s^1 or s^2.

Examples: Lithium ($1s^2$ **$2s^1$**) and magnesium ($1s^2\ 2s^2\ 2p^6$ **$3s^2$**)

2) The **p-block** elements have an outer shell configuration of s^2p^1 to s^2p^6.

Example: Chlorine ($1s^2\ 2s^2\ 2p^6$ **$3s^2\ 3p^5$**)

3) The **d-block** elements have electron configurations in which d sub-shells are being filled.

Example: Cobalt ($1s^2\ 2s^2\ 2p^6\ 3s^2\ 3p^6$ **$3d^7$** $4s^2$)

Even though the 3d sub-shell fills last in cobalt, it's not written at the end of the line.

When you've got the periodic table **labelled** with the **shells** and **sub-shells** like the one up there, it's pretty easy to read off the electron structure of any element by starting at the top and working your way across and down until you get to your element.

Example

Electron structure of phosphorus (P):

Period 1 — $1s^2$ ← Complete sub-shells
Period 2 — $2s^2\ 2p^6$
Period 3 — $3s^2\ 3p^3$ ← Incomplete outer sub-shell

So it's: $1s^2\ 2s^2\ 2p^6\ 3s^2\ 3p^3$

Example

Electron structure of vanadium (V):

Period 1 — $1s^2$ ← Complete sub-shells
Period 2 — $2s^2\ 2p^6$
Period 3 — $3s^2\ 3p^6\ 3d^3$ ← Incomplete outer sub-shell
Period 4 — $4s^2$

So it's: $1s^2\ 2s^2\ 2p^6\ 3s^2\ 3p^6\ 3d^3\ 4s^2$

But... watch out for chromium and copper — they're a bit weird. See next page for more details.

A wee apology...
This bit's really hard to explain clearly in words. If you're confused, just look at the examples until you get it...

Electronic Structure

Chromium and **Copper** Behave Unusually

Chromium (Cr) and **copper** (Cu) are badly behaved. They donate one of their **4s** electrons to the **3d sub-shell**. It's because they're happier with a **more stable** full or half-full d sub-shell.

Cr atom (24 e^-): $1s^2\ 2s^2\ 2p^6\ 3s^2\ 3p^6\ 3d^5\ 4s^1$ Cu atom (29 e^-): $1s^2\ 2s^2\ 2p^6\ 3s^2\ 3p^6\ 3d^{10}\ 4s^1$

Electronic Structure Decides the **Chemical Properties** of an Element

The number of **outer shell electrons** decides the chemical properties of an element.

1) The **s block** elements (Groups 1 and 2) have 1 or 2 outer shell electrons. These are easily **lost** to form positive ions with an **inert gas configuration**. E.g. Na — $1s^2\ 2s^2\ 2p^6\ 3s^1 \rightarrow$ Na^+ — $1s^2\ 2s^2\ 2p^6$ (the electronic configuration of neon).
2) The elements in Groups 5, 6 and 7 (in the p block) can **gain** 1, 2 or 3 electrons to form negative ions with an **inert gas configuration**. E.g. O — $1s^2\ 2s^2\ 2p^4 \rightarrow$ O^{2-} — $1s^2\ 2s^2\ 2p^6$. Groups 4 to 7 can also **share** electrons when they form covalent bonds.

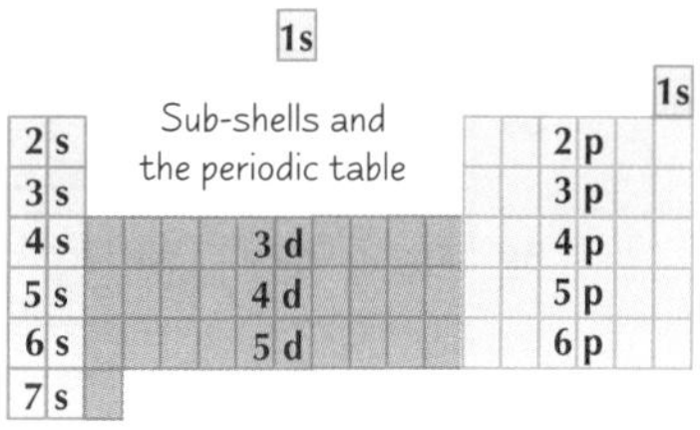

3) Group 0 (the inert gases) have **completely filled** s and p sub-shells and don't need to bother gaining, losing or sharing electrons — their full sub-shells make them **inert**.
4) The **d block elements** (transition metals) tend to **lose** s and d electrons to form positive ions.

Practice Questions

Q1 Write down the sub-shells in order of increasing energy up to 4*f*.

Q2 How many electrons would full s, p and d sub-shells contain?

Q3 What does the term 'spin-pairing' mean?

Q4 Write down the electron configuration of krypton.

Exam Questions

Q1 Potassium reacts with oxygen to form potassium oxide, K_2O.

a) Give the electron configurations of the potassium atom. [1 mark]

b) Using arrow-in-box notation, give the electron configuration of the oxygen atom. [2 marks]

c) Explain why it is the outer shell electrons, not those in the inner shells, which determine the chemistry of potassium and oxygen. [2 marks]

Q2 This question concerns the electron configurations of atoms and ions.

a) What is the electron configuration of a manganese atom? [1 mark]

b) Identify the element with the 4th shell configuration of $4s^2\,4p^2$. [1 mark]

c) Using arrow-in-box notation, give the electron configuration of the aluminium atom. [2 marks]

d) Suggest the identity of an atom, a positive ion and a negative ion with the configuration $1s^2\ 2s^2\ 2p^6\ 3s^2\ 3p^6$. [3 marks]

She shells sub-sells on the sea shore...

The way electrons fill up the orbitals is kind of like how strangers fill up seats on a bus. Everyone tends to sit in their own seat till they're forced to share. Except for the huge, scary, smelly man who comes and sits next to you. Make sure you learn the order the sub-shells are filled up, so you can write electron configurations for any atom they throw at you.

Oxidation and Reduction

This next bit has more occurrences of "oxidation" than the Beatles' "All You Need is Love" features the word "love".

If Electrons are Transferred, it's a ***Redox Reaction***

1) A **loss** of electrons is called **oxidation**. A **gain** in electrons is called **reduction**.
2) Reduction and oxidation happen **simultaneously** — hence the term "**redox**" reaction.
3) An **oxidising agent accepts** electrons and gets reduced.
4) A **reducing agent donates** electrons and gets oxidised.

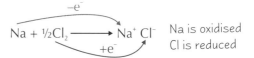

$$Na + \tfrac{1}{2}Cl_2 \longrightarrow Na^+\ Cl^-$$

($-e^-$ from Na; $+e^-$ to Cl)

Na is oxidised
Cl is reduced

Sometimes it's Easier to Talk about ***Oxidation States***

(They're also called oxidation <u>numbers</u>.)

1) **Oxidation state** (or **number**) is a way of showing the charge an atom *would have* if all its bonds were totally ionic.
2) Here's the nice simple bit:
   - When **metals** react and form ions they normally lose electrons and are oxidised to form positive ions. This **increases** their oxidation number.
   - **Non-metals** normally react by gaining electrons — they're reduced to negative ions. This **decreases** their oxidation number.
3) And here's the harder bit — there are several **rules** for working out oxidation states. Take a deep breath...

   1) All atoms are treated as **ions** for this, even if they're covalently bonded.
   2) Uncombined **elements** have an oxidation state of **0**.
   3) Elements just bonded to **identical atoms**, like O_2 and H_2, also have an oxidation state of **0**.
   4) The oxidation state of a simple **monatomic ion**, e.g. Na^+, is the same as its **charge**.
   5) In **compounds** or **compound ions**, the **overall oxidation state** is just the ion charge.

      SO_4^{2-} — **overall oxidation state = –2**, oxidation state of **O = –2** (total = –8), so oxidation state of **S = +6**

      Within an ion, the most electronegative element has a negative oxidation state (equal to its ionic charge). Other elements have more positive oxidation states.

   6) The sum of the oxidation states for a **neutral compound** is 0.

      Fe_2O_3 — **overall oxidation state = 0**, oxidation state of **O = –2** (total = –6), so oxidation state of **Fe = +3**

   7) Combined **oxygen** is nearly always -2, except in peroxides, where it's -1, (and in the fluorides OF_2, where it's +2, and O_2F_2, where it's +1 (and O_2 where it's 0).

      In H_2O, oxidation state of **O = –2**, but in H_2O_2, oxidation state of **H** has to be **+1** (an H atom can only lose one electron), so oxidation state of **O = –1**

   8) Combined **hydrogen** is +1, except in metal hydrides where it is –1 (and H_2 where it's 0).

      In **HF**, oxidation state of **H = +1**, but in **NaH**, oxidation state of **H = –1**

4) Oxidation states are sometimes shown in chemical names as **Roman numerals**. This is because some elements can have several oxidation states — there's more about this on the next page.

   E.g. copper has oxidation state **+2** in **copper(II) sulfate** and manganese has oxidation state **+7** in a **manganate(VII) ion** (MnO_4^-)

Oxidation and Reduction

You Can Work Out *Oxidation States* from *Formulas* or *Systematic Names*

1) Many elements can have **more than one** oxidation state. For example, **iron** can form Fe^{2+} or Fe^{3+} ions. So it's not good enough to call a substance 'iron oxide' — the name has to show which oxidation state the Fe atoms are in.
2) **Systematic names** of compounds make it clear which oxidation state such elements are in. E.g. iron(III) oxide is formed from $\mathbf{Fe^{3+}}$ and O^{2-} ions, whereas iron(II) oxide contains $\mathbf{Fe^{2+}}$ ions and O^{2-}.
3) This systematic naming process doesn't just apply to ionic substances.

For example, **silicon** can exist in **several oxidation states**.

The compound $\mathbf{SiO_2}$ contains **two oxygen atoms** for every **one silicon atom**. The oxygen atoms are in oxidation state **–2** (giving –2 × 2 = –4), so the silicon must be in oxidation state **+4** (to make the overall oxidation number for the compound **0**).

So its systematic name is silicon(IV) oxide — but it's often called silicon dioxide.

(Silicon(II) oxide is SiO — its overall oxidation number is 0 too.)

4) Many common substances contain **compound ions**. For example, the sulfate, carbonate and nitrate ions are all compound ions. Their systematic names tell you the oxidation states of the atoms that make them up. Take **potassium sulfate(VI)** for example:
   - The **ate** ending in 'sulfate' shows that the ion contains oxygen as well as sulfur (just as a nitrate ion contains nitrogen and oxygen, a carbonate ion contains carb... OK, you've got it, I'll stop). **BUT...**
   - **Sulfate(VI)** tells you that the **sulfur** has oxidation state **+6**. (The oxidation state applies to the sulfur not the oxygen, because oxygen is always –2.)
5) Several ions have widely used common names that are different from their correct systematic names.

   For example, the systematic name for the compound ion SO_3^{2-} is **sulfate(IV)**. (Oxygen is –2, and 2 × 3 = –6, so sulfur must have oxidation state +4 to give the overall state of –2.) But this ion is often called the **sulfite** ion.

   In the old naming system, compound ions of oxygen and an element with two possible oxidation states had names ending in either '-ate' or '-ite'. The '-ite' ending indicated one less oxygen atom (i.e. the 'other' atom was in its lower oxidation state).
6) You might have to work out the systematic name for a compound, given its formula. Here's how:

Example: Give the systematic name of the compound KNO_3.

Potassium always forms K^+ ions. The nitrate ion must be NO_3^-.
Each oxygen atom in the NO_3^- ion has oxidation state –2. This gives 3 × –2 = **–6**.
The ion has an overall state of **–1**, so the nitrogen must be in the **+5** state.
So the compound is called **potassium nitrate(V)**.

It's called the nitrate(V) ion.

7) Here are some common ions you need to know about. A couple of them have **systematic names** as well as their more common names.

   Like with all ions, to form a compound you just **balance** the positive and negative charges.

   For instance, **ammonium sulfate** would have formula $\mathbf{(NH_4)_2SO_4}$.

Ion	Common name	Systematic name
NO_3^-	nitrate	nitrate(V)
SO_4^{2-}	sulfate	sulfate(VI)
CO_3^{2-}	carbonate	
OH^-	hydroxide	
NH_4^+	ammonium	
HCO_3^-	hydrogencarbonate	

Oxidation States go *Up* or *Down* as Electrons are *Lost* or *Gained*

1) The oxidation state for an atom will **increase by 1** for each **electron lost**.
2) The oxidation state will **decrease by 1** for each **electron gained**.
3) In a **redox** reaction, some oxidation numbers will **change** — like in this reaction between iron(III) oxide and **carbon(II) oxide** (aka carbon monoxide). The products are the element iron and **carbon(IV) oxide** (more commonly known as carbon dioxide).

Fe oxidation number reduced from +3 to 0 — reduction

$$Fe_2O_3 + 3CO \rightarrow 2Fe + 3CO_2$$

C oxidation number increased from +2 to +4 — oxidation

Hands up if you like Roman numerals...

4) Remember... when **metals** form compounds, they generally **donate** electrons to form **positive ions** — meaning they usually have **positive oxidation numbers**. When **non-metals** form compounds, they generally **gain** electrons — meaning they usually have **negative oxidation numbers**.

Oxidation and Reduction

You Can Combine Half-Equations into Full Reaction Equations

Ionic half-equations show oxidation or reduction.

You can **combine** half-equations for different oxidising or reducing agents together to make **full equations** for reactions.

Magnesium burns in oxygen to form magnesium oxide.

Magnesium is oxidised: $Mg \rightarrow Mg^{2+} + 2e^-$

Oxygen is reduced: $\frac{1}{2}O_2 + 2e^- \rightarrow O^{2-}$

Combining the half-equations gives: $Mg + \frac{1}{2}O_2 \rightarrow MgO$

The electrons balance on each side so they aren't included in the full equation.

Many Metals Reduce Dilute Acids

You need to be able to say what's been **oxidised** and what's been **reduced** in a reaction. Here's an example:

1) **Dilute acids** contain hydrogen ions, H^+, in solution. Many metals react with dilute acid to produce hydrogen gas. This is a redox reaction:
   - The metal atoms are **oxidised**, losing electrons and forming soluble metal ions.
   - The hydrogen ions in solution are **reduced**, gaining electrons and forming hydrogen molecules.
2) For example, magnesium reacts with dilute hydrochloric acid like this:

$$Mg_{(s)} + 2HCl_{(aq)} \rightarrow MgCl_{2\,(aq)} + H_{2\,(g)}$$

Magnesium is oxidised: $Mg_{(s)} \rightarrow Mg^{2+}_{(aq)} + 2e^-$

Hydrogen ions are reduced: $2H^+_{(aq)} + 2e^- \rightarrow H_{2\,(g)}$

Notice that the chloride ions don't change oxidation state — they're still chloride ions, with oxidation state −1. That's why you don't need to include them in the ionic half-equations.

And here's another example:

When a Group 2 metal reacts with water, **oxidation** and **reduction** also take place. For example...

$$Ca_{(s)} + 2H_2O_{(l)} \rightarrow Ca(OH)_{2\,(aq)} + H_{2\,(g)}$$

Calcium is oxidised: $Ca_{(s)} \rightarrow Ca^{2+}_{(aq)} + 2e^-$

Hydrogen is reduced: $2H^+_{(aq)} + 2e^- \rightarrow H_{2\,(g)}$

The electrons in the two half-equations should balance.

Practice Questions

Q1 What is a reducing agent?

Q2 What is the usual oxidation number for oxygen combined with another element?

Q3 Is a metal atom usually oxidised or reduced when it forms a compound?

Exam Question

Q1 When hydrogen iodide gas is bubbled through warm concentrated sulfuric acid, hydrogen sulfide and iodine are produced.

a) Balance the equation below for the reaction. [1 mark]

$$H_2SO_{4(l)} + HI_{(g)} \rightarrow H_2S_{(g)} + I_{2(s)} + H_2O_{(l)}$$

b) Calculate the oxidation state of sulfur in H_2SO_4 and in H_2S. [2 marks]

c) In this reaction, which is the reducing agent? Give a reason. [2 marks]

d) Write a half-equation to show the conversion of iodide, I^-, into iodine, I_2. [1 mark]

e) Write a half-equation to show the conversion of sulfuric acid into hydrogen sulfide. [2 marks]

Redox — relax in a lovely warm bubble bath...

Ionic equations are so evil even Satan wouldn't mess with them. But they're on your specification, so you can't ignore them. Have a flick back to p52 if they're freaking you out.

And while we're on the oxidation page, I suppose you ought to learn the most famous memory aid thingy in the world...

OIL RIG
- **Oxidation Is Loss**
- **Reduction Is Gain**

(of electrons)

Electronegativity

Pulling power... that's what we're talking about here. The ability to pull electrons.

*There's a Gradual **Transition** from Ionic to Covalent Bonding*

1) Very few compounds come even close to being **purely ionic**.
2) And only bonds between atoms of a **single element**, like diatomic gases such as hydrogen (H_2) or oxygen (O_2), can be **purely covalent**.
3) So really, most compounds come somewhere **in between** the two extremes — meaning they've often got ionic **and** covalent properties.

   For example, covalent hydrogen chloride gas molecules dissolve to form hydrochloric acid, which is an ionic solution.

$$HCl_{(g)} \xrightarrow{H_2O_{(l)}} H^+_{(aq)} + Cl^-_{(aq)}$$

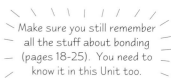

Make sure you still remember all the stuff about bonding (pages 18-25). You need to know it in this Unit too.

*Some Atoms **Attract** Bonding Electrons More than Other Atoms*

The ability to attract the bonding electrons in a covalent bond is called electronegativity.

1) Electronegativity is usually measured using the **Pauling scale**.
2) **Fluorine** is the most electronegative element — it's given a value of **4.0** on the Pauling scale. Oxygen, nitrogen and chlorine are also very strongly electronegative.

Sounds a bit like 'pulling'.

Element	H	C	N	Cl	O	F
Electronegativity	2.1	2.5	3.0	3.0	3.5	4.0

3) Electronegativity **increases across periods** and **decreases down groups** (ignoring the noble gases).

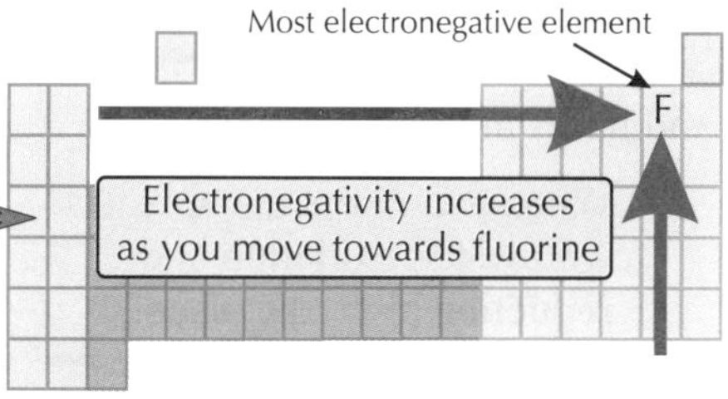

*Covalent Bonds may be Polarised by **Differences** in **Electronegativity***

In a covalent bond between two atoms of **different** electronegativities, the bonding electrons are **pulled towards** the more electronegative atom. This makes the bond **polar**.

1) The covalent bonds in diatomic gases (e.g. H_2, Cl_2) are **non-polar** because the atoms have **equal** electronegativities and so the electrons are equally attracted to both nuclei.

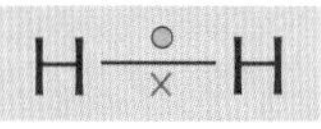

Permanent polar bonding

2) Some elements, like carbon and hydrogen, have pretty **similar** electronegativities, so bonds between them are essentially **non-polar**.
3) But in a **polar bond**, the difference in electronegativity between the two atoms causes a **dipole**. A dipole is a **difference in charge** between the two atoms caused by a shift in **electron density** in the bond.

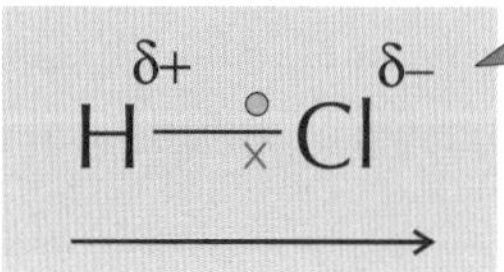

The chlorine atom drags the electrons slightly towards itself — meaning it has a small negative charge.

'δ' (delta) means 'slightly', so 'δ+' means 'slightly positive'.

4) So what you need to **remember** is that the greater the **difference** in electronegativity, the **more polar** the bond.

Electronegativity

Polar Bonds **Don't** Always Make **Polar Molecules**

Whether a molecule has a **permanent dipole** depends on its **shape** and the **polarity** of its bonds.

1) So in a simple molecule, such as **hydrogen chloride**, the polar bond gives the whole molecule a permanent dipole — it's a **polar molecule**.

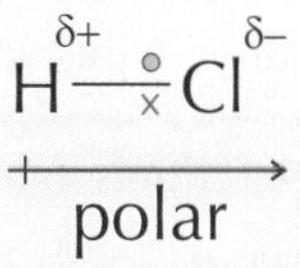

2) A more complicated molecule may have **several polar bonds**. If the polar bonds are arranged so they point in opposite directions, they'll **cancel each other out** — the molecule is **non-polar** overall.

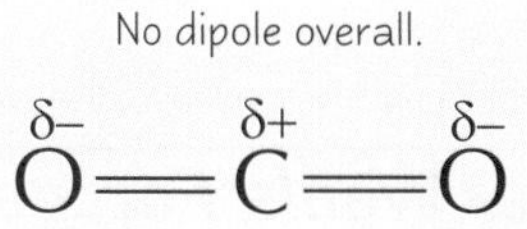

3) If the polar bonds all point in roughly the **same direction**, then the molecule will be **polar**.

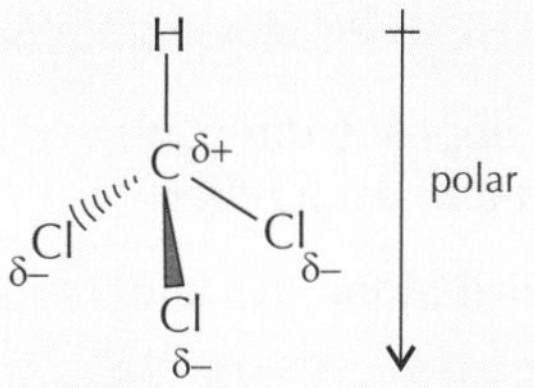

4) **Lone pairs of electrons** on the central atom also have an effect on the overall polarity and may **cancel out** the dipole created by the bonding pairs.

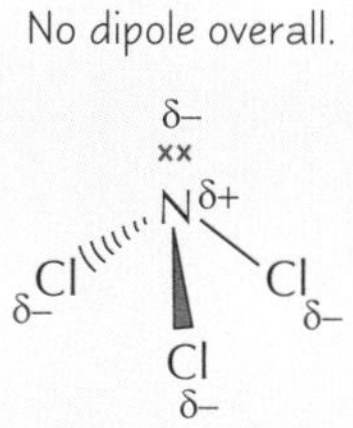

Practice Questions

Q1 What are the only bonds which can be purely covalent?

Q2 What is the most electronegative element?

Q3 What is a dipole?

Exam Questions

Q1 Many covalent molecules have a permanent dipole, due to differences in electronegativities.

a) Define the term electronegativity. [2 marks]

b) Draw the shapes and predict the overall polarity of the following molecules, marking any bond polarities clearly on your diagram:
(i) Br_2 (ii) H_2O (iii) CCl_4 (iv) NH_3 [8 marks]

c) Fluorine is the most electronegative element.
NF_3 is the same shape as NH_3, yet it has no permanent dipole. Why is this? [2 marks]

Q2 Draw diagrams to show the shape of the covalently bonded molecules below.
Indicate any permanent dipoles on your diagrams.

a) Boron(III) chloride (BCl_3), [2 marks]

b) Nitrogen(III) chloride (NCl_3). [2 marks]

Enough of this chemistry rubbish. Here are some interesting facts...

If you chop the head off a beetle, it wouldn't die of being beheaded, but actually starvation. It's true. If you ate 14 lbs of almonds, you'd die of cyanide poisoning. It's true! Daddy-long-legs are actually the most poisonous insects in the world, but they can't pierce the skin... it's TRUE. Every night, the human body sweats enough to fill a swimming pool. It's true...

Intermolecular Forces

Intermolecular forces hold molecules together. They're pretty important, cos we'd all be gassy clouds without them.

Intermolecular Forces are **Very Weak**

Intermolecular forces are forces **between** molecules. They're much **weaker** than covalent, ionic or metallic bonds. There are three types you need to know about:

1) **Instantaneous dipole-induced dipole bonds** or **van der Waals** forces (this is the weakest type)
2) **Permanent dipole-permanent dipole bonds**
3) **Hydrogen bonding** (this is the strongest type — see page 100)

Van der Waals Forces are Found Between **All** Atoms and Molecules

Van der Waals forces cause **all** atoms and molecules to be **attracted** to each other.

1) **Electrons** in charge clouds are always **moving** really quickly. At any particular moment, the electrons in an atom are likely to be more to one side than the other. At this moment, the atom would have a **temporary dipole**.
2) This dipole can cause **another** temporary dipole in the opposite direction on a neighbouring atom. The two dipoles are then **attracted** to each other.
3) The second dipole can cause yet another dipole in a **third atom**. It's kind of like a domino rally.

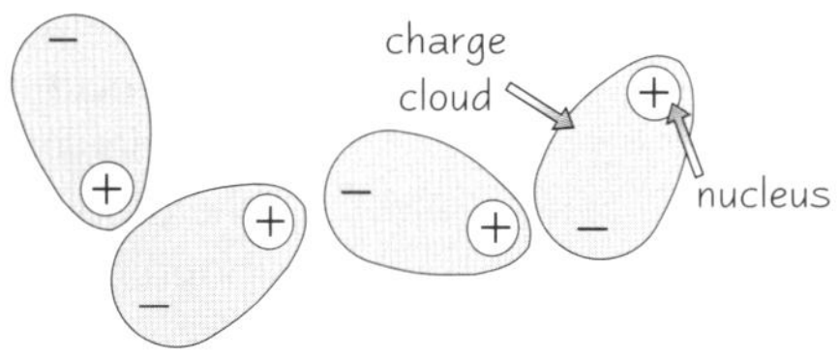

4) Because the electrons are constantly moving, the dipoles are being **created** and **destroyed** all the time. Even though the dipoles keep changing, the **overall effect** is for the atoms to be **attracted** to each other.

Hence the catchy name... "instantaneous dipole-induced dipole forces".

Polar Molecules have **Permanent Dipole-Permanent Dipole** Forces

The $\delta+$ and $\delta-$ charges on **polar molecules** cause **weak electrostatic forces** of attraction **between** molecules.

E.g. **hydrogen chloride gas** has polar molecules.

$$\overset{\delta+}{H}—\overset{\delta-}{Cl}$$

Even though they're weak, these **permanent dipole-permanent dipole** forces are still much stronger than van der Waals forces.

<u>Now this bit's pretty cool</u>:

If you put an **electrostatically charged rod** next to a jet of a polar liquid, like water, the liquid will **move** towards the rod. I wouldn't believe me either, but it's true. It's because **polar liquids** contain molecules with **permanent dipoles**. It doesn't matter if the rod is **positively** or **negatively** charged. The polar molecules in the liquid can **turn around** so the oppositely charged end is attracted towards the rod.

You can use this experiment to find out if the molecules of a jet of liquid are **polar or non-polar**.

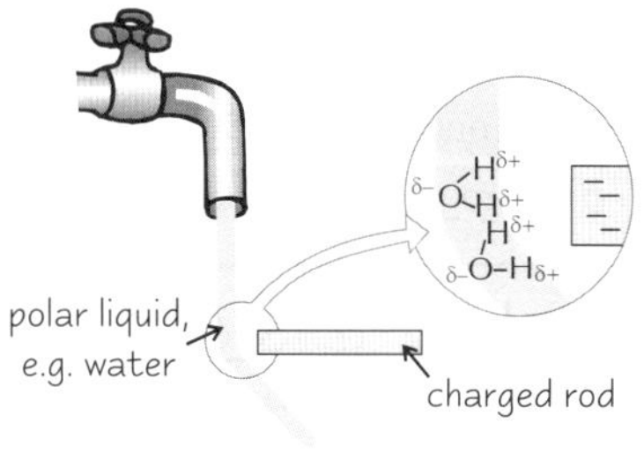

Intermolecular Forces

Intermolecular Forces in Organic Molecules Depend on Their Shape

The **shape** of an organic compound's molecules affects the **strength** of the **intermolecular forces**.
Take alkanes, for example...

1) Alkanes have **covalent bonds** inside the molecules.
   Between the molecules there are **van der Waals** forces, which hold them all together.
2) The **longer** the carbon chain, the **stronger** the van der Waals forces — because there's **more molecular surface area** and more electrons to interact.
3) So as the molecules get longer, it takes **more energy** to overcome the van der Waals forces and separate them.

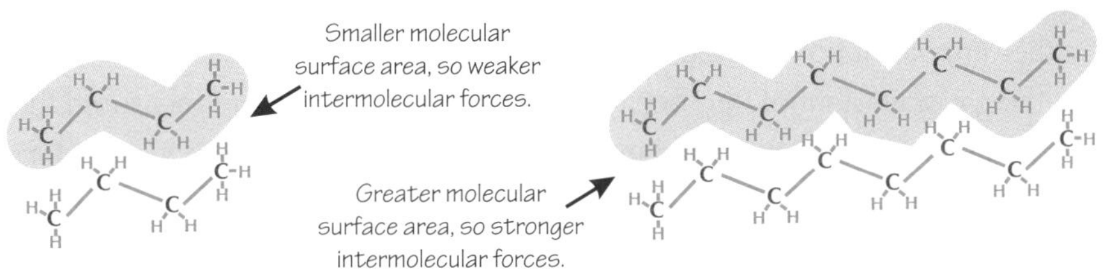
Smaller molecular surface area, so weaker intermolecular forces.
Greater molecular surface area, so stronger intermolecular forces.

4) Branched-chain alkanes can't **pack closely** together and they have smaller **molecular surface areas** — so the van der Waals forces are reduced.

Look at these **isomers** of C_4H_{10}, for example...

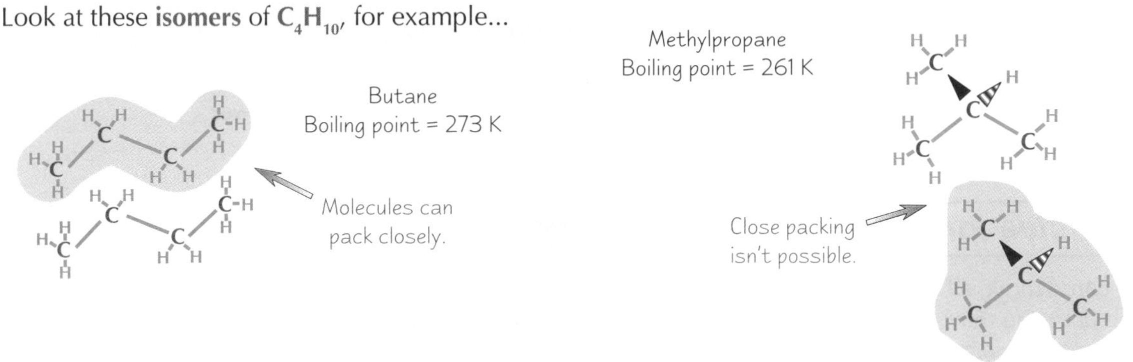
Butane
Boiling point = 273 K
Molecules can pack closely.
Methylpropane
Boiling point = 261 K
Close packing isn't possible.

Practice Questions

Q1 What's the weakest type of intermolecular force?

Q2 Explain what instantaneous dipole-induced dipole bonds are.

Q3 Explain what gives rise to permanent dipole-permanent dipole intermolecular forces.

Exam Question

Q1 The molecules in the table on the right all have the molecular formula C_5H_{12}.
Explain the differences in the strengths of the intermolecular forces.

[6 marks]

Molecule	Relative strength of intermolecular forces
Pentane	Strong
2-methylbutane	Intermediate
2,2-dimethylpropane	Weak

Van der Waal — a Dutch hit for Oasis...

Just because intermolecular forces are a bit wimpy and weak, don't forget they're there. It'd all fall apart without them. Make especially sure you understand everything about van der Waals forces and permanent dipole-dipole forces. Then try that "pulling water towards a rod" trick. Go on, treat yourself to a real-life demonstration of Chemistry at work.

Ionisation Enthalpies

This page gets a trifle brain-boggling, so I hope you've got a few aspirin handy...

Ionisation is the *Removal* of One or More *Electrons*

When electrons have been removed from an atom or molecule, it's been **ionised**.
The energy you need to remove the first electron is called the **first ionisation enthalpy**:

> The **first ionisation enthalpy** is the energy needed to remove 1 electron from **each atom** in **1 mole** of **gaseous** atoms to form 1 mole of gaseous 1+ ions.

You can write **equations** for this process — here's the equation for the **first ionisation of oxygen**:

$$O_{(g)} \rightarrow O^{+}_{(g)} + e^{-} \quad \textbf{1st ionisation enthalpy = +1314 kJ mol}^{-1}$$

Here are a few rather important points about ionisation enthalpies:

1) You **must** use the gas state symbol, **(g)**, because ionisation enthalpies are measured for gaseous atoms.
2) Always refer to **1 mole** of atoms, as stated in the definition, rather than to a single atom.
3) The **lower** the ionisation enthalpy, the **easier** it is to form an ion.

There are **3 main things** that affect the size of ionisation enthalpies:

1) **Atomic radius** — the further the outer shell electrons are from the positive nucleus, the less they'll be attracted towards the nucleus. So, the ionisation enthalpy will be **lower**.
2) **Nuclear charge** — the **more protons** there are in the nucleus, the more it'll attract the outer electrons — it'll be harder to remove the electrons, so the ionisation enthalpy will be **higher**.
3) **Electron shielding** — the inner electron shells **shield** the outer shell electrons from the attractive force of the nucleus. Because more inner shells mean more shielding, the ionisation enthalpy will be **lower**.

Successive Ionisation Enthalpies Involve Removing *Additional* Electrons

1) You can remove **all** the electrons from an atom, leaving only the nucleus.
   Each time you remove an electron, there's a **successive ionisation enthalpy**.
2) The definition for the **second ionisation enthalpy** is —

> The **second ionisation enthalpy** is the energy needed to remove 1 electron from **each ion** in **1 mole** of **gaseous** 1+ ions to form 1 mole of gaseous 2+ ions.

And here's the equation for the **second ionisation of oxygen**:

$$O^{+}_{(g)} \rightarrow O^{2+}_{(g)} + e^{-} \quad \textbf{2nd ionisation enthalpy = +3388 kJ mol}^{-1}$$

3) A **graph** of successive ionisation enthalpies (like the one for sodium below) shows the **shell structure** of atoms.

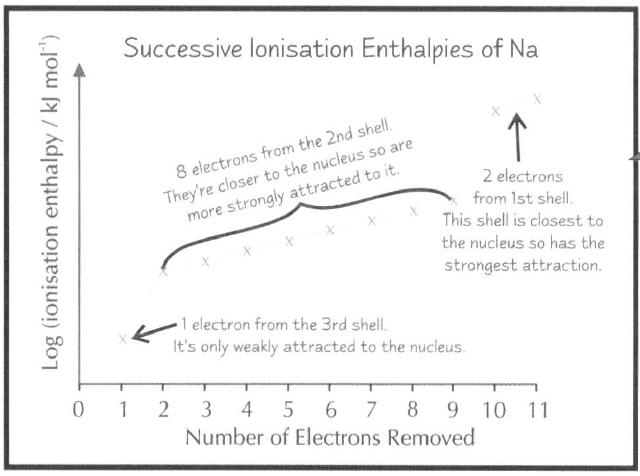

1) **Within each shell**, successive ionisation enthalpies **increase**.
   This is because electrons are being removed from an **increasingly positive ion**, so the attraction between the nucleus and the remaining electrons increases.
   Also, there's **less repulsion** amongst the remaining electrons.
2) The **big jumps** in ionisation enthalpies happen when a new shell is broken into — an electron is being removed from a shell **closer** to the nucleus.

Ionisation Enthalpies

First Ionisation Enthalpies **Decrease** Down a **Group**

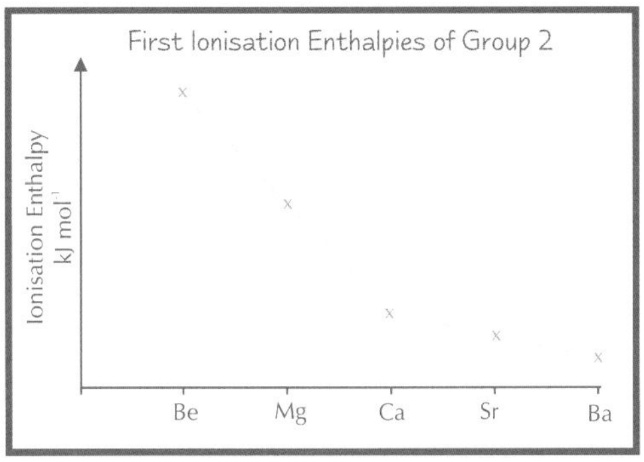

The first ionisation enthalpy **decreases** down a group (the graph shows the pattern for Group 2) because there's **less attraction** between the nucleus and outer electrons. This shows that the electrons are arranged in **energy levels**:

1) As you go down the group, the outer electrons are in shells **further** from the nucleus, so they're attracted to the nucleus **less**.
2) The amount of shielding **increases** because there are more filled inner shells. This means **less nuclear attraction** for the outer shell electrons.
3) Although the number of **protons** increases down the group, this **doesn't** lead to an increase in ionisation enthalpy because it's a less important factor than either shielding or the distance of the outer electrons from the nucleus.

First Ionisation Enthalpies **Increase** Across a **Period**

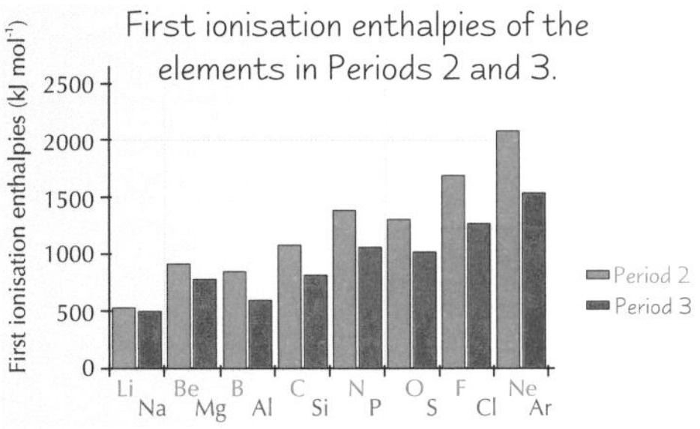

1) As you **move across** a period, the trend is for the ionisation enthalpies to **increase** — it gets harder to remove outer electrons.
2) This is because the number of protons is increasing, which means a stronger **nuclear attraction**.
3) And since all the outer-shell electrons are at **roughly the same** energy level — there's generally little **extra shielding** effect or **extra distance** to lessen the attraction from the nucleus.
4) But, there are **small drops** between Groups 2 and 3, and 5 and 6.

Between Groups 2 and 3: Boron's outer electron is in a **2p orbital** rather than a 2s, so on average the electron is **further** from the nucleus. Also, the 2p orbital is screened not only by the $1s^2$ **electrons**, but also **partially** by the $2s^2$ **electrons**. These factors **override** the effect of the increased nuclear charge, resulting in the ionisation enthalpy **dropping** slightly.

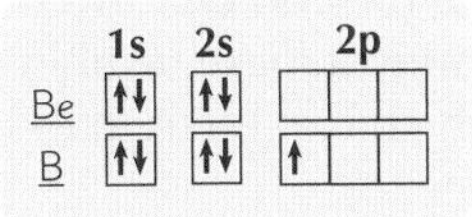

Between Groups 5 and 6: The **screening is identical** in nitrogen and oxygen, and the electron is being removed from an identical orbital. The difference is that in oxygen, the **electron** being **removed** is one of a pair. The **repulsion** between the two electrons in the same orbital means that an electron is **easier to remove**. The same is true for the drop in ionisation enthalpy at **sulfur**.

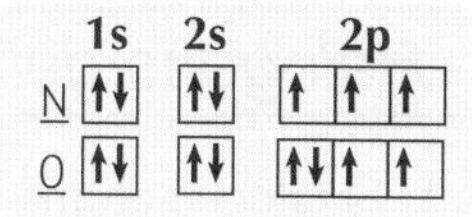

Practice Questions

Q1 Define first ionisation enthalpy and give an equation as an example.

Q2 Describe the three main factors that affect ionisation enthalpies.

Q3 How do first ionisation enthalpy plots give you information about atomic sub-shell structure?

Exam Question

Q1 The graph shows how first ionisation enthalpy varies across Period 2.

a) Explain why there is a general increase in ionisation enthalpy across the period. [2 marks]

b) Explain how the graph provides evidence for the electronic structure of these elements. [3 marks]

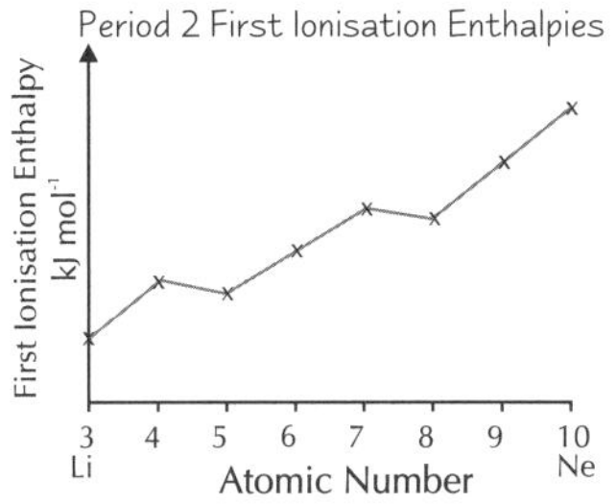

Shirt crumpled — ionise it...

When you're talking about ionisation enthalpies in exams, always use the 3 main factors — shielding, nuclear charge and atomic radius. It's really important that you know what's going on in the graphs and why they look like dog's hind legs. Recite the definition of the first and second ionisation enthalpies to yourself until the men in white coats get to you. Then stop.

Group 7 — The Halogens

Hold on to your hats... here come the halogens...

Halogens are the **Highly Reactive Non-Metals** of Group 7

The table below gives some of the main properties of the first 4 halogens.

The word <u>halogen</u> should be used when describing the atom (X) or molecule (X_2), but the word <u>halide</u> is used to describe the negative ion (X^-).

halogen	formula	colour	physical state	electronic structure	electronegativity
fluorine	F_2	pale yellow	gas	$1s^2\ 2s^2\ 2p^5$	increases
chlorine	Cl_2	green	gas	$1s^2\ 2s^2\ 2p^6\ 3s^2\ 3p^5$	up
bromine	Br_2	red-brown	liquid	$1s^2\ 2s^2\ 2p^6\ 3s^2\ 3p^6\ 3d^{10}\ 4s^2\ 4p^5$	the
iodine	I_2	grey	solid	$1s^2\ 2s^2\ 2p^6\ 3s^2\ 3p^6\ 3d^{10}\ 4s^2\ 4p^6\ 4d^{10}\ 5s^2\ 5p^5$	group

1) **Their boiling points increase down the group**
This is due to the increasing strength of the **van der Waals forces** as the size and relative mass of the atoms increases. This trend is shown in the changes of **physical state** from chlorine (gas) to iodine (solid).
(A substance is said to be **volatile** if it has a low boiling point. So volatility **decreases** down the group.)

2) **Electronegativity decreases down the group**.
Electronegativity, remember, is the tendency of an atom to **attract** a bonding pair of **electrons**.
The halogens are all highly electronegative elements. But larger atoms attract electrons **less** than smaller ones. So, going down the group, as the atoms become **larger**, the electronegativity **decreases**.

Fluorine is the most electronegative element.

Halogens are **More Soluble** in **Organic Solvents** than in Water

Halogens in their natural state exist as covalent diatomic molecules (e.g. Br_2, Cl_2).
Because they're covalent, they have **low solubility in water**.

But they do dissolve easily in **organic compounds** like hexane. Some of these resulting solutions have distinctive colours which can be used to identify them.

	colour in water	colour in hexane
chlorine	virtually colourless	virtually colourless
bromine	yellow/orange	orange/red
iodine	brown	pink/violet

Halogens get **Less Reactive** Down the Group

1) Halogen atoms react by **gaining an electron** in their outer p sub-shell. This means they're **reduced**. As they're reduced, they **oxidise** another substance (it's a redox reaction) — so they're **oxidising agents**.

$$X + e^- \rightarrow X^-$$
ox. state: 0 → -1

2) As you go down the group, the atoms become **larger** so the outer electrons are **further** from the nucleus. The outer electrons are also **shielded** more from the attraction of the positive nucleus, because there are more inner electrons. This makes it harder for larger atoms to attract the electron needed to form an ion, so larger atoms are less reactive.

3) Another way of saying that the halogens get **less reactive** down the group is to say that they become **less oxidising**. (See the next page for more on this.)

You Can Use **Patterns** To **Predict Properties**

1) The smallest halogen, **fluorine**, is the **most reactive** non-metal element. Fluorine isn't used in schools and colleges because it's so dangerous, but you can **predict** its properties by looking at those of the other halogens.

2) The **melting** and **boiling points** increase down the group, so you can predict that fluorine would be a gas at room temperature, like chlorine below it. Similarly, fluorine should be **coloured** as all the other halogens are. In fact, fluorine is a very pale yellow gas at room temperature.

3) Astatine (below iodine in the periodic table) is a solid. You'd expect it to be the **least reactive** halogen, but its properties haven't been studied because it's highly radioactive and decays quickly.

Halogen (Increasing Reactivity ↑)	Melting Point / °C	Boiling Point / °C
F		
Cl	–101	–34
Br	–7	58
I	114	183
At		

Group 7 — The Halogens

Halogens **Displace** Less Reactive Halide Ions from Solution

1) The halogens' **relative oxidising strengths** can be seen in their **displacement reactions** with halide ions. For example, if you mix bromine water, $Br_{2\,(aq)}$, with potassium iodide solution, the bromine displaces the iodide ions (it oxidises them), giving iodine, $I_{2\,(aq)}$ and potassium bromide, $KBr_{(aq)}$. You can see what happens by following the **colour changes**.

	Potassium chloride solution $KCl_{(aq)}$ - colourless	Potassium bromide solution $KBr_{(aq)}$ - colourless	Potassium iodide solution $KI_{(aq)}$ - colourless
Chlorine water $Cl_{2(aq)}$ - colourless	no reaction	orange solution (Br_2) formed	brown solution (I_2) formed
Bromine water $Br_{2(aq)}$ - orange	no reaction	no reaction	brown solution (I_2) formed
Iodine solution $I_{2(aq)}$ - brown	no reaction	no reaction	no reaction

2) You can make the changes easier to see by shaking the reaction mixture with an **organic solvent** like hexane. The halogen that's present will dissolve readily in the organic solvent, which settles out as a distinct layer above the aqueous solution. This example shows the presence of **iodine**.
(The colours of the other solutions are on the previous page.)

3) These displacement reactions can be used to help **identify** which halogen (or halide) is present in solution.

A **halogen** will **displace a halide** from solution if the halide is **below it** in the periodic table, e.g.

Periodic table	Displacement reaction	Ionic equation
Cl	chlorine (Cl_2) will displace bromide (Br^-) and iodide (I^-)	$Cl_{2(aq)} + 2Br^-_{(aq)} \rightarrow 2Cl^-_{(aq)} + Br_{2(aq)}$ $Cl_{2(aq)} + 2I^-_{(aq)} \rightarrow 2Cl^-_{(aq)} + I_{2(aq)}$
Br	bromine (Br_2) will displace iodide (I^-)	$Br_{2(aq)} + 2I^-_{(aq)} \rightarrow 2Br^-_{(aq)} + I_{2(aq)}$
I	no reaction with F^-, Cl^-, Br^-	

You can also say a halogen will **oxidise** a halide if the halide is below it in the periodic table.

	$Cl_{2(aq)}$ +	$2Br^-_{(aq)}$	→	$2Cl^-_{(aq)}$ +	$Br_{2(aq)}$	
ox. state of Cl	**0**		→	**–1**		reduction
ox. state of Br		**–1**	→		**0**	oxidation

Practice Questions

Q1 Place the halogens F, Cl, Br and I in order of increasing: (a) boiling point (b) volatility (c) electronegativity

Q2 What would be seen when chlorine water is added to potassium iodide solution?

Q3 What colour solution is formed when iodine dissolves in: (a) water (b) hexane

Exam Questions

Q1 a) Write an ionic equation for the reaction between iodine solution and sodium astatide (NaAt). [1 mark]
b) For the equation in (a), deduce which substance is oxidised. [1 mark]

Q2 The extraction of bromine from seawater can be represented by the following equation:

$$Cl_{2\,(aq)} + 2Br^-_{(aq)} \rightarrow Br_{2\,(aq)} + 2Cl^-_{(aq)}$$

a) Explain why this is classed as a redox reaction. [1 mark]
b) Identify the oxidising agent in this reaction. [1 mark]
c) Using your knowledge of periodic trends, suggest which halogen(s) could be used to extract chlorine from a concentrated solution of chloride ions. [1 mark]

Don't skip this page — it could cost you £31 000...

Let me explain... the other night I was watching Who Wants to Be a Millionaire, and this question was on for £32 000:

Which of the these elements is a halogen?
A Argon B Nitrogen
C Fluorine D Sodium

Bet Mr Redmond from Wiltshire wishes he paid more attention in Chemistry now, eh. Ha sucker...

More About The Halogens

I know a nice song about the halogens... : "The halogens are here again, the skies above are clear again. So let's sing a song of cheer again, halogens are here again." Sing it loud in Chemistry lessons... it'll impress your teacher.

Silver Ions React with Halide Ions to Form a Precipitate

This can be used as a **test** for halides. First you add **dilute nitric acid** to remove ions which might interfere with the reaction. Then you just add **silver nitrate solution** ($AgNO_{3(aq)}$). A **precipitate** is formed (of the silver halide).

$$Ag^+_{(aq)} + X^-_{(aq)} \rightarrow AgX_{(s)}$$ ...where X is F, Cl, Br or I

For example, if you add silver nitrate to **sodium chloride**:

$$Ag^+_{(aq)} + Cl^-_{(aq)} \rightarrow AgCl_{(s)}$$

The **colour** of the precipitate identifies the halide present in the original solution.

SILVER NITRATE TEST FOR HALIDE IONS...	
Fluoride F^-:	no precipitate (AgF is soluble)
Chloride Cl^-:	white precipitate
Bromide Br^-:	cream precipitate
Iodide I^-:	yellow precipitate

Most Halogens Can Be Extracted by Electrolysis of Halide Solutions

1) When you **electrolyse** aqueous solutions containing **iodide** or **bromide** ions, the **halogen** element is released at the **anode** (the positive electrode).
2) The **halide ions lose electrons** to the electrode and are **oxidised** to atoms, which combine to form **molecules**.
   For example, electrolysing sodium **bromide** solution produces **bromine** at the anode.

$$2Br^-_{(aq)} \rightarrow 2e^- + Br_{2\,(aq)}$$

3) At the **cathode**, hydrogen ions (from the water) form hydrogen gas:

$$2H^+_{(aq)} + 2e^- \rightarrow H_{2\,(g)}$$

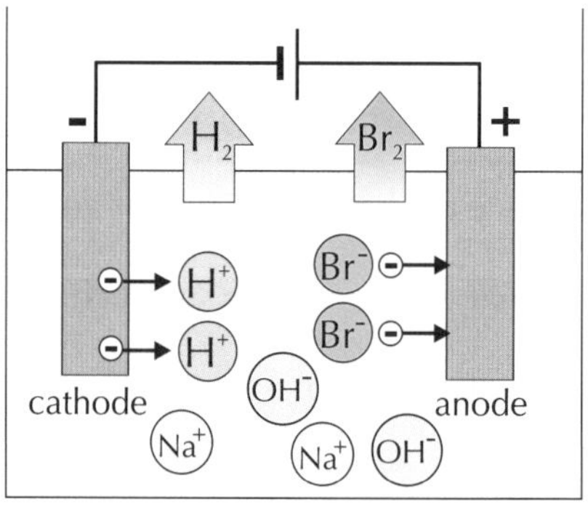

You can only extract **chlorine** from **concentrated sodium chloride** solution:

1) In sodium chloride solution, there are two cations present (Na^+ and H^+) and two anions (Cl^- and OH^-). Which anion is discharged depends on the **concentration** of the solution.
2) In very **dilute** solutions, the chloride ions (Cl^-) **aren't discharged** — they hang on to their extra electrons. The **OH^-** ions lose their extra electron instead and the products at the anode are **oxygen** and water. ⟹ $4OH^-_{(aq)} \rightarrow 4e^- + 2H_2O_{(l)} + O_{2\,(g)}$
3) But if the solution is **concentrated**, chloride ions are discharged and **chlorine** is produced. $2Cl^-_{(aq)} \rightarrow 2e^- + Cl_{2\,(aq)}$
4) In both cases, **hydrogen** is released at the cathode (as it is with other halide solutions). Here's a summary. ⟹

	anode	cathode
Dilute	O_2	H_2
Concentrated	Cl_2	H_2

Fluorine can't be produced by electrolysis of aqueous fluoride solutions — even with concentrated fluoride solutions the hydroxide ions are discharged instead (as above).

More About The Halogens

Storing and Transporting Halogens — It's a Risky Business...

The more reactive halogens can be quite dangerous. They must be kept away from **flammable materials** (being oxidising agents, they increase fire risks). And they're **toxic** and **corrosive**, so must be kept away from **skin** and **eyes**.

1) **Fluorine** is the most reactive halogen, and the most hazardous. Wherever possible, it's produced where it will be used — to **avoid** transporting or storing it. It reacts with most metals and non-metals and can only be stored in expensive containers lined with nickel or copper-nickel alloys — and these containers have to be **small**, so that if there's an accident the damage is limited.
2) **Chlorine** is used a lot in industry. It can be stored as a **liquid** under **pressure** in small cylinders. Like fluorine, it's only transported if no alternative is possible — usually it's produced on site or is made into less hazardous compounds before being transported.
3) **Bromine** is a **liquid** at room temperature, so it's easier to store, but it is volatile (evaporates readily). It can be transported in small quantities but more often it's converted into bromine compounds first.
4) **Iodine** is a solid at room temperature, and much less reactive, so is relatively easy to transport.

... But They are Very Useful

1) Although they're pretty hazardous, both **fluorine** and **chlorine** are widely used because they're needed to make many useful compounds.
   You're expected to know some of those compounds, and examples of their uses.

Halogen	is used to make:	which has these useful properties:	and is used for:
Fluorine	PTFE (polytetrafluoro-ethene)	inert, low-friction, thermally stable	non-stick coating on pans
	HCFCs (hydrochloro-fluorocarbons)	inert, gas at room temperature	refrigerant
	sodium fluoride	strengthens tooth enamel	toothpaste
Chlorine	PVC (polyvinyl chloride)	electrical insulator	electrical wires
	bleach	kills bacteria	water treatment

2) **Bromine** is used in **medicines**, and in many **agricultural** chemicals, e.g. pesticides. It's also an ingredient of **flame retardants** used in electronics, clothing and furniture.
3) **Iodine** is used in **medicines** too. It's also an essential **nutrient** — table salt often contains added potassium iodide.

Practice Questions

Q1 Write an equation for the reaction between silver ions and halide ions.

Q2 What is the anode product if a dilute solution of sodium chloride is electrolysed?

Q3 Outline the dangers of trying to store and transport fluorine. How are these dangers dealt with?

Q4 Which common plastic is made using chlorine?

Exam Questions

Q1 Chlorine is a very important industrial chemical.

a) Explain why chlorine is normally produced on the same site where it is to be used. [3 marks]

b) Name two important compounds made using chlorine, and give one example of how each is used. [2 marks]

c) Write the equations for the electrolysis of concentrated sodium chloride solution. [4 marks]

Q2 Bromine can be extracted by the electrolysis of a concentrated solution of potassium bromide.

a) Write the equations for the reactions at the anode and the cathode. [2 marks]

b) Bromine can be used to make the pesticide bromomethane.
Suggest why bromomethane is likely to be made on the site where the bromine is produced. [2 marks]

Just take a look at these pages... you know what you've got to do...

Never in all my years have I seen an AS Chemistry page so screaming out with the words — "learn me, learn me, learn ALL OF ME, up a bit, across a bit, oh yes that's it, learn me..." ahem, you get the idea. It's quite nice to learn about some real uses of chemicals after all of that theory stuff about periodic trends, don't you think? No? Just me then. Again.

The Chemical Industry

I'm sure that with all your chemistry knowledge, you're thinking of starting up a chemical business. But there are a few things you'll need to bear in mind before you do...

*Production Processes are either **Batch** or **Continuous***

This bit is relatively straightforward. You can either make your product **continuously**, or in **batches**...

	Continuous	Batch
What is it?	Reactants continually enter the vessel, and products continually leave — the reaction doesn't need to be stopped.	Reactants enter the vessel and react. The product is removed, the vessel is cleaned and then used again.
Advantages	Lower labour costs as the process can be easily automated. Can make large quantities of product non-stop. Less variation in quality.	Small quantities can be made. The reaction vessel can be used to make other products.
Disadvantages	More expensive to build. More expensive to run unless the plant runs at full capacity.	More labour intensive as emptying and cleaning needed. Contamination can occur if cleaning is not thorough.
Examples	Making industrial ethanol (see p96). Haber process for making ammonia. Contact process for making sulfuric acid. Blast furnace.	Dye manufacture. Aspirin and paracetamol manufacture. Steel making. Production of ethanol by fermentation.

*It's Important to Choose a **Suitable Site***

This is where things get more complicated. You probably **won't** find a place that's absolutely **perfect** to build your plant. You'll probably need to find the best **compromise** to satisfy **competing demands**.

1) Ideally, you'd like your chemical plant to be near a source of **raw materials**, since they can be expensive to **transport** — especially if they're hazardous, bulky, or you just need lots of them. So it might make sense to build your plant near a **source** of your raw materials, or near a **port** you can ship them to.
2) But ideally, you'd also like to put your plant near your **customers** — to save on **delivery costs**. (If a product's going to be used by another plant to make other chemicals, it's usually a good idea to site the plants close together.)
3) Chemical processes often use large amounts of **water** for cooling. So you might want access to a **river** or the **sea**.
4) And if your process needs loads of **energy** (as in, say, the production of aluminium), you need to think about that too. (Aluminium ore is shipped long distances to get it to cheap sources of power, e.g. near a hydroelectric power station.)

5) You'll also need to think about your **workforce**. Are people with the necessary **skills** available **nearby**? If not, will people be willing to **relocate**?
6) It's pretty unlikely you'll be able to find a spot that satisfies **all** of these requirements. So what you have to do is pick the place that offers the best **compromise**. You might be able to accept being far from your customers as long as the bulky, hazardous raw materials are nearby. What you compromise on will depend on the exact nature of the chemical plant you're building.

Atom Economy** is Important When Choosing **Reactions

Atom economy tells you what **proportion** of the **starting materials** end up in **useful products**. It can be used to measure the **efficiency** of a chemical process.

$$\%\text{ atom economy} = \frac{\text{mass of desired product}}{\text{total mass of reactants}} \times 100$$

1) Businesses want to make **efficient** use of their raw materials — especially if they're in limited supply.
2) Atoms from raw materials can end up in **either**: a) products that you can use, **or** b) products that are useless (waste).
3) Industries want to make as **little waste** as possible, since waste products have to be **separated** from the useful ones, and then disposed of **safely** (governments have tight controls on all kinds of **pollution**).
4) So where possible, businesses use **reactions** with **high atom economies**.
5) Ideally, they'd also choose reactions where the raw materials, waste products, intermediate products, and the process itself are as **safe** as possible. Apart from reducing the **risks** generally, it also avoids having to take potentially expensive **safety precautions**, which are strictly controlled by **health and safety legislation**.

The Chemical Industry

Reaction Conditions are Often a Compromise

You've got your chemical plant. You've chosen your reaction. Now you need to decide the **reaction conditions**.

1) Reaction conditions will affect your **percentage yield**, the **speed** of the reaction, and the **equipment** you need (high pressures will need expensive **pipes** and **vessels** to withstand it, for example).
2) Ideally, you'd choose the conditions that give you the **highest percentage yield**, the **fastest reaction** and that **reduce your costs** as much as possible. This will make for the greatest **efficiency**.

Percentage yield (see p53) compares the amount of product actually produced with the theoretical amount you'd expect according to the reaction equation.

3) Unfortunately though, you'll probably have to **compromise** again...
   For example, it could be that you can get a really **high percentage yield** and a really **fast reaction** if you use a **high temperature** and **pressure**. Unfortunately, this will mean you need to **spend more** on:
   (i) **energy costs** (high temperature and pressure are expensive to make),
   (ii) **tougher equipment** (to cope with the high temperatures and pressures),
   (iii) **stricter safety measures** (high temperatures and pressures are more dangerous, requiring more stringent procedures and better training).
   So maybe you'll compromise, and choose a **lower temperature and pressure**, meaning:
   (i) your equipment costs are **cheaper**, and you'll probably need less stringent **safety procedures**, but...
   (ii) you'll have a **slower reaction**, which will **increase** your **costs** anyway (time is money in industry).
   Or maybe you could think about how using a high temperature and low pressure would affect things...
4) There's not always an **obvious** answer. In reality, chemists and **accountants** would have to sit down and work out how much the various possible options would cost, and choose the one that works best for the business.
5) One thing that will usually help though is a **catalyst**. Catalysts are great. They can save heaps of money — see page 38.
   (But you'd still have to think about the time and money needed to **separate** catalysts from the product, the likelihood of the catalyst being **poisoned**, and so on. Nothing's ever straightforward, is it.)

Which do you favour, atom economy or percentage yield?
I don't really care, I'm a used car salesman.

Practice Questions

Q1 What is meant by the phrase 'high atom economy'?

Q2 Give two advantages of batch production over continuous production.

Q3 Give three factors that affect the siting of a chemical plant.

Exam Questions

Q1 Ethanol is made by the addition of steam to ethene: $C_2H_{4(g)} + H_2O_{(g)} \rightleftharpoons C_2H_5OH_{(g)}$
   a) The atom economy of this reaction is 100%. Explain why reactions with high atom economies are used as often as possible in industry. [2 marks]
   b) Suggest one reason why the percentage yield of this reaction is always less than 100%. [1 mark]
   c) Ethene is made by cracking oil or natural gas.
   Explain how this might affect the choice of location for a plant producing ethanol. [2 marks]

Q2 Chemical A is used to make chemical B. Using 500 kg of chemical A, the reaction equation indicates that you should theoretically get 300 kg of Chemical B. You actually get 250 kg.
   a) Calculate the percentage yield of this reaction. [2 marks]
   b) Chemical B is made from chemical A in a continuous process.
   Give one advantage and one disadvantage of using a continuous process compared to using a batch process. [2 marks]

I've got a chemical plant — it's a chemis-tree...

You need to be able to compare different chemical processes by thinking about all the factors mentioned on these pages. To get rich, all you need is to find a clean, safe chemical process with high atom economy and yield that you can carry out cheaply and easily anywhere you like, and sell the product for loads of money. And if you can find one, let me know...

Halogenoalkanes

Don't worry if you see halogenoalkanes called haloalkanes. It's a government conspiracy to confuse you.

***Halogenoalkanes** are **Alkanes** with **Halogen** Atoms*

A **halogenoalkane** is an alkane with at least one **halogen atom** in place of a hydrogen atom.

E.g.

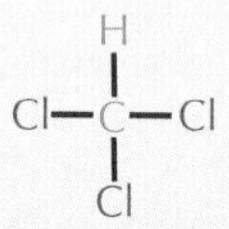

trichloromethane

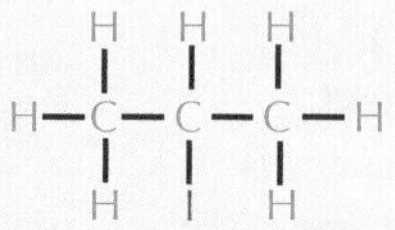

2-iodopropane

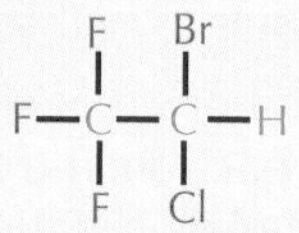

2-bromo-2-chloro-1, 1, 1-trifluoroethane

Naming Halogenoalkanes

1) Look for the longest carbon chain — this gives you the **last** part of the compound's name.
2) The **names** and **positions** of the halogen atoms are described at the **start**.
   - Add '**chloro-**', '**bromo-**' or '**iodo-**' depending on the type of halogen(s) present. If there's more than one type, then put them in alphabetical order.
   - Show the **positions** of halogen atoms on the carbon chain by including the numbers of the carbon atoms they're attached to.
   - If there's more than one identical halogen atom, use **di-** (2), **tri-** (3) or **tetra-** (4) before that part of the name.

See page 41 for a more complete set of rules on naming organic compounds.

*The **Boiling Points** of the **Halogenoalkanes Increase Down** the Group*

1) The boiling points of the halogenoalkanes depend on the **strength** of their **intermolecular forces** – the stronger the forces between the molecules, the higher the boiling point.
2) As you go **down** Group 7 from fluorine to iodine, the **atomic radius** of the halogen atoms, and the **number of electron shells** that they have, **increases**.
3) This leads to stronger **van der Waals forces** (see page 64) between molecules — you have to put in **more energy** to overcome them.
4) So the boiling point of the halogenoalkanes **increases** down the group.

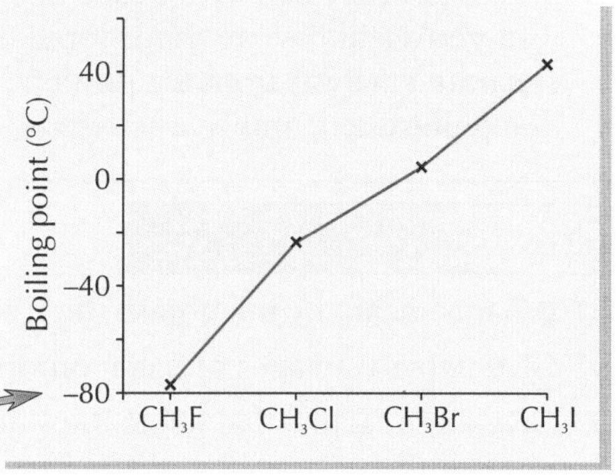

Chloroalkanes** can be Made from **Alcohols

1) **Alcohols** are a good starting point for making halogenoalkanes. You need to replace the alcohol's **-OH** group with a **halogen**.
2) One way to make a **chloroalkane** from an alcohol is to add **concentrated hydrochloric acid** and give the mixture a **shake**.

   This gives you an **impure** chloroalkane, which you can purify using the method shown on the next page.

   For example...

This method doesn't work with all alcohols, but it's the only method you need to know about.

It works a treat with tertiary alcohols (the most reactive type of alcohol), but isn't so good with primary or secondary alcohols.

See page 97 for more info on primary, secondary and tertiary alcohols.

To make **2-chloro-2-methylpropane** you just need to shake **2-methylpropan-2-ol** (a tertiary alcohol) with **concentrated hydrochloric acid** at room temperature.

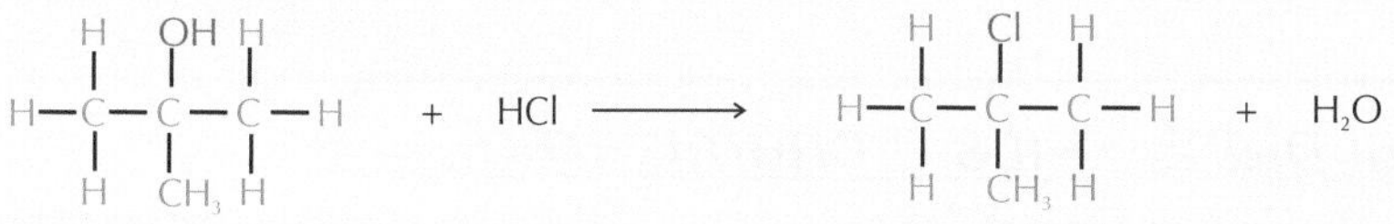

2-methylpropan-2-ol → 2-chloro-2-methylpropane

Halogenoalkanes

Organic Chemistry uses some **Specific Techniques**

There are some **practical techniques** that get used a lot in organic chemistry. The products from organic reactions are often **impure** — so you've got to know how to get rid of the unwanted by-products or leftover reactants. The method for turning an **alcohol** into a **chloroalkane** is a really useful example because it involves quite a few of those techniques.

Making a Chloroalkane from an Alcohol

Stage 1 — the reaction

Shake some 2-methylpropan-2-ol with concentrated hydrochloric acid in a separating funnel for about 20 minutes. You have to keep releasing the pressure (because the product is volatile — it evaporates easily, which raises the pressure in the funnel).

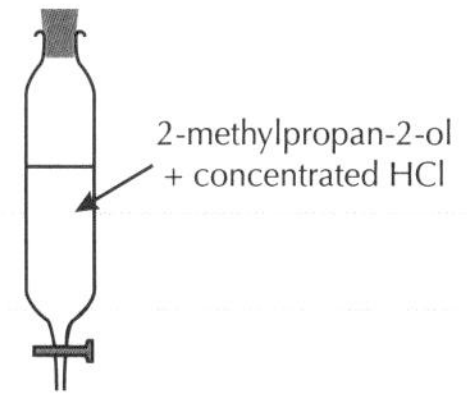

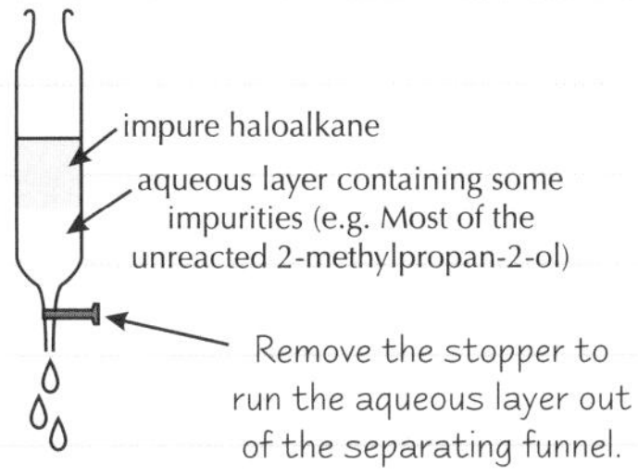

Stage 2 — separation

Allow the mixture to settle into layers.
Run off the aqueous lower layer, leaving the impure halogenoalkane.

Stage 3 — purification

To get a pure sample of your chloroalkane, you need to get rid of the excess acid, water and alcohol.

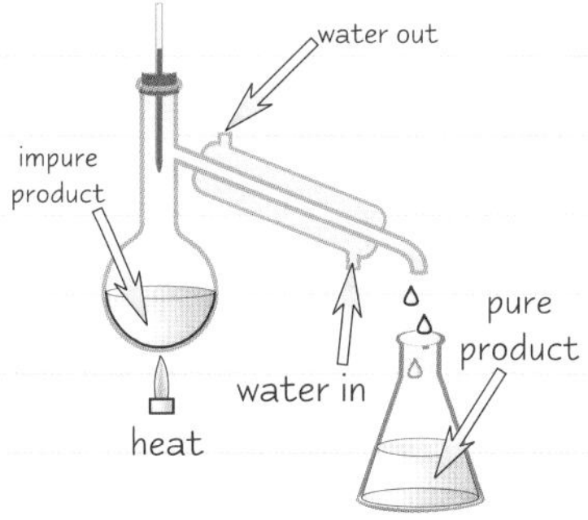

a) Neutralize the excess acid by adding sodium hydrogencarbonate solution to the product and shaking until no more gas is produced (releasing the pressure frequently). Run the lower layer off. Add some distilled water to the product and shake, and again run off the lower layer (this gets rid of remaining inorganic impurities).

b) Remove any remaining water by adding anhydrous sodium sulfate (a drying agent) and shaking the mixture.

c) Remove remaining organic impurities (e.g. unreacted alcohol) by distilling the mixture.
Collect the fraction that boils between 48 and 53 °C — that'll be the chloroalkane.

Practice Questions

Q1 What is a halogenoalkane?

Q2 Describe one factor that influences the boiling points of halogenoalkanes.

Q3 Describe how you could make an impure sample of a chloroalkane.

Exam Questions

Q1 In 1956 the anaesthetic "Halothane" was developed by ICI. It has the chemical formula $CF_3CHBrCl$.
Give the chemical name for this structure and draw its displayed formula. [2 marks]

Q2 A chemist has samples of three halogenoalkanes in tubes labelled A, B and C.
The boiling points of the three halogenoalkanes are: Tube A = 71 °C, Tube B = 46 °C, Tube C = 102 °C.
The halogenoalkanes in the three tubes are 1-chloropropane, 1-bromopropane and 1-iodopropane.
Which halogenoalkane is in which tube? Explain your answer. [4 marks]

Bromochlorofluoroiodomethane — yeah, like that's a real word...

Oh... really? It is?

I don't reckon there's anything too complicated about this stuff. Well... apart from the experimental stuff — that's really fiddly. The best thing to do is write a brief description of the different steps involved in purifying an organic compound, and make sure you can draw the distillation apparatus. Don't just assume you'll be able to do it on exam day — practise it now.

More About Halogenoalkanes

*If you haven't had enough of halogenoalkanes yet, there's more. If you **have** had enough — there's still more.*

The **Carbon–Halogen Bond** in Halogenoalkanes is **Polar**

1) Halogens are much more **electronegative** than carbon.
   So, the **carbon–halogen bond** is **polar**.
2) The **δ+ carbon** doesn't have enough electrons. This means it can be attacked by a **nucleophile**. A nucleophile's an **electron-pair donor.** It donates an electron pair to somewhere without enough electrons.
3) **OH^-**, **NH_3** and **H_2O** are all **nucleophiles** that can react with halogenoalkanes.

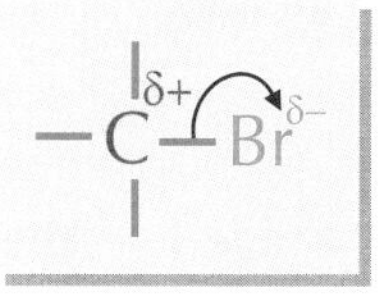

Halogenoalkanes can Undergo **Nucleophilic Substitution**

Halogenoalkanes react with **hydroxide ions** by **nucleophilic substitution**.
You have to use **warm aqueous sodium hydroxide** or it won't work.
Here's how the reaction happens:

The OH^- ion acts as a nucleophile, attacking the positive carbon atom.

The C–Br bond is polar. The $C^{\delta+}$ attracts a lone pair of electrons from the OH^- ion.

The C–Br bond breaks heterolytically, and a new bond forms between the C and the OH^- ion

Heterolytic fission is when both the electrons are taken by one of the atoms — in this case, the Br.

Here's the general equation for this reaction: **R–X + NaOH → ROH + NaX**

R represents an alkyl group. X stands for one of the halogens (F, Cl, Br or I).

Water Can Act as a **Nucleophile** Too

Warming a **halogenoalkane** with **water** also results in a **nucleophilic substitution** reaction:

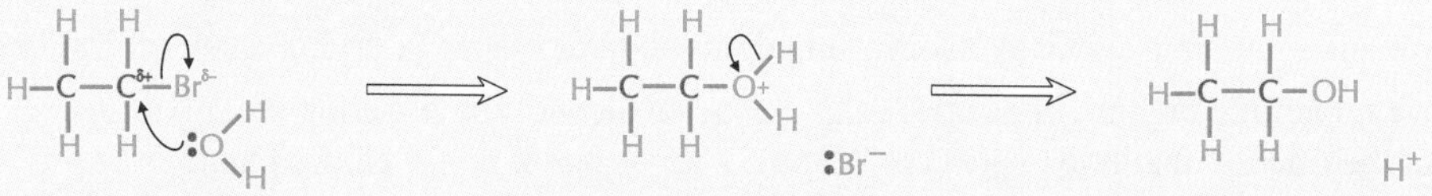

The reaction starts in the same way — the $C^{\delta+}$ attracts a lone pair from the H_2O, and the polar C–Br bond breaks.

An intermediate forms with an oxygen that has three bonds. This is unstable, so one O–H bond breaks.

An alcohol is formed.

This is a **hydrolysis** reaction — a molecule is broken up by water.

Halogenoalkanes React With **Ammonia** to Form **Amines**

1) Amines are organic compounds. They're based on **ammonia** (NH_3), but one or more of the **hydrogen** atoms are **replaced** by **alkyl** groups.

Alkyl groups are shown by the letter R. They're alkanes with one H removed. E.g. $-CH_3$, $-C_2H_5$.

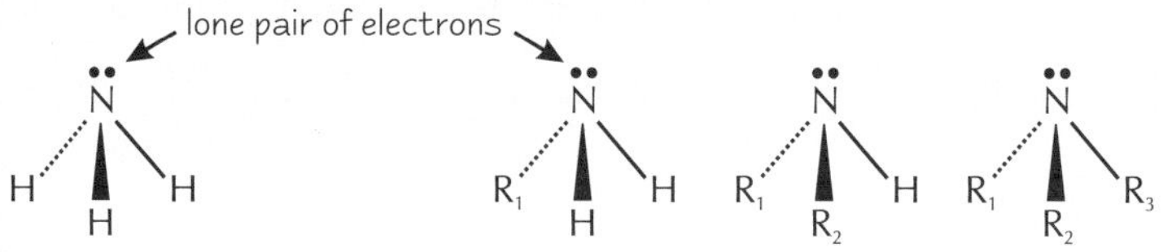

This is ammonia... ...but these are amines.

2) If you **warm** a haloalkane with excess **ethanolic** ammonia, the **ammonia** swaps places with the **halogen** — yes, it's another one of those **nucleophilic substitution reactions**.

Ethanolic ammonia is just ammonia dissolved in ethanol.

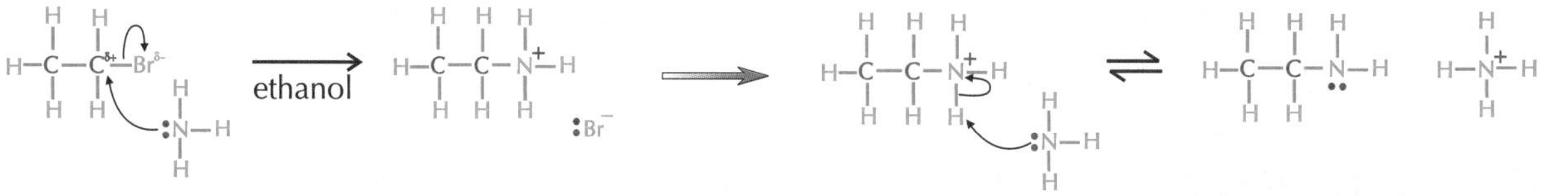

The first step is the same as in the mechanisms above, except this time the nucleophile is NH_3.

In the second step, an ammonia molecule removes a hydrogen from the NH_3 group to leave an amine.

More About Halogenoalkanes

Iodoalkanes are the *Most Reactive* Halogenoalkanes

Bonds between carbon atoms and halogen atoms are polarised, with **C–F** the **most polar** and **C–I** the **least**.
You might expect that the more polar the bond is, the more likely it is to break, but this turns out **not** to be the case.
Experimental evidence shows that **iodoalkanes** are the **most reactive** of the first four haloalkanes — so reactivity can't be due to bond polarisation. Here are two experiments you can use to show this reactivity series:

React the Halogenoalkanes with Water:

1) To compare the **reactivities** of the halogenoalkanes, you need to see which reacts **fastest**.
Put a **chloroalkane**, a **bromoalkane**, and an **iodoalkane** in three different test tubes. To each of these, add some **silver nitrate** solution (this contains the water) and some **ethanol** (as a solvent).

$$Ag^+ (aq) + X^- (aq) \rightarrow AgX (s)$$

This is the reaction from p70.

2) A precipitate forms fastest with the **iodoalkane** — so that must be the **most reactive**.
Bromoalkanes react slower than iodoalkanes, and **chloroalkanes** the slowest of all.

or: **React the Halogenoalkanes with NaOH:**

1. Warm **aqueous NaOH** with the **halogenoalkanes**. The **OH^- ion** acts as the nucleophile (as on previous page).
2. Add dilute **nitric acid** to **neutralise** any spare OH^- ions **before** adding the **silver nitrate** solution (or else the silver nitrate will react with the OH^- ions to form a silver oxide precipitate, which messes up your results).

It's actually the carbon-halogen bond strength that decides reactivity:

Despite being the most polar, the **C-F bond** is the **strongest** — it has the highest **bond enthalpy**. For any reaction to occur the carbon-halogen bond needs to **break**. The **stronger** that bond is, the **slower** the reaction will be.

bond	bond enthalpy kJ mol^{-1}
C–F	467
C–Cl	346
C–Br	290
C–I	228

Faster hydrolysis as bond enthalpy decreases (the bonds are getting weaker).

Practice Questions

Q1 What is a nucleophile?

Q2 Why is the carbon-halogen bond polar?

Q3 Why does iodoethane react faster than chloro- or bromoethane with warm, aqueous sodium hydroxide?

Q4 Give two examples of nucleophiles that can react with halogenoalkanes.

Exam Question

Q1 The equation for the reaction between water and 2-bromopropane is shown below.

$$CH_3CHBrCH_3 + H_2O \rightarrow CH_3CH(OH)CH_3 + HBr$$

a) (i) Name the type of reaction. [1 mark]
(ii) Name the organic product. [2 marks]

b) Under the same conditions, 2-iodopropane was used in place of 2-bromopropane in the reaction above.
What difference would you expect in the rate of the reaction? Explain your answer. [2 marks]

c) Draw the mechanism for the reaction between 2-bromopropane and aqueous potassium hydroxide. [3 marks]

I get irritable when it rains — it's a precipitation reaction...

Polar bonds get in just about every area of Chemistry. If you still think they're something to do with either bears or mints, flick back to page 62 and have a good read. And make sure you can explain that reaction mechanism, and the different reactivities above. This stuff's always coming up in exams. Ruin the examiner's day and get it right.

Giant Structures

As you saw back on page 22, atoms can form giant structures as well as piddling little molecules — well...'giant' in molecular terms anyway. Compared to structures like the Eiffel Tower, they're still unbelievably tiny.

Diamond and Silicon(IV) Oxide have Giant Molecular Structures

1) **Giant molecular** structures have a huge network of **covalently** bonded atoms. They're sometimes called **macromolecular structures**.
2) **Diamond** (a form of **carbon**) and **silicon(IV) oxide** are two examples of substances with macromolecular structures.
3) The reason **carbon** and **silicon** atoms can form this type of structure is that they can each form four strong, covalent bonds.

Diamond is the Hardest known Substance

1) In diamond, each carbon atom is **covalently bonded** to **four** other carbon atoms.
2) The atoms arrange themselves in **tetrahedral** shapes, and form a **crystal lattice** structure.

Remember... a tetrahedron is a triangular-based pyramid.

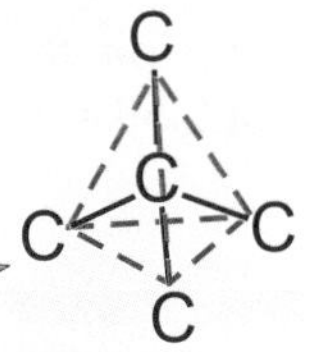

Diamond

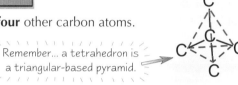

Because of its **strong covalent** bonds:
1) Diamond is extremely **hard** — it's used in diamond-tipped drills and saws.
2) **Vibrations** travel easily through the stiff lattice, so it's a **good thermal conductor**.
3) Diamond has a **very high melting point** — it actually sublimes at over 3800 K.
4) It **can't conduct** electricity — all the outer electrons are held in localised bonds.
5) It won't dissolve in **any** solvent.

'Sublimes' means it changes straight from a solid to a gas, skipping the liquid stage.

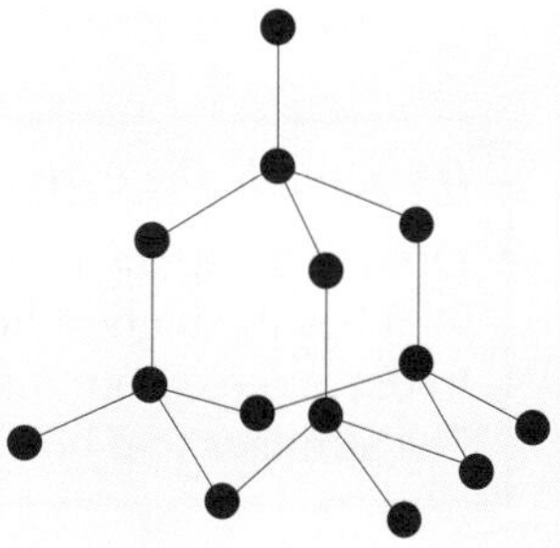

You can 'cut' diamond to form gemstones. Its structure makes it refract light a lot, which is why it sparkles.

Silicon(IV) Oxide also has a Tetrahedral Structure

Silicon(IV) oxide (**SiO_2**) also forms a **giant lattice**. It has a structure fairly similar (but **not** identical) to diamond.

Silicon(IV) oxide

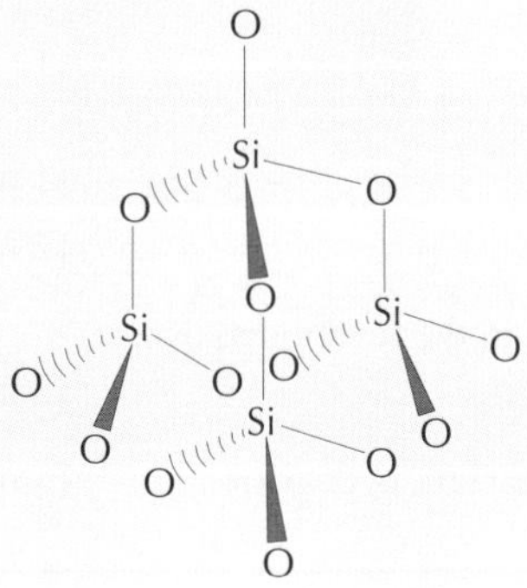

1) **Silicon dioxide** or **silica** (SiO_2) is found as **quartz** or **sand** (sand's not pure — it's got lots of bits of other stuff in too).
2) Each silicon atom **covalently bonds** with **four oxygen atoms** in a **tetrahedral** arrangement to form a big **crystal lattice**.
3) Its structure **isn't** exactly the same as diamond's, because the oxygen atoms can only bond with **two silicon atoms**.
4) Like diamond, silica is a **hard crystalline solid** with a **high melting point**. It is **insoluble** in any solvent. This is down to its strong **covalent bonds**.
5) Silica **doesn't conduct electricity** — all of its bonding electrons are used for making covalent bonds.

Giant Structures

CO_2 and SiO_2 Have **Very Different Structures**...

1) Carbon and silicon are in the **same Group** of the periodic table, so they have similar arrangements of outer-shell electrons — both have 2 electrons in their outermost p sub-shell. And so you'd expect them to be similar in some ways. And they are... for example, pure **silicon** has a similar structure to diamond.
2) But in some ways they act quite differently. Both elements react with oxygen to form **dioxides**, **but**... the **structures** of CO_2 and SiO_2 couldn't be more different.

- **Carbon dioxide** (CO_2) consists of **small molecules**, with each carbon forming a **double bond** with the oxygen atoms.

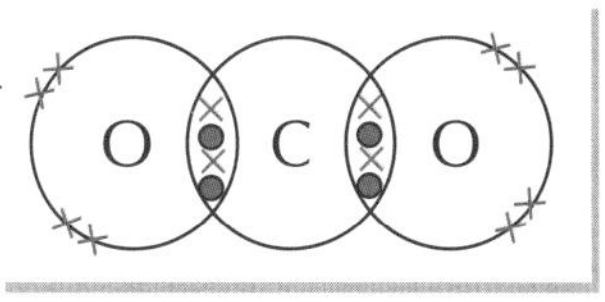

- **Silicon dioxide** forms a giant lattice structure (as shown on the previous page). Each silicon atom forms **single bonds** with four oxygen atoms (allowing each oxygen to bond to another silicon).

...and so **Very Different Properties**

Because the **structures** of CO_2 and SiO_2 are so different, you'd expect the two compounds to have very different **physical properties**. The most obvious difference is in the melting and boiling points...

1) Carbon dioxide is a gas at room temperature (the molecules are non-polar, so the only forces holding them together are weak **instantaneous dipole – induced dipole forces**).
2) Silicon dioxide doesn't even melt until it reaches over 1700 °C, and has a boiling point of over 2000 °C.
3) The **solubilities** in water of the two substances are very different as well. Whereas silicon dioxide is **insoluble**, carbon dioxide **will** dissolve (even though it's covalent). *The 'fizz' in fizzy pop is because of dissolved carbon dioxide.*

Practice Questions

Q1 Explain why carbon and silicon are both able to form giant molecular structures.

Q2 Explain why diamond won't conduct electricity.

Q3 In silicon(IV) oxide, how many oxygen atoms are bonded to each silicon atom?

Q4 Explain why the boiling points of CO_2 and SiO_2 are so different.

Exam Question

Q1 Look at the data below on the compound boron nitride (BN).

Melting point: 2700 °C (sublimes)
Electrical conductivity of liquid: zero
Solubility in water: insoluble

a) On the basis of this data suggest the bond type and structure in boron nitride. Explain your choices. [4 marks]

b) Boron(III) chloride has a boiling point of –107 °C.
(i) Suggest the bond type and structure in boron(III) chloride. [2 marks]
(ii) Explain why boron(III) chloride has a much lower melting point than boron nitride. [3 marks]

Carbon is a girl's best friend...

You've seen some of these ideas before — but that's no reason to be complacent. If you reckon you know all this stuff, then don't just skim quickly over the pages — test yourself using the questions above, and double check that you know it as well as you think. The Exam is not the place to find out that one or two of the important details had slipped your mind.

Reaction Rates

The rate of a reaction is just how quickly it happens. Lots of things can make it go faster or slower — like heating it up.

Particles **Must** Collide to **React**

Can I talk to you about collision theory dear?
If you do, my croquet mallet might collide with your head.
Ah ha ha!

1) Particles in liquids and gases are **always moving** and **colliding** with **each other**. They **don't** react every time though — only when the **conditions** are right. A reaction **won't** take place between two particles **unless** —

   - They collide in the **right direction**. They need to be **facing** each other the right way.
   - They collide with at least a certain **minimum** amount of kinetic (movement) **energy**.

   This stuff's called **Collision Theory**.
2) The **minimum amount of kinetic energy** particles need to react is called the **activation enthalpy** or **activation energy**. The particles need this much energy to **break the bonds** to start the reaction.
3) Reactions with **low activation enthalpies** often happen **pretty easily**. But reactions with **high activation enthalpies** don't. You need to give the particles extra energy by **heating** them.

To make this a bit clearer, here's an **enthalpy profile diagram**.
It shows the energy of the reacting particles before, during and after they react.

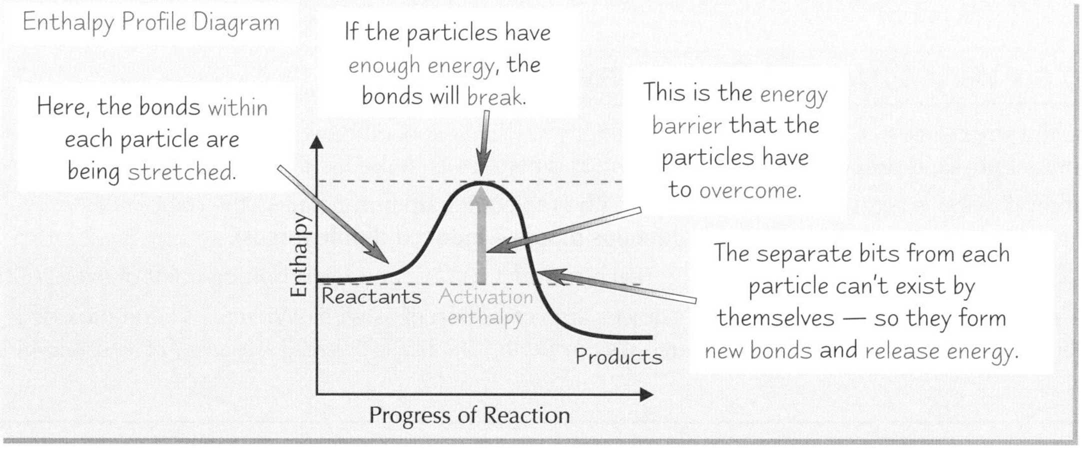
Enthalpy Profile Diagram
If the particles have enough energy, the bonds will break.
Here, the bonds within each particle are being stretched.
This is the energy barrier that the particles have to overcome.
The separate bits from each particle can't exist by themselves — so they form new bonds and release energy.
Enthalpy
Reactants
Activation enthalpy
Products
Progress of Reaction

Molecules in a Gas **Don't** all have the **Same Amount of Energy**

You need to be really clear about how **temperature** affects the rate of a reaction. It's all down to the **energy** of the particles — and **Maxwell-Boltzmann distributions** are a good way to get your head round what's going on.

1) Imagine looking down on Oxford Street when it's teeming with people. You'll see some people ambling along **slowly**, some hurrying **quickly**, but most of them will be walking with a **moderate speed**.
2) It's the same with the **molecules** in a **gas**. Some **don't have much kinetic energy** and move **slowly**. Others have **loads of kinetic energy** and **whizz** along. But most molecules are somewhere **in between**.
3) If you plot a **graph** of the **numbers of molecules** in a **gas** with different **kinetic energies** you get a **Maxwell-Boltzmann distribution**. It looks like this —

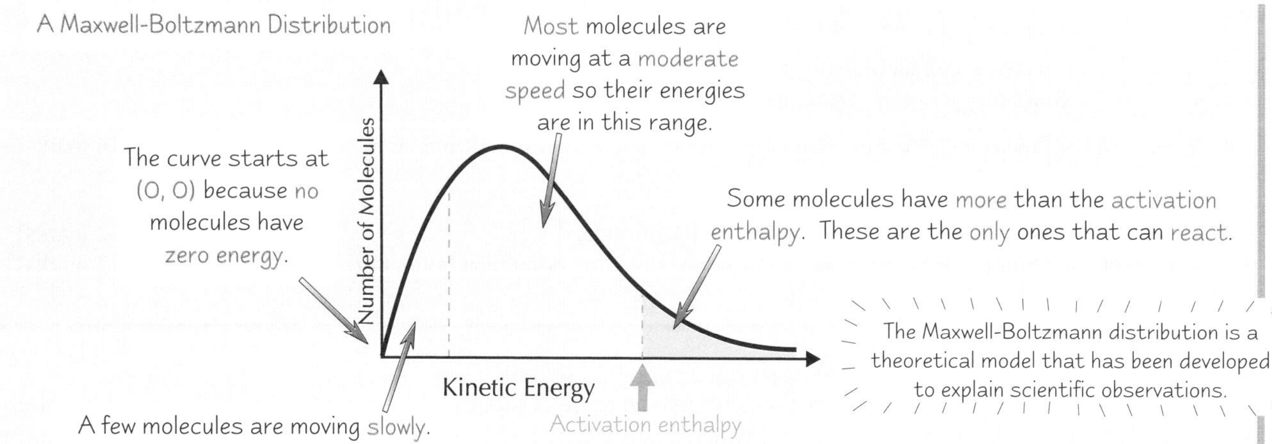
A Maxwell-Boltzmann Distribution
Most molecules are moving at a moderate speed so their energies are in this range.
The curve starts at (0, 0) because no molecules have zero energy.
Some molecules have more than the activation enthalpy. These are the only ones that can react.
Number of Molecules
Kinetic Energy
Activation enthalpy
A few molecules are moving slowly.

The Maxwell-Boltzmann distribution is a theoretical model that has been developed to explain scientific observations.

Reaction Rates

Increasing the *Temperature* makes Reactions *Faster*

1) If you increase the **temperature**, the particles will on average have more **kinetic energy** and will move **faster**.
2) So, a **greater proportion** of molecules will have the **activation energy** and be able to **react**. This changes the **shape** of the **Maxwell-Boltzmann distribution curve** — it pushes it over to the **right**.

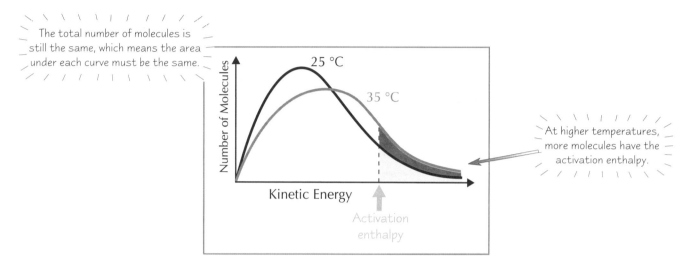

The total number of molecules is still the same, which means the area under each curve must be the same.

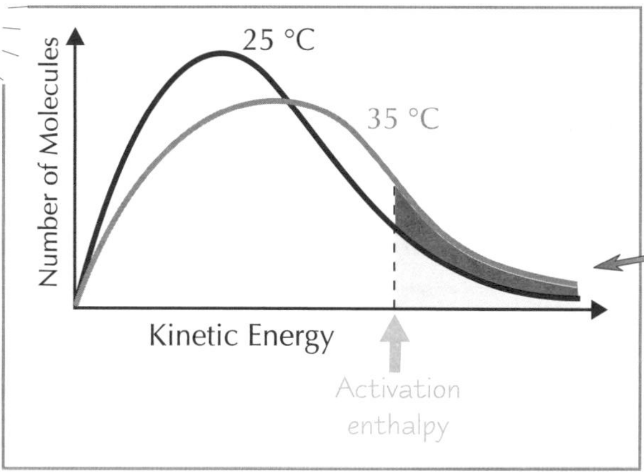

At higher temperatures, more molecules have the activation enthalpy.

3) Because the molecules are flying about **faster**, they'll **collide more often**. This is **another reason** why increasing the temperature makes a reaction faster.
So **small temperature increases** can lead to **large increases in reaction rate**.

Practice Questions

Q1 Explain the term 'activation enthalpy'.

Q2 Sketch an enthalpy profile diagram for a reaction.

Q3 Sketch the distribution of the energies of molecules at two different temperatures.

Exam Questions

Q1 Nitrogen monoxide (NO) and ozone (O_3) sometimes react to produce nitrogen dioxide (NO_2) and oxygen (O_2).
A collision between the two molecules does not always lead to a reaction. Explain why. [2 marks]

Q2 Use collision theory to explain why the reaction between a solid and a liquid is generally faster than that between two solids. [2 marks]

Q3 This graph shows the rate that oxygen is evolved when hydrogen peroxide decomposes at 25 °C.

Which of the curves X, Y or Z shows the rate that oxygen is evolved when the same amount of hydrogen peroxide decomposes at 15 °C. Explain your answer. [4 marks]

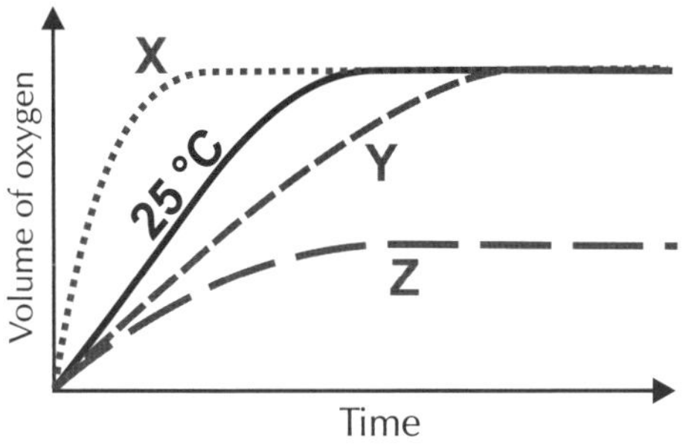

Reaction Rates — cheaper than water rates

This page isn't too hard to learn — no equations, no formulas... what more could you ask for. The only tricky thing might be the Maxwell-Boltzmann thingymajiggle. Remember, particles don't react every time they collide — only if they have enough energy, and are at the correct angle. The more often they collide and the more energy they have, the faster the reaction is.

More On Reaction Rates

Carrots and sticks won't do a lot of good. But here's some more things that will.

Concentration, Surface Area and Catalysts Affect the Reaction Rate Too

Increasing Concentration Speeds Up Reactions

Increasing the **concentration** of reactants in a **solution** means the particles are **closer together** on average. If they're closer, they'll **collide more often**. **More collisions** mean **more chances** to react.

Increasing Pressure Speeds Up Reactions

Increasing the **pressure** of a **gas** works for exactly the same reason that increasing concentration works — particles are **closer together** on average, they **collide more often**, and so have **more chances** to react.

Increasing Surface Area Speeds Up Reactions

If one reactant is in a **big lump** then most of the particles won't collide with other reactants. You need to **crush** these lumps so that more of the particles can come in **contact** with the other **reactants**. A **smaller particle size** means a **larger surface area**. This leads to a **speedier** reaction.

Catalysts Can Speed Up Reactions

Catalysts are really useful. They **lower the activation enthalpy** by providing a **different way** for the bonds to be broken and remade. If the activation enthalpy's **lower**, more particles will have **enough enthalpy** to react.
There's more about catalysts below.

And Don't Forget About Temperature

Temperature is a biggie. I told you about why it affects reaction rate on the last page, but it's so important that I'll tell you again. Increasing the temperature gives the particles **more energy**, so that they're **more likely to react** when they collide. And because they're moving faster, they collide more often too. It's win-win all the way.

Homogeneous Catalysts are in the Same State as the Reactants

1) Catalysts **increase** the **rate** of a reaction.
2) They do this by providing an **alternative reaction pathway** with a lower activation enthalpy. The catalyst is **chemically unchanged** at the end of the reaction.
3) There are two types of catalyst — **heterogeneous** catalysts (see page 38-39) and **homogeneous** catalysts.
4) A **homogeneous catalyst** is in the **same state** as the **reactants**. So, if the reactants are **gases**, the catalyst must be a **gas** too. And if the reactants are **aqueous** (dissolved in water), the catalyst has to be **aqueous** too.
5) When enzymes (biological catalysts) catalyse reactions in your body cells, everything's **aqueous** — so that's an example of **homogeneous catalysis**.

More On Reaction Rates

Homogeneous Catalysts Work by Forming **Intermediates**

1) A homogeneous catalyst speeds up reactions by forming one or more **intermediate compounds** with the reactants. The products are then formed from the intermediate compounds.
2) The activation enthalpy needed to form the **intermediates** (and to form the products from the intermediates) is **lower** than that needed to make the products directly from the reactants.
3) If a reaction is speeded up by a **homogeneous catalyst**, its enthalpy profile will have **two humps** in it.

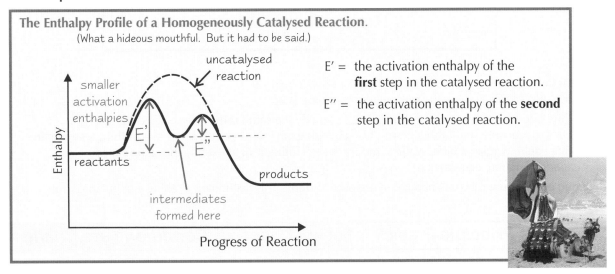

The Enthalpy Profile of a Homogeneously Catalysed Reaction.
(What a hideous mouthful. But it had to be said.)

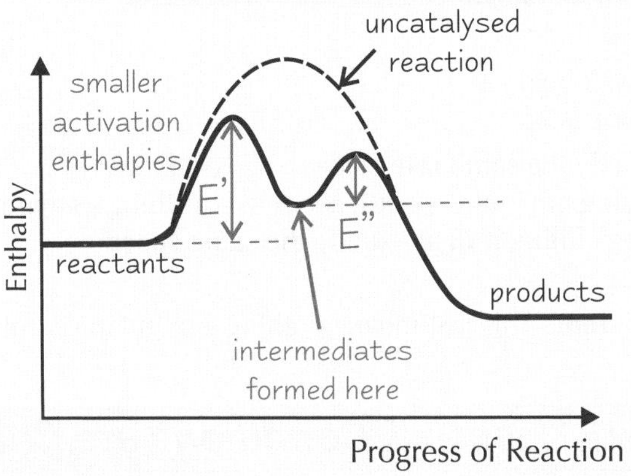

E′ = the activation enthalpy of the **first** step in the catalysed reaction.

E″ = the activation enthalpy of the **second** step in the catalysed reaction.

4) The catalyst is **reformed** again and carries on **catalysing** the reaction.

Mrs Watson tried everything to lower the camel's activation enthalpy.

Practice Questions

Q1 Name the five factors that affect the rate of a reaction.

Q2 Why does decreasing concentration decrease the rate of a reaction.

Q3 Describe two reasons why increasing the temperature can speed up the rate of a reaction.

Q4 Enzymes are homogeneous catalysts. Explain what a homogeneous catalyst is.

Q5 Why are there two humps in the enthalpy profile of a homogeneously catalysed reaction?

Exam Questions

Q1 Explain how homogeneous catalysts speed up chemical reactions. [2 marks]

Q2 Enzymes are proteins that catalyse specific biological reactions.
Draw a fully labelled enthalpy profile for an enzyme-catalysed reaction and an uncatalysed reaction. [4 marks]

Q3 Homogeneous catalysts speed up a reaction by forming intermediate compounds.
Explain why they are classed as catalysts, even though they are chemically altered during the reaction. [1 mark]

I'm a catalyst — I like to speed up arguments without getting too involved...

Remember, increasing concentration and pressure do exactly the same thing. The only difference is you increase the concentration of a ***solution*** *and the pressure of a* ***gas****. Don't get them muddled... And don't go thinking that, just because this stuff is (a bit) easier than some topics, you can relax. No way... easy topics mean easy marks if you know your stuff.*

Reversible Reactions

There's a lot of to-ing and fro-ing on this page. Mind your head doesn't start spinning.

Reversible Reactions Can Reach **Dynamic Equilibrium**

1) Lots of chemical reactions are **reversible** — they go **both ways**. To show a reaction's reversible, you stick in a $\rightleftharpoons$. Here's an example:

$$H_{2(g)} + I_{2(g)} \rightleftharpoons 2HI_{(g)}$$

This reaction can go in **either direction** —

forwards $H_{2(g)} + I_{2(g)} \rightarrow 2HI_{(g)}$ ....or **backwards** $2HI_{(g)} \rightarrow H_{2(g)} + I_{2(g)}$.

2) As the **reactants** get used up, the **forward** reaction **slows down** — and as more **product** is formed, the **reverse** reaction **speeds up**.
3) After a while, the forward reaction will be going at exactly the **same rate** as the backward reaction. The amounts of reactants and products **won't be changing** any more, so it'll seem like **nothing's happening**. It's a bit like you're **digging a hole**, while someone else is **filling it in** at exactly the **same speed**. This is called a **dynamic equilibrium**.
4) A **dynamic equilibrium** can only happen in a **closed system**. This just means nothing can get in or out.

Le Chatelier's Principle Predicts what will Happen if **Conditions are Changed**

If you **change** the **concentration**, **pressure** or **temperature** of a reversible reaction, you're going to **alter** the **position of equilibrium**. This just means you'll end up with **different amounts** of reactants and products at equilibrium.

If the position of equilibrium moves to the **left**, you'll get more **reactants**.

$$H_{2(g)} + I_{2(g)} \rightleftharpoons 2HI_{(g)}$$

If the position of equilibrium moves to the **right**, you'll get more **products**.

$$H_{2(g)} + I_{2(g)} \rightleftharpoons 2HI_{(g)}$$

Mr and Mrs Le Chatelier celebrate another successful year in the principle business

Le Chatelier's principle tells you how the **position of equilibrium** will change if a **condition changes**:

If there's a change in **concentration**, **pressure** or **temperature**, the equilibrium will move to help **counteract** the change.

So, basically, if you **raise the temperature**, the position of equilibrium will shift to try to **cool things down**.
And, if you **raise the pressure or concentration**, the position of equilibrium will shift to try to **reduce it again**.

Catalysts **Don't Affect** The Position of Equilibrium

Catalysts have **NO EFFECT** on the **position of equilibrium**.
They **can't** increase **yield** — but they **do** mean equilibrium is reached **faster**.

Reversible Reactions

Here's Some Handy Rules for Using Le Chatelier's Principle

CONCENTRATION $2SO_{2(g)} + O_{2(g)} \rightleftharpoons 2SO_{3(g)}$

1) If you **increase** the **concentration** of a **reactant** (SO_2 or O_2), the equilibrium tries to **get rid** of the extra reactant. It does this by making **more product** (SO_3). So the equilibrium's shifted to the **right**.
2) If you **increase** the **concentration** of the **product** (SO_3), the equilibrium tries to remove the extra product. This makes the **reverse reaction** go faster. So the equilibrium shifts to the **left**.
3) **Decreasing** the concentrations has the **opposite effect**.

PRESSURE (changing this only affects **equilibria involving gases**)

1) **Increasing** the pressure shifts the equilibrium to the side with the **fewest** gas molecules. This **reduces** the pressure.
2) **Decreasing** the pressure shifts the equilibrium to the side with **most** gas molecules. This **raises** the pressure again.

There's 3 moles on the left, but only 2 on the right.
So, an increase in pressure shifts the equilibrium to the right. ⟹ $2SO_{2(g)} + O_{2(g)} \rightleftharpoons 2SO_{3(g)}$

TEMPERATURE

1) **Increasing** the temperature means **adding heat**.
   The equilibrium shifts in the **endothermic (positive ΔH) direction** to absorb this heat.
2) **Decreasing** the temperature **removes heat**.
   The equilibrium shifts in the **exothermic (negative ΔH) direction** to try to replace the heat.
3) If the forward reaction's **endothermic**, the reverse reaction will be **exothermic**, and vice versa.

This reaction's exothermic in the forward direction.
If you increase the temperature, the equilibrium shifts to the left to absorb the extra heat.

Exothermic ⟹

$$2SO_{2(g)} + O_{2(g)} \rightleftharpoons 2SO_{3(g)} \quad \Delta H = -197\ \text{kJ mol}^{-1}$$

⟸ Endothermic

Practice Questions

Q1 Using an example, explain the terms 'reversible' and 'dynamic equilibrium'.

Q2 If the equilibrium moves to the right, do you get more products or reactants?

Q3 A reaction at equilibrium is endothermic in the forward direction.
What happens to the position of equilibrium as the temperature is increased?

Exam Question

Q1 Nitrogen and oxygen gases were reacted together in a closed flask and allowed to reach equilibrium with the nitrogen monoxide formed. The forward reaction is endothermic.

$$N_{2(g)} + O_{2(g)} \rightleftharpoons 2NO_{(g)}$$

a) State Le Chatelier's principle. [1 mark]

b) Explain how the following changes would affect the position of equilibrium of the above reaction:
(i) Pressure is **increased**. [2 marks]
(ii) Temperature is **reduced**. [2 marks]
(iii) Nitrogen monoxide is removed. [1 mark]

c) What would be the effect of a catalyst on the composition of the equilibrium mixture? [1 mark]

Only going forward cos we can't find reverse...

Equilibria never do what you want them to do. They always ***oppose*** *you. Be sure you know what happens to an equilibrium if you change the conditions. A word about pressure — if there's the same number of gas moles on each side of the equation, then you can raise the pressure as high as you like and it won't make a blind bit of difference to the position of equilibrium.*

The Atmosphere

The atmosphere wasn't always like it is today. A few billion years ago it was full of carbon dioxide, with just a teeny-weeny bit of oxygen. Luckily, it evolved so we could breathe and stuff. We're starting to mess it up again with pollutants though.

Most of the ***Atmosphere*** *is* ***Nitrogen*** *and* ***Oxygen***

Here's what the atmosphere's made of. The percentages are by **volume** of dry air (in the lower atmosphere).

Nitrogen	**78%**
Oxygen	**21%**
Argon	**1%**
Carbon dioxide	**0.035%**

Also:
1) Varying amounts of **water vapour**.
2) **Other gases** in tiny amounts.

It comes to over 100% because the figures are rounded off slightly.

So every **100 cm³** of air contains about **78 cm³** of nitrogen, **21 cm³** of oxygen and **1 cm³** of argon. And **tiny bits** of other stuff too.

We're also putting **pollutants** like **particulates**, **oxides of sulfur and nitrogen**, **carbon monoxide** and **unburnt hydrocarbons** into the atmosphere. This is mainly by burning fossil fuels in vehicle engines and power stations.

See p48 for more details.

And then there's methane and extra carbon dioxide — they add to the **greenhouse effect** (page 88).

Parts Per Million *is used for* ***Really Small Quantities***

1) The **major gases** in the atmosphere are normally given as **percentages** of the **total volume**. But some gases are present in such **tiny amounts** that it's **not very convenient** to write their quantities like this. For instance, **xenon** makes up only **0.000 009%** of the atmosphere. Numbers this small are a pain to work with.
2) So to get round this problem, another type of measurement is used. It is called **parts per million** or **ppm**.
3) So if there's **0.000 009 parts** of xenon in every **one hundred parts of air**, you can multiply both quantities by **10 000** to make the quantity **large enough** to work with, like this:

0.000 009% = 0.000 009 parts per 100 parts of air ⟶ **0.000 009 × 10 000 = 0.09; 100 × 10 000 = 1 000 000** ⟶ **0.09 parts per million**

4) So there's 0.09 ppm xenon. The atmosphere also contains **0.1 ppm** carbon monoxide and **0.3 ppm** nitrous oxide.

The ***Earth's Atmosphere*** *Absorbs* ***Radiation***

1) The Sun gives out **electromagnetic radiation** because of the nuclear processes going on in its core. Electromagnetic radiation is energy that's transmitted as waves, with a **spectrum** of different frequencies.
2) The Sun mainly gives out **visible** radiation (light) and **infrared** radiation (heat), along with a smaller amount of **ultraviolet** radiation.

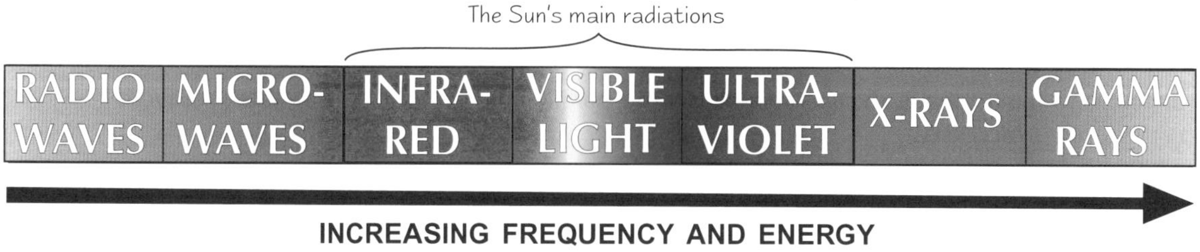

3) The **Earth's atmosphere** absorbs some of the Sun's infrared radiation and most of the ultraviolet radiation — more on this on the next page.
4) The **Earth's surface** also absorbs radiation from the Sun and is warmed. It then re-emits **radiation**, mostly as **infrared**. The Earth emits much **lower frequency** radiation than the Sun (because it's much cooler).

The Atmosphere

Infrared Radiation Makes Some Bonds Vibrate More

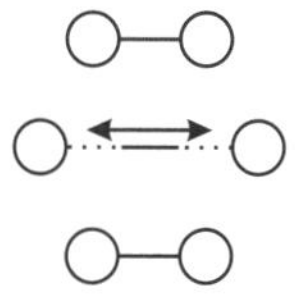

Vibration movement

This happens when the bonds stretch and bend.

1) Some molecules absorb energy from **infrared radiation**. The extra energy makes their covalent bonds **vibrate** more.
2) Only molecules made of **different atoms** can absorb infrared radiation. This is because the **polarities** of their bonds change as they vibrate.
3) So, oxygen (O_2) and nitrogen (N_2) don't absorb infrared radiation, but **carbon dioxide**, **water**, **nitric oxide (NO)** and **methane** do. Gases that **do** absorb infrared radiation are called **greenhouse gases** because they stop some of the radiation emitted by the Earth from escaping into space (see page 88).
4) Gas molecules' bonds have **certain fixed vibrational energy levels**. These are called **quantised** levels. So a bond's energy can only **jump** from one level to another — like moving up a **staircase** in steps.
5) This means that only frequencies of radiation corresponding to particular amounts of energy are absorbed. **Different molecules** absorb **different frequencies** of radiation.

UV and Visible Light Radiation Give Electrons More Energy

1) The **electrons** in molecules also have **fixed energy levels** that they can **jump between**.
2) When **ultraviolet radiation** or **visible light** hit a molecule of **gas** the **electrons** can **absorb** the energy and **jump up** to their **next energy level**. Because the energy needed for these changes is **quantised** too, **only specific frequencies** are absorbed.
3) If enough energy is absorbed bonds **break**, forming **free radicals**.

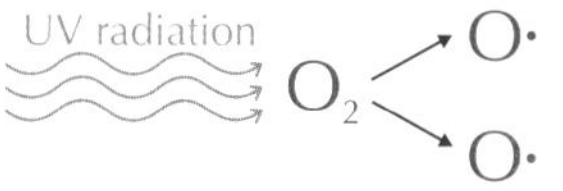

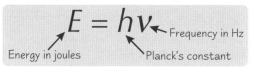

If O_2 molecules absorb the right amount of UV energy they split into oxygen atoms or free radicals — this is the first step in the formation of ozone, O_3 (see page 92).

The Energy from Radiation can be Calculated

You saw this equation on page 16.

The **energy** depends on the **frequency** of the radiation. I reckon we're about due for an **equation**:

$$E = h\nu$$

E = Energy in joules, h = Planck's constant, ν = Frequency in Hz

Planck's constant $= 6.63 \times 10^{-34}$ Js

So, if you know **Planck's constant** and the **frequency**, you can calculate **how much energy** the molecule absorbed.

Example: What is the energy supplied to a molecule by infra-red radiation of frequency 0.5×10^{14} Hz?

$E = h\nu = (6.63 \times 10^{-34}) \times (0.5 \times 10^{14}) = \mathbf{3.315 \times 10^{-20}\ J}$

Practice Questions

Q1 What is the difference between 'percent' and 'parts per million'?

Q2 What does the word 'quantised' mean?

Q3 Name two greenhouse gases and two non-greenhouse gases.

Q4 What happens when molecules absorb UV radiation?

Exam Questions

Q1 The Earth absorbs radiation from the Sun. It also emits radiation.

a) What are the main types of radiation emitted by the Sun and by the Earth? [2 marks]

b) Name the type of radiation that can cause an increase in some covalent bonds' vibrational energy. What types of molecule are not affected? [2 marks]

Q2 Calculate the energy absorbed when one molecule of HCl changes from its ground vibrational level to the next level, given that the frequency of radiation absorbed is 8.19×10^{13} Hz. [2 marks]

The atmosphere — it ain't made of custard...

If there were no atmospheric gases to absorb the Sun's radiation, bad sunburn would be the least of our worries. There'd be no oxygen, so we wouldn't be able to breathe. But at least there'd be no AS Chemistry either. This hasn't been too bad a page — I hope you weren't too bored by the stuff on Planck's constant. Cor blimey, if ever there was a lame joke, that was it.

The Greenhouse Effect

Now I'm sure you know this already but it's good to be sure — the greenhouse effect, global warming and climate change are all different things. They're linked (and you need to know how) — but they are not the same. Ahem.

The **Greenhouse Effect** Keeps Us **Alive**

1) The Sun emits **electromagnetic radiation**, mostly as visible light, UV radiation and infrared radiation.
2) When radiation from the Sun reaches **Earth's atmosphere**, most of the UV and infrared is **absorbed by atmospheric gases**, and some radiation is **reflected back into space** from **clouds**.
3) The energy that reaches the **Earth's surface** is mainly **visible light** and UV. Some of this radiation is reflected into space by light-coloured, shiny surfaces like ice and snow. The rest is **absorbed** by the Earth, which causes it to heat up.
4) The Earth then **radiates energy** back towards space as **infrared radiation** (heat).
5) Some of this infrared (IR) radiation **escapes** (through the so-called 'IR window' — the range of IR frequencies that are not absorbed by atmospheric gases). But various gases in the troposphere (the lowest layer of the atmosphere) **absorb** other infrared radiation... and **re-emit** it in **all directions** — including back towards Earth, keeping us warm.
6) This is called the '**greenhouse effect**' (even though a real greenhouse doesn't actually work like this, annoyingly).
   Without this absorption and re-emission of heat by 'greenhouse gases', the average surface temperature on Earth would be about 30 °C cooler than it is — and we wouldn't be here.

Visible and UV radiation from the Sun
Some infrared radiation emitted by the Earth is absorbed by greenhouse gases
Some infrared radiation emitted by the Earth escapes through the 'IR window'

1) The main greenhouse gases are **water vapour**, **carbon dioxide** and **methane**. They're greenhouse gases because their molecules **absorb IR radiation** to make the bonds in the molecule **vibrate more** (see page 87).
2) This extra vibrational energy is passed on to other molecules in the air by **collisions**, giving the other molecules more kinetic energy and so raising the overall temperature.
3) The greenhouse gas you hear about all the time is **carbon dioxide**, but actually **water vapour** makes a far greater contribution to the effect. The contribution of any particular gas depends on:
   - **how much radiation** one molecule of the gas absorbs
   - **how much of that gas** there is in the atmosphere (concentration in ppm, say)

   For example, one methane molecule traps far more heat than one carbon dioxide molecule, but there's much less methane in the atmosphere, so its overall contribution to the greenhouse effect is smaller.

An **Enhanced Greenhouse Effect** Causes **Global Warming...**

Vegetarians can't feel entirely smug though. Paddy fields, in which rice is grown, kick out a fair amount of methane too.

1) Over the last 150 years or so, the world's **human population** has shot up and we've become more **industrialised**. To supply our energy needs, we've been **burning fossil fuels** at an ever-increasing rate, releasing **tons and tons** of CO_2 into the atmosphere. We've also been **chopping down forests** which used to absorb CO_2 by photosynthesis.
2) And it's not just carbon dioxide. **Methane** levels have also risen as we've had to grow more food for our rising population. **Cows** are responsible for large amounts of methane. From both ends. (Though a change of diet is quite a simple way to reduce this problem.)
3) These **human activities** have caused a rise in greenhouse gas concentrations, which **enhances** the greenhouse effect, since less IR can escape. So now **too much heat** is being trapped and the Earth is **getting warmer**.
4) This is **global warming**. It leads to the **sea-levels rising** and **climate change** — bad news.

Climate Change **Isn't New...**

Climate change has happened quite **naturally** throughout the Earth's history, on various different timescales:

1) For example, regular changes in the Earth's orbit around the Sun are linked to **ice age** cycles — long cold periods (ice ages) with warmer periods (**interglacials**) in between. (We're in an interglacial period now).

2) Various changes in the **Sun**'s activity (e.g. **sunspot** cycles every 11 years) also cause warming or cooling.
3) Not all natural changes are caused by regular cycles. For example, huge **volcanic eruptions** or **meteor impacts** have thrown vast amounts of smoke or dust into the air and caused significant global cooling.

The Greenhouse Effect

... But Anthropogenic Change Is

A lot of scientific evidence shows that global warming **is** taking place now, more quickly than in the past.

1) For example, scientists regularly sample the air in unpolluted places (like remote islands). Both average temperatures and carbon dioxide levels are going up (they both change over the seasons, of course, so it's the yearly averages that count).
2) Monitoring of **sea water** shows that the oceans have become **more acidic** as more carbon dioxide dissolves in the water (because it forms carbonic acid, H_2CO_3). So we know that the chemistry of the oceans is changing.
3) Scientists use **mass spectrometry** to analyse the composition of **air** trapped inside the ice in polar regions, to see how the atmosphere changed in the past (when older, deeper ice formed), and compare that with recent changes.
4) Putting all the evidence together, it seems to show that the Earth's average temperature has increased **dramatically** in the last 50 years, and that carbon dioxide levels have increased at the same time.
5) The **correlation** between CO_2 and temperature is pretty clear, but there's been debate about whether rising carbon dioxide levels have **caused** the recent temperature rise, and if so, what's caused the rising CO_2 levels. Just showing a correlation doesn't prove that one thing causes another — there has to be a plausible mechanism for how one change causes the other (in this case, the explanation is the enhanced greenhouse effect).
6) Most climate scientists now agree that the link **is** causal, and that recent warming is **anthropogenic** — **human activities** are to blame for the rise in CO_2 levels (see previous page).

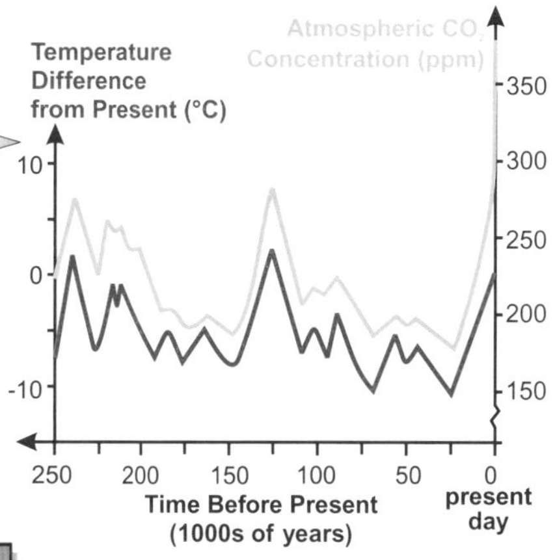

Scientists are Seeking Ways to Limit Global Warming

Scientists are investigating various ways to help **reduce** carbon dioxide emissions. These include:

1) Finding ways to burn fewer fossil fuels — e.g. by developing **alternative fuels** (see p50-51) and more **fuel-efficient** technologies, e.g. 'lean-burn' car engines.
2) **Carbon capture and storage** (CCS). This means removing waste CO_2 from, say, power stations, and either
   - injecting it as a **liquid** into the **deep ocean** (although this runs the risk of making the oceans more acidic).
   - storing it under pressure deep **underground** — one possibility is to use old oil- or gas-fields under the seabed, or
   - reacting it with metal oxides to form stable, easily stored **carbonate minerals**, e.g. calcium carbonate.
3) Trying to **increase photosynthesis** to soak up more CO_2 — one idea is to increase the growth of **phytoplankton** (teeny green plants in the ocean) by 'seeding' the oceans with iron, an essential nutrient for the plankton.

Practice Questions

Q1 What type of electromagnetic radiation does the Earth emit?

Q2 What's the difference between the greenhouse effect and global warming?

Q3 What is the 'IR window'?

Q4 Carbon dioxide could be stored by injecting it into the ocean. Give one problem this may cause.

Exam Questions

Q1 a) Name three greenhouse gases. [3 marks]

b) Explain how greenhouse gases keep the temperature in the lower layer of the Earth's atmosphere higher than it would otherwise be. [4 marks]

Q2 The concentration of carbon dioxide in the Earth's atmosphere has increased over the last 50 years.

a) Describe one piece of scientific evidence for the increase. [1 marks]

b) Describe two methods that chemists are developing as a way of reducing carbon dioxide emissions. [2 marks]

Global Warming probably just isn't funny...

You may be sick of global warming, because it's all over the news these days. Well, tough — just think of all those poor, seasick chemists hauling bucketfuls of water out of the ocean and sticking litmus paper in to test its acidity (that's not actually what they do, clearly, but there is a lot of careful measuring involved to monitor what's changing and how).

Halogenoalkanes and CFCs

Oooh, eh... mechanisms. You might like them. You might not. But you've gotta learn 'em.
Reactions don't happen instantaneously — there are often a few steps. And mechanisms show you what they are.

There are Two Types of Bond Fission — Homolytic and Heterolytic

Breaking a covalent bond is called **bond fission**. A single covalent bond is a shared pair of electrons between two atoms. It can break in two ways:

Heterolytic Fission:
In heterolytic fission **two different** substances are formed — a positively charged **cation** (X^+), and a negatively charged **anion** (Y^-).

$$X{-}Y \rightarrow X^+ + Y^-$$

('hetero' means 'different')

Homolytic Fission:
In homolytic fission two electrically uncharged **'radicals'** are formed. Radicals are particles that have an unpaired electron.

$$X{-}Y \rightarrow X\bullet + Y\bullet$$

Because of the unpaired electron, these radicals are very reactive.

A double-headed arrow shows that a pair of electrons move. A single-headed arrow shows the movement of a single electron. Makes sense.

Halogens React with Alkanes, Forming Halogenoalkanes

1) Halogens react with alkanes in **photochemical** reactions. Photochemical reactions are started by **ultraviolet** light.
2) A hydrogen atom is **substituted** (replaced) by chlorine or bromine. This is a **free-radical substitution reaction**.

Chlorine and **methane** react with a bit of a bang to form **chloromethane**: $CH_4 + Cl_2 \xrightarrow{U.V.} CH_3Cl + HCl$

The **reaction mechanism** has three stages:

Initiation reactions — free radicals are produced.

1) Sunlight provides enough energy to break the Cl-Cl bond — this is **photodissociation**.

$$Cl_2 \xrightarrow{U.V.} 2Cl\cdot$$

2) The bond splits **equally** and each atom gets to keep one electron — **homolytic fission**. The atom becomes a highly reactive **free radical**, Cl·, because of its **unpaired electron**.

Propagation reactions — free radicals are used up and created in a chain reaction.

1) Cl· attacks a **methane** molecule: $Cl\cdot + CH_4 \rightarrow CH_3\cdot + HCl$
2) The new **methyl free radical**, $CH_3\cdot$, can attack another Cl_2 molecule: $CH_3\cdot + Cl_2 \rightarrow CH_3Cl + Cl\cdot$
3) The new Cl· can attack **another** CH_4 molecule, and so on, until all the Cl_2 or CH_4 molecules are wiped out.

Termination reactions — free radicals are mopped up.

1) If two free radicals join together, they make a **stable molecule**.
2) There are **heaps** of possible termination reactions.
Here's a couple of them to give you the idea: $Cl\cdot + CH_3\cdot \rightarrow CH_3Cl$
$CH_3\cdot + CH_3\cdot \rightarrow C_2H_6$

Some products formed will be trace impurities in the final sample.

The reaction between bromine and methane works in exactly the same way.
$CH_4 + Br_2 \xrightarrow{U.V.} CH_3Br + HBr$

UV Radiation Can Also Break Carbon-Halogen Bonds

1) All halogenoalkanes contain bonds between **carbon** atoms and **halogen** atoms. **Ultraviolet radiation** can break these bonds — the carbon-halogen bond splits **homolytically** to create two **free radicals**.
2) The ease with which the carbon-halogen bond is broken by UV depends on the halogen. It turns out (see p77) that the **carbon-iodine** bond is the **most likely** to break, and the **carbon-fluorine** bond the **least likely**. This is because the C-I bond has the **lowest bond enthalpy**, and the C-F bond the **highest**.

Halogenoalkanes and CFCs

Chlorofluorocarbons (CFCs) Have Some Really **Useful** Properties...

1) **CFCs (chlorofluorocarbons)** are a group of compounds made by replacing all of the hydrogen atoms in alkanes with chlorine and fluorine. They're **halogenoalkanes** — see page 74.
2) They're **unreactive**, **non-flammable** and **harmless**. It's also possible to make CFCs with a range of boiling points.

Examples of CFCs:

trichlorofluoromethane   chlorotrifluoromethane

3) These properties made them useful for fire extinguishers, as propellants in aerosols, as the coolant gas in fridges. They were also used to expand polystyrene for use as packaging and insulating material.

...But **Alternatives** to CFCs Had to be Found

But **CFCs** helped create 'holes' in the **ozone layer** of the Earth's atmosphere (see pages 92-93 for all the details). And because of the damage that CFCs do, it became clear that we really couldn't carry on using them.

1) The **Montreal Protocol** of 1989 was an **international treaty** to phase out the use of CFCs and other ozone-destroying halogenoalkanes by the year 2000. There were a few **permitted uses** such as in medical inhalers and in fire extinguishers used in submarines.
2) Scientists supported the treaty, and worked on finding **alternatives** to CFCs.

- **HCFCs(hydrochlorofluorocarbons)** and **HFCs(hydrofluorocarbons)** are being used as temporary alternatives to CFCs until safer products are developed. **Hydrocarbons** are also used.
- **HCFCs** are broken down in the atmosphere in 10-20 years. They still damage the ozone layer, but their effect is much smaller than CFCs.

These all have drawbacks, but they're currently the least environmentally damaging of all the alternatives.

- **HFCs** are broken down in the atmosphere too **and** they don't contain chlorine, so don't affect the ozone layer. Unfortunately, **HFCs and HCFCs are greenhouse gases** — they're 1000 times worse than carbon dioxide.
- Some **hydrocarbons** are being used in fridges but these are greenhouse gases too.
- Nowadays, most aerosols have been replaced by **pump spray systems** or use **nitrogen** as the propellant. Many fridges now use **ammonia** as the coolant gas, and **carbon dioxide** is used to make foamed polymers.

3) The ozone holes **still** form in the spring but the **rate of decrease** of ozone is **slowing** — so things are looking up.

Practice Questions

Q1 What is bond fission? Describe the two types of bond fission.

Q2 What is a photochemical reaction?

Q3 Describe the mechanism of the reaction between chlorine and methane.

Q4 What are CFCs? Why were they useful? What problem did they cause? What alternatives are now used instead?

Exam Questions

Q1 1-chloro-1,1-difluoroethane is an example of a hydrochlorofluoroalkane (HCFC) .

a) Draw the displayed formula of this molecule. [1 mark]

b) In the presence of strong sunlight, 1-chloro-1,1-difluoroethane undergoes homolytic fission to generate a chlorine radical and a molecular radical. Write an equation to represent this reaction. [2 marks]

Q2 CFCs were invented in 1928. They were widely used in the 20th century.

a) Give three important uses of CFCs. [3 marks]

b) What useful properties do CFCs have? [3 marks]

c) Why was the use of CFCs banned by the Montreal Protocol? [1 mark]

d) What alternatives to CFCs have been used and what are their drawbacks? [6 marks]

Bond fission — almost happened with that laser in You Only Live Twice...

Free radicals are a bit hyperactive. They won't just relax and chill out — they've got to be doing something, such as reacting with other particles. That would be okay if they only went around taking part in helpful reactions, but sadly that isn't always the case (as the ozone layer found out). But at least something was done to help the ozone layer — good to know.

Ozone

The ozone layer seems to have been forgotten about lately, what with all the worries about climate change.

The Earth has a Layer of **Ozone** at the Edge of the **Stratosphere**

The **ozone layer** is in a layer of the atmosphere called the **stratosphere**. It contains most of the atmosphere's **ozone molecules**, O_3. Ozone is formed when **UV radiation** from the Sun hits oxygen molecules.

If the right amount of **UV radiation** is absorbed by an oxygen molecule, the oxygen molecule splits into separate atoms or **free radicals** (see page 90). The free radicals then **combine** with other oxygen molecules to form **ozone molecules**, O_3.

$$O_2 + h\nu \rightarrow O\bullet + O\bullet \longrightarrow O_2 + O\bullet \rightarrow O_3$$

a quantum of UV radiation ($h\nu$)

The Ozone Layer is Constantly Being **Replaced**

1) UV radiation can also **reverse** the formation of ozone.

$$O_3 + h\nu \rightarrow O_2 + O\bullet$$

The radical produced then forms more ozone with an O_2 molecule, as shown above.

2) So, the ozone layer is continuously being **destroyed** and **replaced** as UV radiation hits the molecules. An **equilibrium** is set up, so the concentrations stay fairly constant:

$$O_2 + O\bullet \rightleftharpoons O_3$$

The **Ozone Layer** High in the Atmosphere **Protects** Against UV Radiation

1) The ozone layer is incredibly **important** for us — it **protects** us from most of the harmful effects of the Sun's **ultraviolet** (**UV**) **radiation**. The ozone layer removes all the high energy **UVC radiation** and about 90% of the **UVB**. These types of UV radiation are harmful to humans and most other life of Earth.

The **UV radiation** from the Sun is made up of **different frequencies**, grouped into **three bands**:

UVA UVB UVC

INCREASING FREQUENCY AND ENERGY →

2) **UVB** can damage the DNA in cells and cause **skin cancer**, and is the main cause of **sunburn**. **UVA** can also lead to **skin cancer**. Both types cause the skin to **age faster**.
3) **BUT...** UV radiation isn't all bad — in fact it's **essential** for us humans. We need it to produce **vitamin D**. Also, when the skin's exposed to UV, it **tans**. This helps protect **deeper tissues** from the effects of the radiation.

Scientists Discovered that the **Ozone Layer** Was a **Bit Thin** in Places

1) In the 1970s, the **British Antarctic Survey** found that the concentration of ozone over Antarctica was very low compared to previous measurements. The decrease was so dramatic they thought their measuring instruments must be faulty. But **new instruments** gave the same results. Eeeek.
2) A **satellite** mapped the ozone levels at about the same time. But it was programmed to treat measurements below a certain value as **errors** and to ignore them — so this evidence for the thinning of the ozone layer was overlooked. When the British Antarctic Survey published their findings the satellite data was re-examined and found to show the 'hole' too.
3) The ozone layer over the **Arctic** has been found to be thinning too. These 'holes' in the ozone layer are bad because they allow more harmful **UV radiation** to reach the Earth.

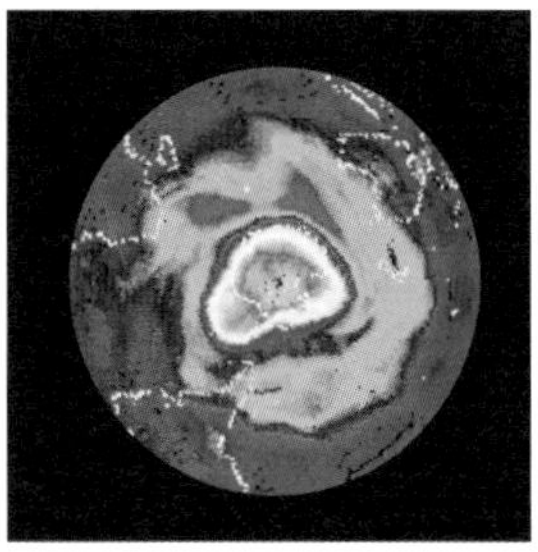

LABORATORY FOR ATMOSPHERES, NASA GODDARD SPACE FLIGHT CENTER/SCIENCE PHOTO LIBRARY

The 'hole' in the Antarctic ozone layer is shown by the white and pink area.

It Took Time to **Prove** the Link Between **Ozone Holes** and **Halogenoalkanes**

Like a lot of things in science, the **evidence** needed to prove this explanation took **time** to collect.

1) Scientists knew that **CFCs affected ozone**. They also knew that the **ozone layer was thinning**. But it took a while to **prove** that man-made emissions of CFCs causes the observed ozone depletion.
2) It took several **Antarctic expeditions**, some **high-altitude flights** in a **converted spy plane**, and lots of **satellite data** before enough evidence was gathered to **confirm** this hypothesis, and **rule out natural causes** for the ozone holes.

Ozone

The Ozone Layer's being Destroyed by Homogeneous Catalysis

You've heard of how the **ozone layer's** being destroyed by **CFCs**, right. Well, here's what's happening.

- **Chlorine free radicals**, Cl•, are formed when **CFCs** (chlorofluorocarbons) are broken down by **ultraviolet radiation**.

E.g. $CCl_3F_{(g)} \rightarrow CCl_2F\bullet_{(g)} + Cl\bullet_{(g)}$

- These free radicals are **catalysts**. They react with **ozone** to form an **intermediate** (ClO•), and an oxygen molecule.

These are all gases, so it's homogeneous catalysis.

$$Cl\bullet_{(g)} + O_{3(g)} \rightarrow O_{2(g)} + ClO\bullet_{(g)}$$

$$ClO\bullet_{(g)} + O_{3(g)} \rightarrow 2O_{2(g)} + Cl\bullet_{(g)}$$

The chlorine free radical is regenerated. It goes straight on to attack another ozone molecule. It only takes one little chlorine free radical to destroy loads of ozone molecules.

- So the **overall reaction** is: $2O_{3(g)} \rightarrow 3O_{2(g)}$ ... and Cl• is the catalyst.

1) Other free radicals can destroy ozone too — e.g. NO• from **nitrogen oxides** and free radicals are produced from other **halogenoalkanes**.
2) These affect ozone in the **same** way as chlorine radicals. The overall reactions can be represented by these equations, where R represents your free radical.

Nitrogen oxides are produced by car and aircraft engines and thunderstorms.

$$\mathbf{R} + O_3 \rightarrow \mathbf{RO} + O_2$$

$$O\bullet + \mathbf{RO} \rightarrow O_2 + \mathbf{R}$$

Formed when UV breaks down O_2.

The harmful radical is regenerated.

Ozone Occurs at Ground Level Too

1) Ozone (O_3) also occurs in the **troposphere** (the lowest part of the atmosphere) due to the effect of **sunlight** on mixtures of **nitrogen dioxide and hydrocarbons**. These occur **naturally** from a variety of sources but **vehicle engines** and **power stations** contribute large amounts too.
2) In heavily industrialised areas and cities with lots of cars, the ozone mixes with **solid particles** of carbon and many other substances — the effect is called **photochemical smog**. Mexico City is particularly badly affected.
3) Ozone is **toxic** to humans. At the levels often found in cities it can affect the **lungs** and trigger **asthma attacks**.

Practice Questions

Q1 What is ozone, and where is the ozone layer?

Q2 Which has higher energy — UVA, UVB, or UVC? Which types are absorbed by ozone?

Q3 Write out equations to show how ozone is destroyed by chlorine radicals.

Exam Questions

Q1 The 'ozone layer' lies mostly between 15 and 30 km above the Earth's surface.
  a) Explain how ozone forms in this part of the atmosphere. [3 marks]
  b) What are the benefits to humans of the ozone layer? [1 mark]
  c) How does the ozone layer absorb harmful radiation without being permanently destroyed? [2 marks]

Q2 a) Explain why large amounts of ground-level ozone can be a problem. [1 mark]
  b) Why are these problems most frequently encountered in heavily industrialised areas? [2 marks]

A scarecrow won a Nobel Prize — He was outstanding in his field...

I know it's completely irrelevant, but I like it.

How scientists found the hole in the ozone layer, repeated their experiments, then published their results is a super example of How Science Works. What's more, the evidence was used to instigate an international treaty — it's a beauty of an example of how science informs decision-making. And remember — think about any anomalous results before chucking them away.

Addition Reactions of Alkenes

I'll warn you now — some of this stuff gets a bit heavy. But stick with it, as it's pretty important.

Alkenes are **Unsaturated Hydrocarbons**

I know, I know... you've seen alkenes before. This is just a quick reminder of the basics, and then it's on with new stuff.

1) Alkenes have the **general formula C_nH_{2n}**. They're **hydrocarbons** — made of carbon and hydrogen atoms only.
2) Alkene molecules **all** have at least one **C=C double covalent bond**. Molecules with C=C double bonds are **unsaturated** because they can make more bonds with extra atoms in **addition** reactions (see next page).

   Here are a few pretty diagrams of **alkenes** to help it all come flooding back to you:

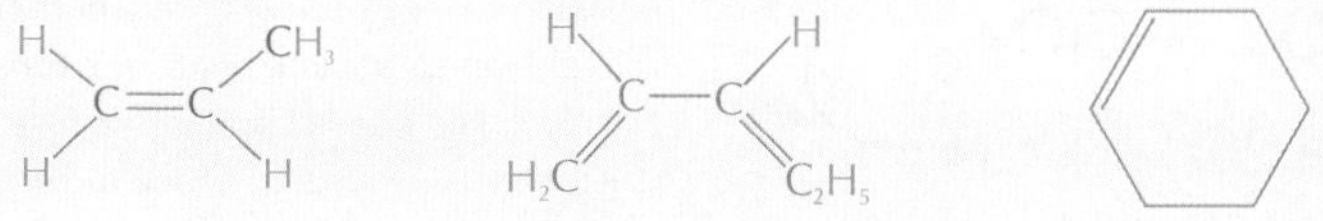

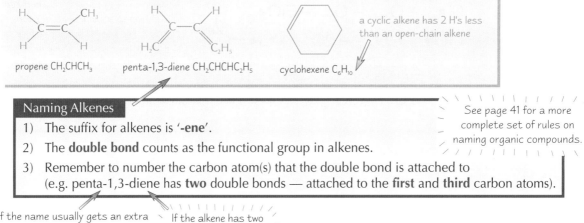

propene CH_2CHCH_3 — penta-1,3-diene $CH_2CHCHC_2H_5$ — cyclohexene C_6H_{10}

a cyclic alkene has 2 H's less than an open-chain alkene

Naming Alkenes

1) The suffix for alkenes is **'-ene'**.
2) The **double bond** counts as the functional group in alkenes.
3) Remember to number the carbon atom(s) that the double bond is attached to (e.g. penta-1,3-diene has **two** double bonds — attached to the **first** and **third** carbon atoms).

See page 41 for a more complete set of rules on naming organic compounds.

The stem of the name usually gets an extra 'a' (e.g. buta-, penta- not but-, pent-) when there's more than one double bond. And you might see the numbers written first, e.g. 1,3-butadiene.

If the alkene has two double bonds the suffix becomes **diene**.

Adding **Hydrogen** to C=C Bonds Produces **Alkanes**

1) Ethene will react with **hydrogen** gas to produce ethane. It needs a **catalyst** though — you can use either a **nickel** catalyst and a temperature of **150 °C** and a **high pressure** or a **platinum** catalyst at **room temperature and pressure**.

$$H_2C{=}CH_2 + H_2 \xrightarrow[150\ ^\circ C]{Ni} CH_3CH_3$$

2) Other alkenes react in the same way — the C=C double bond opens up, then hydrogen atoms join on to give you an alkane.

Use **Bromine Water** to Test for C=C Double Bonds

Something similar happens when you add a halogen, such as bromine (Br_2).

1) When you shake an alkene with **orange bromine water**, the solution quickly **decolourises**.

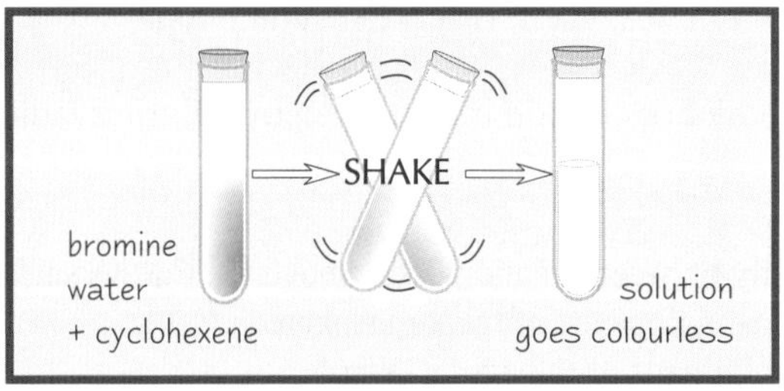

2) Bromine is being added across the double bond to form a (colourless) **dibromoalkane**.

$$\mathbf{H_2C{=}CH_2 + Br_2 \rightarrow CH_2BrCH_2Br}$$

3) Adding bromine water is used as a test for **unsaturation** (i.e. the presence of **double or triple carbon-carbon bonds**). **Saturated** compounds like alkanes **don't react** with it, so the solution **stays brown**.
4) Bromine reacting with an alkene is an example of **electrophilic addition**...

Addition Reactions of Alkenes

Electrophilic Addition Reactions Happen to Alkenes

Electrophilic addition reactions aren't too complicated...

1) The **double bonds** open up and atoms are **added** to the carbon atoms.
2) Electrophilic addition reactions happen because the double bond has got plenty of **electrons** and is easily attacked by **electrophiles**.

> Electrophiles are electron-pair acceptors — they're usually a bit short of electrons, so they're attracted to areas where there's lots of them about.
> Here's a few examples:
> - **Positively charged ions**, like H^+, NO_2^+.
> - **Polar molecules** — the δ+ atom is attracted to places with lots of electrons

See page 62 for a reminder about polar molecules.

3) The double bond is also **nucleophilic** — it's attracted to places that don't have enough **electrons**.

Electrophilic Addition Opens Up the Double Bond

In addition reactions, two small molecules are added together to make a larger molecule.

You need to understand the **mechanism** for these electrophilic addition reactions.
Take the reaction between an alkene and **bromine** as an example...

A carbocation is an organic ion containing a positively charged carbon atom.

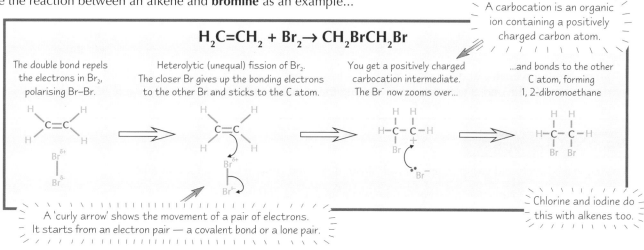

$$H_2C{=}CH_2 + Br_2 \rightarrow CH_2BrCH_2Br$$

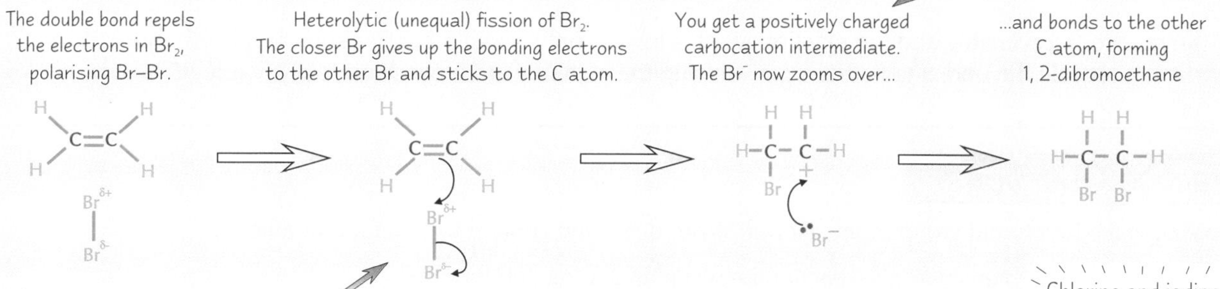

The double bond repels the electrons in Br₂, polarising Br–Br.
Heterolytic (unequal) fission of Br₂. The closer Br gives up the bonding electrons to the other Br and sticks to the C atom.
You get a positively charged carbocation intermediate. The Br⁻ now zooms over...
...and bonds to the other C atom, forming 1, 2-dibromoethane

A 'curly arrow' shows the movement of a pair of electrons. It starts from an electron pair — a covalent bond or a lone pair.

Chlorine and iodine do this with alkenes too.

I know what you're (possibly) thinking — how can scientists know this is what goes on... Well, it's like this...

1) If you add some Cl^- ions to an ethene and bromine mixture, you'll also get some CH_2BrCH_2Cl.
2) This is **evidence** for the above mechanism — once the ethene has reacted with bromine to form the **carbocation** (**positively** charged), it can react with **either** another **bromide ion or** a **chloride ion** (**negatively** charged).

Alkenes also Undergo Addition with Hydrogen Halides

1) Alkenes also undergo **addition** reactions with hydrogen bromide — to form **bromoalkanes**. This is the reaction between **ethene** and HBr:

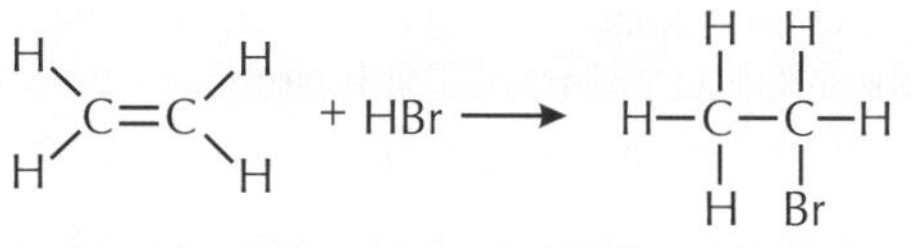

$$C_2H_4 + HBr \rightarrow C_2H_5Br$$

Other alkenes react in a similar way.

2) If the HBr adds to an **unsymmetrical** alkene, like propene, there are two possible products.

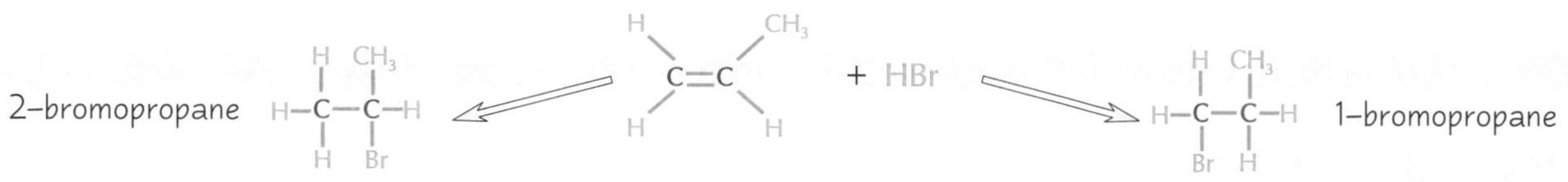

Addition Reactions of Alkenes

That double bond in alkenes is always getting up to something or other...

Reacting Alkenes with **Water** and an H_2SO_4 Catalyst Makes **Alcohols**

1) Cold concentrated **sulfuric acid** reacts with an alkene in an **electrophilic addition** reaction.

$$\underset{\text{ethene}}{H_2C=CH_2} + \underset{\text{sulfuric acid}}{H_2SO_4} \longrightarrow \underset{\text{ethyl hydrogen sulfate}}{CH_3CH_2OSO_2OH}$$

2) If you then add cold **water** and warm the product, it's **hydrolysed** to form an alcohol.

$$\underset{\text{ethyl hydrogen sulfate}}{CH_3CH_2OSO_2OH} + H_2O \longrightarrow \underset{\text{ethanol}}{CH_3CH_2OH} + H_2SO_4$$

The **sulfuric acid** isn't used up — it acts as a **catalyst**.

Hydrolysis is the breaking of covalent bonds by reaction with water.

So the overall reaction is: $H_2C=CH_2 + H_2O \xrightarrow{H_2SO_4} C_2H_5OH$

Ethanol is Manufactured by **Steam Hydration**

1) Ethene can be **hydrated** by **steam** at 300 °C and a pressure of 60 atm. It needs a solid **phosphoric(V) acid catalyst**.

$$H_2C{=}CH_{2(g)} + H_2O_{(g)} \underset{\substack{300\ °C \\ 60\ atm}}{\overset{H_3PO_4}{\rightleftharpoons}} C_2H_5OH_{(g)}$$

2) The reaction's **reversible** and the reaction yield is low — only about 5%. This sounds rubbish, but you can **recycle** the unreacted ethene gas, making the overall yield a much more profitable **95%**.

Practice Questions

Q1 What is the functional group in an alkene? Write down the general formula for an alkene.

Q2 Describe the mechanism for the reaction between an alkene and bromine. What evidence is there for this mechanism?

Q3 Write down the equation of the reaction between ethene and hydrogen bromide.

Exam Questions

Q1 Cyclohexane and hex-1-ene both have the molecular formula C_6H_{12}.
a) Hex-1-ene can be described as an unsaturated hydrocarbon.
Explain what is meant by the term 'unsaturated' as applied to hydrocarbons. [1 mark]
b) Draw the displayed formulae of cyclohexane and hex-1-ene. [2 marks]
c) Give details of a chemical test that would enable you to distinguish between samples of these substances.
You should include details of how your results should be interpreted. [3 marks]

Q2 a) There are two straight-chain alkenes with the molecular formula C_5H_{10}.
Give the structural formulae and names of both isomers. [2 marks]
b) Write an equation for the reaction of one of these alkenes with hydrogen gas. [1 mark]

Q3 Ethene can undergo a hydrolysis reaction with cold water in the presence of a catalyst.
a) Name a catalyst that can be used in the above reaction. [1 mark]
b) Describe the two stages in this reaction. [2 marks]

In the old days, the test for saturation was a bit of seaweed outside the door...

What helped me understand that mechanism was realising that a single bond is just a pair of electrons. And a double bond is just two pairs of electrons. So when you see a curly arrow (and you do have to call them curly arrows — that's their actual name) pointing away from a double bond, all that's happening is that a pair of electrons is moving. That's it.

Alcohols and Other Organic Compounds

Organic compounds come in families. You've met the alcohol family before, but you need to get to know them better now.

Alcohols are **Primary**, **Secondary** or **Tertiary**

1) The alcohol homologous series has the **general formula $C_nH_{2n+1}OH$**.
2) An alcohol is **primary**, **secondary** or **tertiary**, depending on which carbon atom the **hydroxyl group** (**–OH**) is bonded to...

- In a **primary** alcohol, the carbon with the –OH attached is attached to only **one alkyl group**.

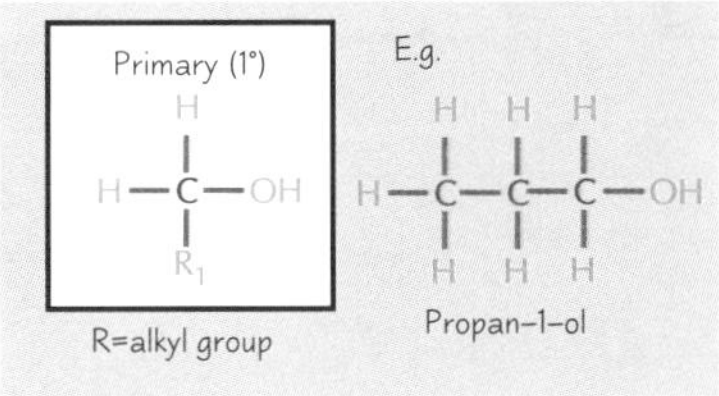

- In a **secondary** alcohol, the carbon with the –OH attached is attached to **two alkyl groups**.

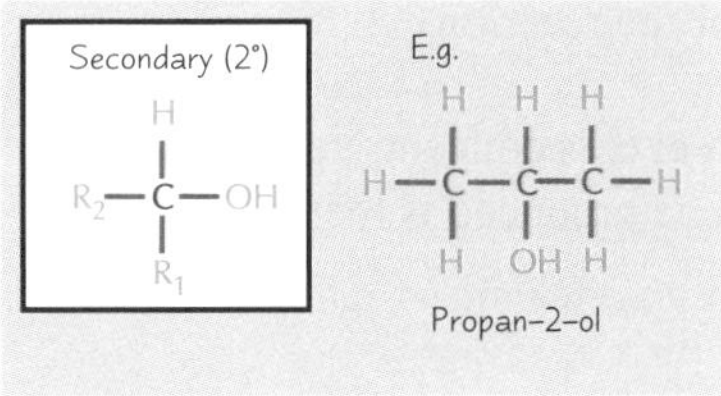

- In a **tertiary** alcohol, the carbon with the –OH attached is attached to **three alkyl groups**.

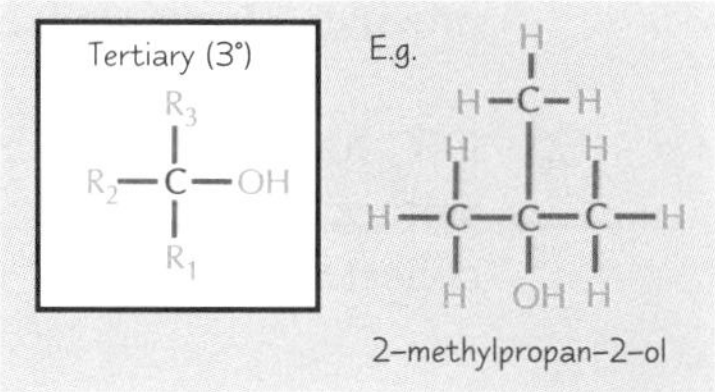

R_1, R_2, R_3 just stand for any alkyl groups (see page 76 for more about alkyl groups).

An (impure) sample of ethanol, a primary alcohol.

Aldehydes and **Ketones** Both Contain a **Double-Bonded Oxygen**

Aldehydes and **ketones** are **carbonyl** compounds — they have the functional group C=O. Their general formula is $\mathbf{C_nH_{2n}O}$.

Aldehydes

Aldehydes have their carbonyl group at the **end** of the carbon chain — for example...

In an aldehyde, the carbonyl group is joined to only **one** other carbon.

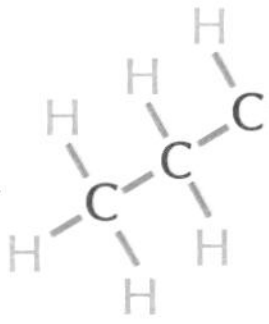

propanal
CH_3CH_2CHO

Ketones

Ketones have their carbonyl group anywhere in the carbon chain, **except** at the end — for example...

In a ketone, the carbonyl group is joined to **two** other carbons.

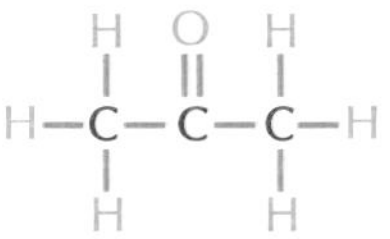

propanone: CH_3COCH_3

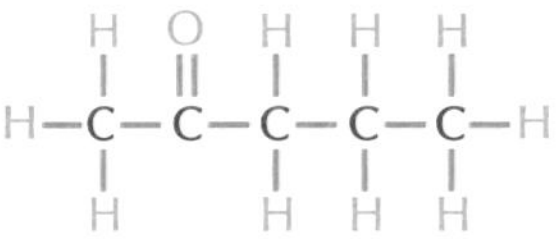

pentan-2-one: $CH_3COC_3H_7$

Carboxylic Acids Contain a **-COOH** Functional Group

1) Carboxylic acids are organic acids.
2) Carboxylic acids contain the **carboxyl** functional group –COOH.

A carboxyl group contains a carbonyl group and a hydroxyl group.

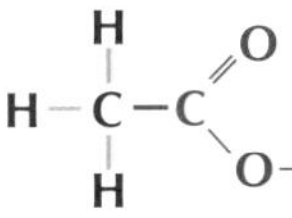

ethanoic acid

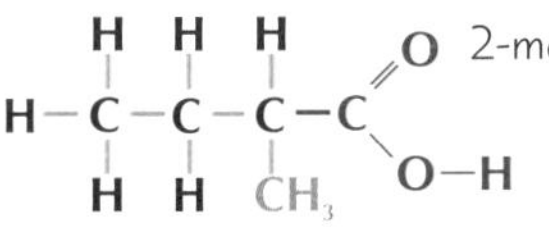

2-methylbutanoic acid

Alcohols and Other Organic Compounds

Another page of organic reactions. But at least you're almost at the end of the book... and your wits, probably.

*Alcohols can be **Dehydrated** to Form **Alkenes***

You can make ethene by **eliminating** water from **ethanol** in a **dehydration reaction**. The experiment isn't too tricky, but there's two ways of doing it...

$$C_2H_5OH \rightarrow CH_2{=}CH_2 + H_2O$$

In an elimination reaction, a small group of atoms breaks away from a larger molecule. This small group is not replaced by anything else

Dehydrating Alcohols to form Alkenes

1) Ethanol vapour is passed over a hot **catalyst** of pumice stone or aluminium oxide, Al_2O_3 — the catalyst provides a **large surface area** for the reaction.

2) **OR**, you can **reflux** ethanol with **excess** concentrated sulfuric acid at 170 °C. The ethene produced is then collected over water. See next page for info on 'refluxing'.

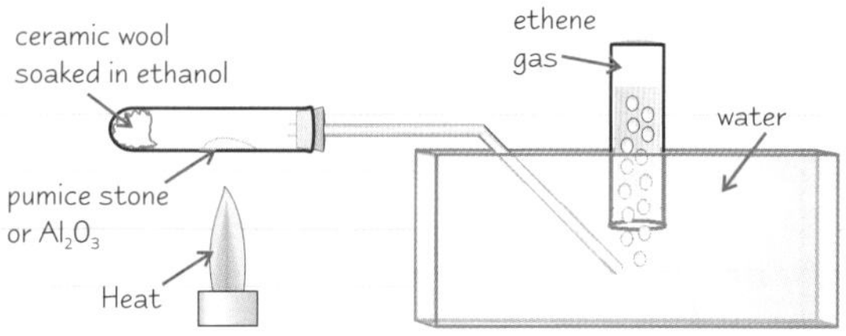

Here's what's going on in the second method (the one with the sulfuric acid)...

The **concentrated sulfuric acid** acts as a **dehydrating agent** in the **elimination** reaction.

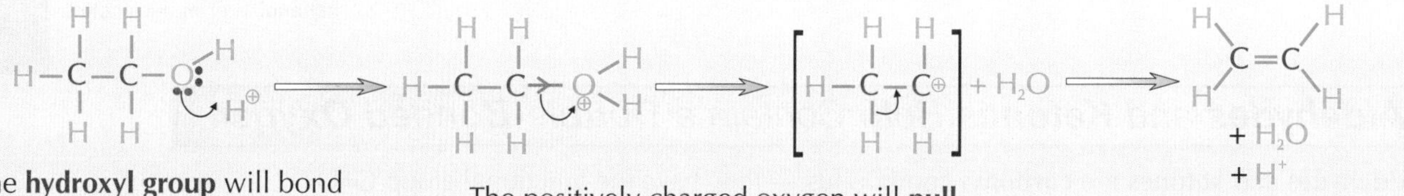

The **hydroxyl group** will bond to **H+ ions** from the strong acid. The alcohol is then **protonated**, giving the oxygen atom a **positive charge**.

The positively charged oxygen will **pull** electrons away from the neighbouring carbon, and water will 'fall off', creating an **unstable carbocation intermediate**.

The carbocation loses H^+ and the **alkene** is formed.

*Alcohols Can be **Oxidised** by: (i) **Burning Them**... (fairly dull)*

It doesn't take much to set ethanol alight, and it then burns with a **pale blue flame**. **Complete oxidation** forms **carbon dioxide** and **water**. This is a **combustion** reaction (see p48 for more about combustion).

But you don't get the most exciting products by doing this. If you want to end up with something more interesting at the end, you need a more sophisticated way of oxidising...

*...or: (ii) by using an **Oxidising Agent** (slightly more interesting)*

How much an alcohol can be oxidised depends on its structure.
You can use the **oxidising agent acidified potassium dichromate(VI)** to oxidise alcohols.

- **Primary** alcohols are oxidised to **aldehydes** and then to **carboxylic acids**.

[O] = oxidising agent

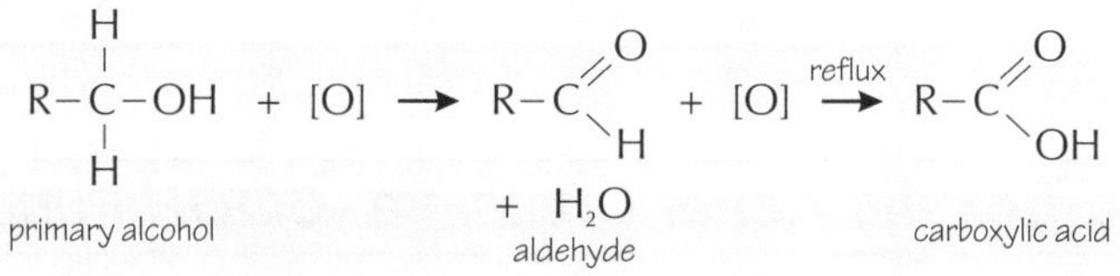

- **Secondary** alcohols are oxidised to **ketones** only.

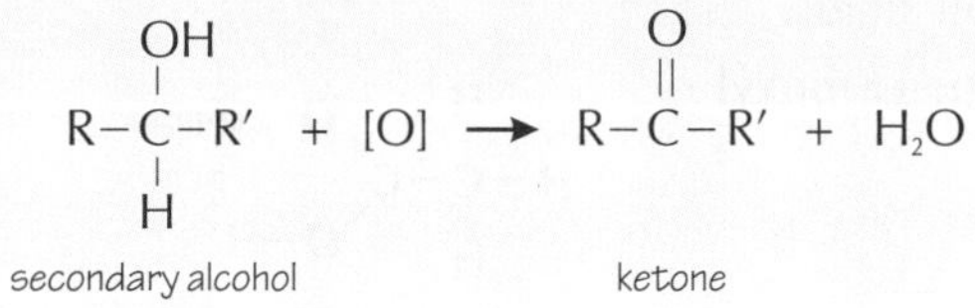

- **Tertiary** alcohols **won't** be oxidised.

The <u>orange</u> dichromate(VI) ion is reduced to the <u>green</u> chromium(III) ion, Cr^{3+}.

Alcohols and Other Organic Compounds

Reaction Conditions *Decide Whether You Get an* ***Aldehyde*** *or* ***Carboxylic Acid***

Whether you get an **aldehyde** or a **carboxylic acid** when you oxidise a **primary** alcohol depends on the **reaction conditions**.

Oxidising Primary Alcohols

1) Gently heating ethanol with potassium dichromate(VI) solution and sulfuric acid in a test tube should produce “apple” smelling **ethanal** (an aldehyde). However, it’s **really tricky** to control the amount of heat and the aldehyde is usually oxidised to form “vinegar” smelling **ethanoic acid**.
2) To get just the **aldehyde**, you need to get it out of the oxidising solution **as soon** as it's formed. You can do this by gently heating excess alcohol with a **controlled** amount of oxidising agent in **distillation apparatus**, so the aldehyde (which boils at a lower temperature than the alcohol) is distilled off **immediately**.

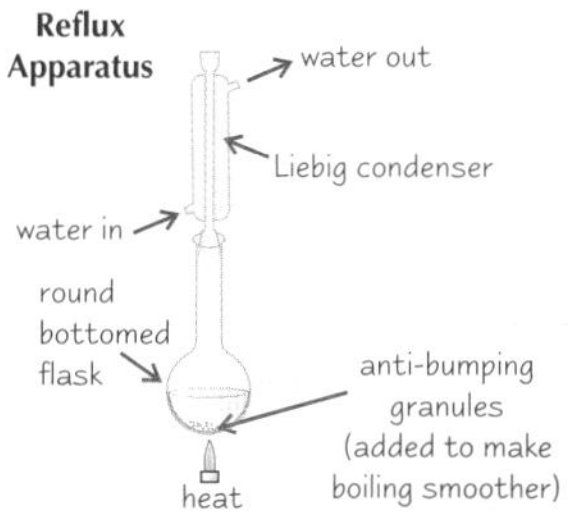

3) To produce the **carboxylic acid**, the alcohol has to be **vigorously oxidised**. The alcohol is mixed with excess oxidising agent and heated under **reflux**. Heating under reflux means you can increase the **temperature** of an organic reaction to boiling without losing **volatile** solvents, reactants or products. Any vaporised compounds are cooled, condense and drip back into the reaction mixture. Handy, hey.

Practice Questions

Q1 What is the difference between a primary alcohol, a secondary alcohol and a tertiary alcohol?

Q2 What’s the difference between an aldehyde, a ketone and a carboxylic acid?

Q3 Describe two ways that alcohols can be dehydrated.

Q4 What will acidified potassium dichromate(VI) oxidise secondary alcohols to?

Exam Questions

Q1 The formula C_4H_9OH can represent the three alcohols shown. Name each alcohol and class it as primary, secondary or tertiary.

a) 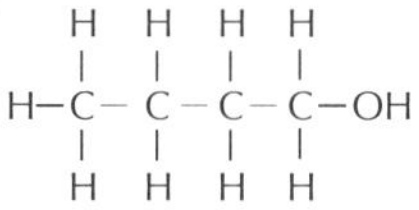

b) 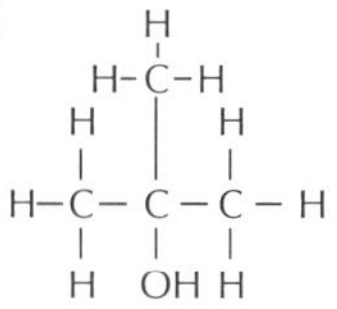

c) 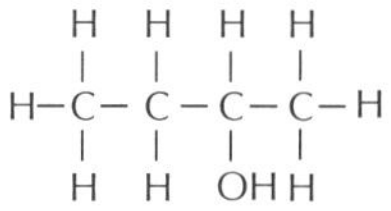

[6 marks]

Q2 Alcohols A and B both have the molecular formula C_3H_8O. Alcohol A is a primary alcohol, alcohol B a secondary alcohol.
- a) State which of these alcohols can be oxidised to a carboxylic acid and name the product formed. [2 marks]
- b) Describe the reagents and conditions used for this oxidation. [2 marks]

Q3 A student wanted to produce an aldehyde from the alcohol propan-1-ol. He set up a reflux apparatus using acidified potassium dichromate(VI) as the oxidising agent.
- a) Draw a labelled diagram of a reflux apparatus. Explain the purpose of the reflux apparatus. [2 marks]
- b) The student tested his product and found that he had not produced an aldehyde.
  - (i) What type of product had the student formed? [1 mark]
  - (ii) Write equations to show the two-stage reaction. Use [O] to represent the oxidising agent. [2 marks]
  - (iii) What technique should the student have used and why? [2 marks]
- c) The student also tried to oxidise 2-methylpropan-2-ol, unsuccessfully.
  - (i) Draw the full structural formula for 2-methylpropan-2-ol. [1 mark]
  - (ii) Why is it not possible to oxidise 2-methylpropan-2-ol with potassium dichromate(VI)? [1 mark]

I.... I .... just can’t do it, R2...

Don’t give up now. You’re so close to the end... Only as a fully-trained Chemistry Jedi, with the force as your ally, can you take on the Examiner. If you quit now, if you choose the easy path as Wader did, all the marks you’ve fought for will be lost. Be strong. Don’t give in to hate — that leads to the dark side...

(Only a few more pages to go now...)

Hydrogen Bonding

Hydrogen bonds form between certain types of molecule. Alcohols have hydrogen bonding, for a start.

Hydrogen Bonding is the Strongest Intermolecular Force

1) Hydrogen bonding **only** happens when **hydrogen** is covalently bonded to **fluorine**, **nitrogen** or **oxygen**.
2) Fluorine, nitrogen and oxygen are very **electronegative**, so they draw the bonding electrons away from the hydrogen atom.

See page 62 for more about electronegativity.

3) The bond is so **polarised**, and hydrogen has such a **high charge density** because it's so small, that the hydrogen atoms form weak bonds with **lone pairs of electrons** on the fluorine, nitrogen or oxygen atoms of **other molecules**.
4) **Water** and **ammonia** both have hydrogen bonding.

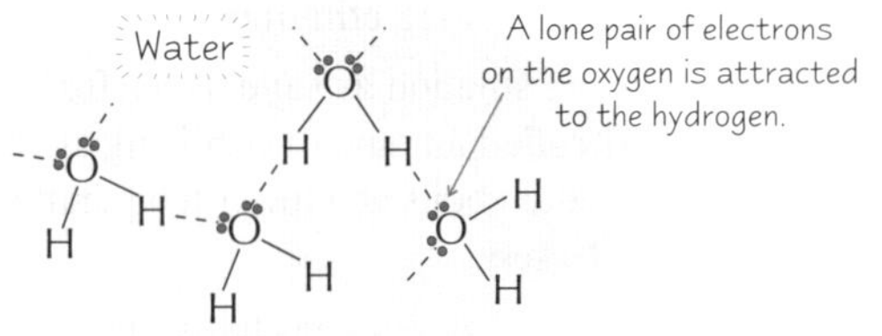

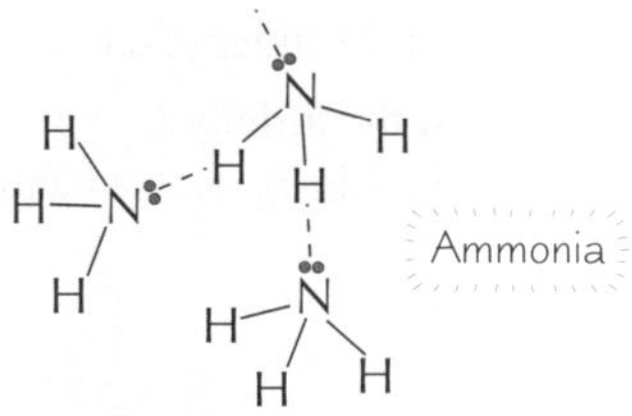

5) **Organic** molecules that form hydrogen bonds often contain **-OH** or **-NH** groups. **Alcohols** form hydrogen bonds, for example.

Hydrogen Bonds Explain Why Ice is Less Dense than Water

1) In **ice**, there is the maximum number of hydrogen bonds — the **lattice structure** formed in this way '**wastes**' lots of space.
2) As the ice **melts**, some of the hydrogen bonds are **broken** and the lattice **breaks down** — allowing molecules to 'fill' the spaces.
3) Water is at its densest at about 4 °C.
(Then as the temperature increases beyond 4 °C, water expands in the 'normal' way... due to the greater vibrations of the molecules.)

Icebergs float because of hydrogen bonds. Most substances get denser (and sink) when they freeze.

Stronger Intermolecular Forces mean Higher Melting and Boiling Points

1) To **boil** a liquid, you need to **overcome** the intermolecular forces, so that the particles can **escape** from the liquid surface.
2) It stands to reason that you need **more energy** to overcome **stronger** intermolecular forces. So liquids with stronger intermolecular forces will have **higher boiling points**.
3) Hydrogen bonding is quite a **strong** intermolecular force, so you'd expect it to have a **huge** effect on the properties of substances. And it does.
4) Substances that form hydrogen bonds have **higher boiling and melting points** than other similar molecules, because of the **extra energy** needed to break the hydrogen bonds. This is the case with **water** and **ammonia**.

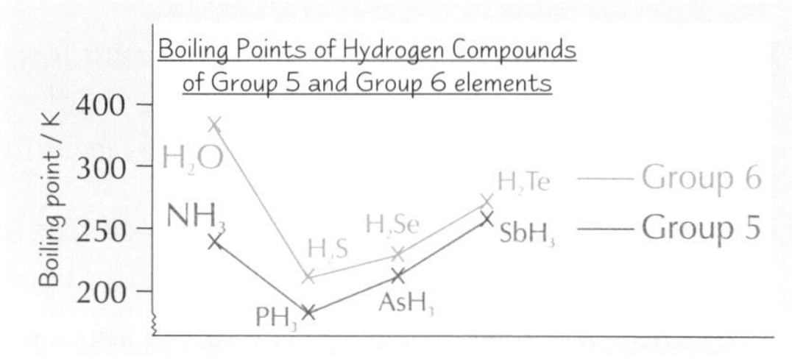

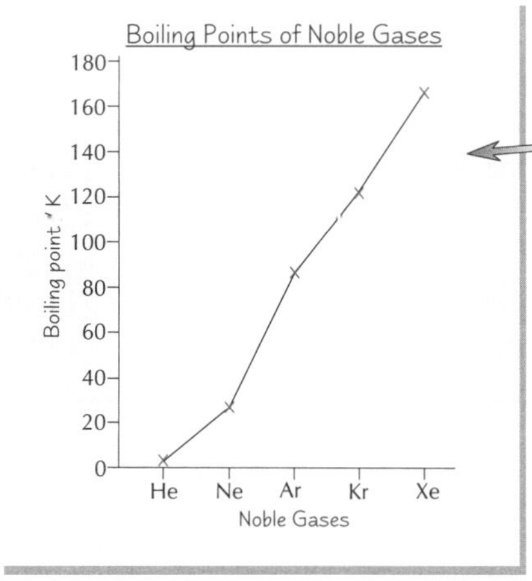

5) Other intermolecular forces (e.g. instantaneous dipole-induced dipole forces — see p64) affect boiling points in a similar way.
Noble gases show this pretty nicely.
As you go down the group of noble gases, the number of **electrons** increases. So the intermolecular forces increase, and so do the **boiling points**.

Hydrogen Bonding

Hydrogen Bonding Means Some Polymers Dissolve in Water

1) A substance will **dissolve** in water if the molecules of the substance are able to form **bonds** with the water molecules instead of with each other.
2) **Polymers** (incredibly long chain molecules — see p102) that have -OH groups can form **hydrogen bonds** with water molecules. For example, this diagram shows how poly(ethanol) forms hydrogen bonds with water, allowing it to dissolve.

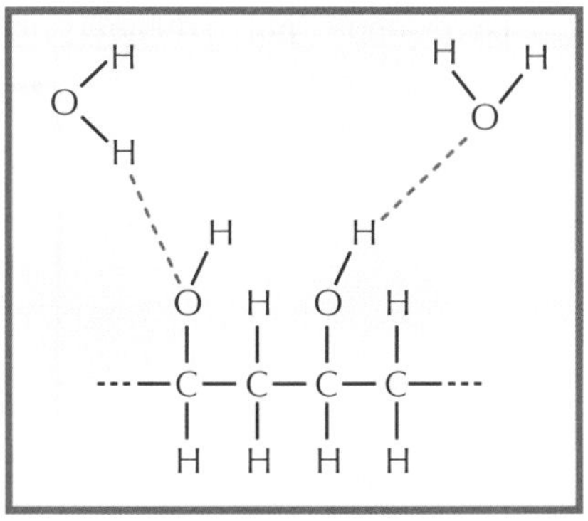

3) But the polymer molecules can also bond to **each other** by hydrogen bonds. There are three possible cases:
   - If the polymer has **loads** of -OH groups, the hydrogen bonding between its molecules will be very **strong** — meaning too much energy is needed to break it down. The polymer will be **insoluble**.
   - If the polymer has **very few** -OH groups, then there won't be many hydrogen bonds formed with water molecules — and the polymer will also be **insoluble**.
   - If the polymer has **not too many** hydrogen bonds and **not too few**, then it'll be **soluble**.

Practice Questions

Q1 What is meant by hydrogen bonding? What atoms need to be present for hydrogen bonding to occur?

Q2 What effect does hydrogen bonding have on the physical properties of a substance?

Q3 Name three substances that undergo hydrogen bonding.

Q4 Which noble gas has the highest boiling point and why?

Q5 Explain why some polymers are soluble, but others are insoluble.

Exam Questions

Q1 For each of the following pairs of compounds, state which will have the higher boiling point. Explain your choices.

A Ammonia (NH_3) and methane (CH_4),

B Water (H_2O) and hydrogen sulfide (H_2S),

C Butane and propan-1-ol. [6 marks]

Q2 An organic compound used as antifreeze is ethan-1,2-diol. Its displayed formula is shown on the right.

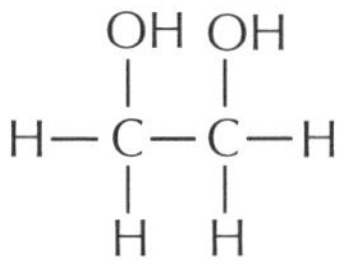

The boiling point of ethan-1,2-diol is 197 °C, whereas the boiling point of ethanol is 76 °C. Suggest a reason for this difference. [2 marks]

Without hydrogen bonding, sweating wouldn't work nearly so well...

Yup... the heat needed to evaporate sweat (i.e. break the hydrogen bonds between water molecules) comes from your body, and removing this heat is what helps keep you cool. So if sweat had weaker intermolecular forces and evaporated more easily, not nearly so much heat would be lost. Now go impress your friends with all your knowledge about sweating.

Polymers

Polymers are long stringy molecules made by joining lots of little molecules together.

*Alkenes **Join up** to form **Addition Polymers***

1) The **double bonds** in alkenes can open up and join together to make long chains called **polymers**. It's kind of like they're holding hands in a big line. The individual, small alkenes are called **monomers**.
2) This is called **addition polymerisation**. For example, **poly(ethene)** is made by the **addition polymerisation** of **ethene**...

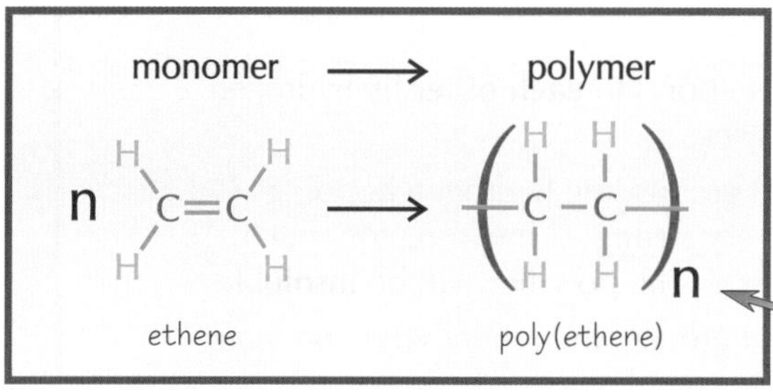

The bit in brackets is the 'repeat unit' (or 'repeating unit'). n represents the number of repeat units.

3) You can polymerise molecules other than basic alkenes. For example:

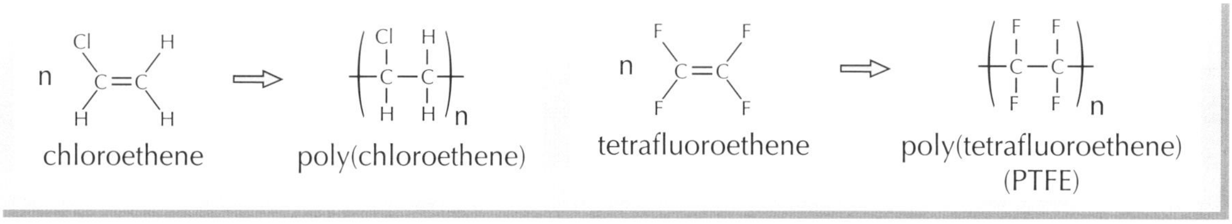

4) **Copolymers** are made from more than one type of monomer — they join together in a **random** order.

nA + mB ⟶ –A–A–B–B–B–A–B–A–A–B–A–A–B–A–A–B–B–

For example, ethene can be combined with propene to produce a polymer with different properties from either poly(ethene) or poly(propene).

Monomers** Will Always Have a **Double Bond

1) To find the **monomer** used to form an addition polymer, take the **repeated unit** and add a **double bond**.
2) Because of the loss of the double bond, poly(alkenes), like alkanes, are **unreactive**.

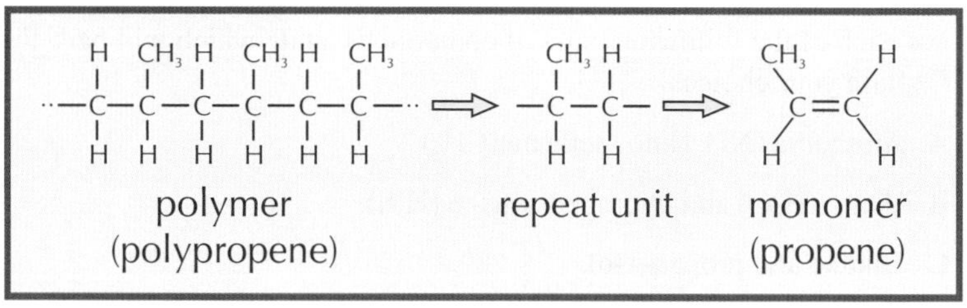

Cross-Linking** Affects how Polymers Behave when they're **Heated

Thermoplastic polymers, like poly(ethene), don't have cross-linking between chains.
It's only **weak intermolecular forces** that hold the chains together.
These forces are really easy to overcome, so it's dead easy to **melt** the plastic.
When it **cools**, the thermoplastic hardens into a new shape.
You can melt these plastics and **remould** them as many times as you like.

Thermosetting polymers, like bakelite, have **covalent cross-links**.
These hold the chains together in a **3D giant covalent structure**.
The polymer doesn't soften when it's heated — but too much heat makes it **char**.
Thermosetting polymers are the **tough guys** of the plastic world.
They're **strong**, **hard**, **rigid** and **insoluble**.

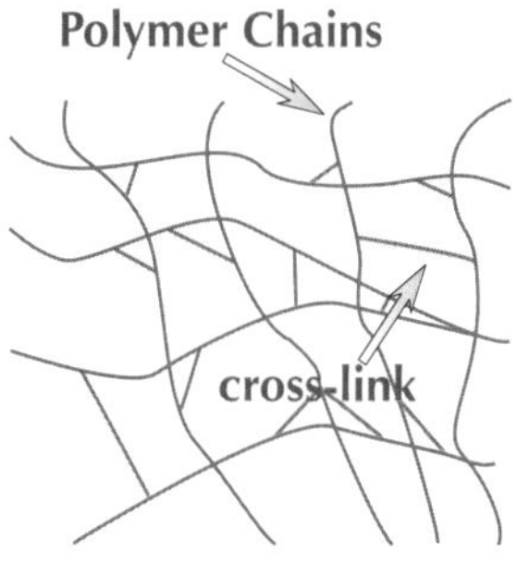

Polymers

A Polymer's **Uses** Depend on its **Properties**

1) Different polymer **structures** have different **properties**, which means they're suited to different **uses**.
Some typical uses of **poly(ethene)** and **poly(propene)** are shown in the table.

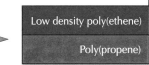

	Properties	Uses
Low density poly(ethene)	Soft Flexible	Plastic bags Squeezy bottles
Poly(propene)	Tough Strong	Bottle crates Rope

2) **Poly(chloroethene)** is **durable** and **flexible**.
It has a wide range of uses — for example, it's used to make **water pipes**, for **insulation** on electric wires and as a **building material**.
It's also used to make outfits — like the one on the right, for example.

Chloroethene is also known as 'vinyl chloride'. Poly(chloroethene) is also called 'polyvinyl chloride' (PVC).

3) **Poly(tetrafluoroethene)** (or PTFE, or Teflon®) is chemically **inert** and has **non-stick** properties.
This makes it ideal as a coating for **frying pans**.

4) **Polystyrene**, or poly(phenylethene), is cheap, and can be made into **expanded polystyrene**, which is light and a good **insulator**.
This means it's good for making things like disposable cups.
It's also used to make the impact-absorbing part of crash helmets.
Perspex™ (another polymer) is transparent and pretty strong, so it can be used in place of glass for certain applications.

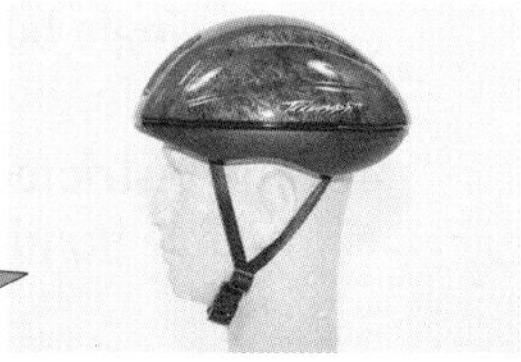

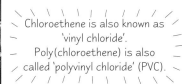

Polystyrene — also useful for making artificial heads.

Practice Questions

Q1 Describe what is meant by addition polymerisation.

Q2 What is a copolymer?

Q3 What is the difference between thermoplastic and thermosetting polymers?

Exam Questions

Q1 Chloroethene CH_2=CHCl forms the polymer poly(chloroethene), commonly known as PVC.
   a) Write an equation to show the polymerisation of chloroethene.
   Your equation should show clearly the structure of the repeating unit in poly(chloroethene). [2 marks]
   b) Poly(chloroethene) is an example of a thermosoftening polymer.
   Explain, in terms of molecular structure, why thermosoftening polymers can be remoulded. [3 marks]

Q2 The polymer poly(propene) can be made by an addition polymerisation reaction involving the monomer propene.
   a) Draw: (i) the displayed formula of propene, (ii) the repeat unit of poly(propene). [2 marks]
   b) A second polymer that can be made by addition polymerisation has the repeat unit shown on the right.
   Name the monomer that gives rise to this polymer. [1 mark]

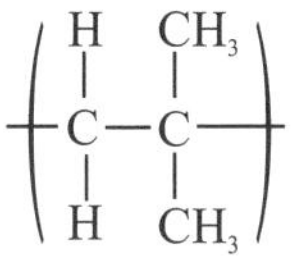

Barbie plastic surgery — gas mark 4, 20 minutes...

You can have hours of fun melting stuff — chocolate, cheese, CDs, candles, crayons, laundry baskets, snails. You're only limited by your imagination. But the potential for setting stuff on fire is a bit of a problem, and some things'll give off nasty fumes. So maybe you'd better find yourself a different pastime instead. Like learning AS Chemistry. That'll keep you busy.

E/Z Isomerism

The chemistry on these pages isn't so bad. And don't be too worried when I tell you that a good working knowledge of both German and Latin would be useful. It's not absolutely essential... and you'll be fine without.

*Atoms **Can't Rotate** Around **Double Bonds***

1) You've already seen how **single bonds** allow atoms to **rotate freely** — a bit like wheels on an axle. For example, the two molecules on the right are **exactly the same.**
(They're **not** isomers — they're the **same** molecule.
If you not sure of the difference, have another look at page 43.)

SAME

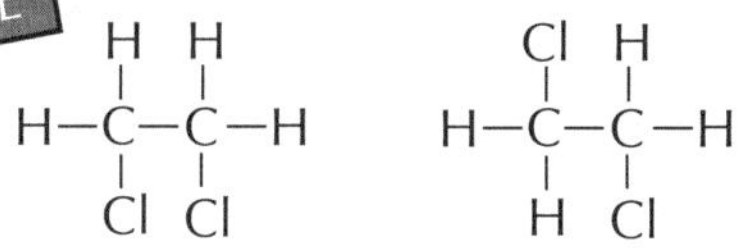

DIFFERENT

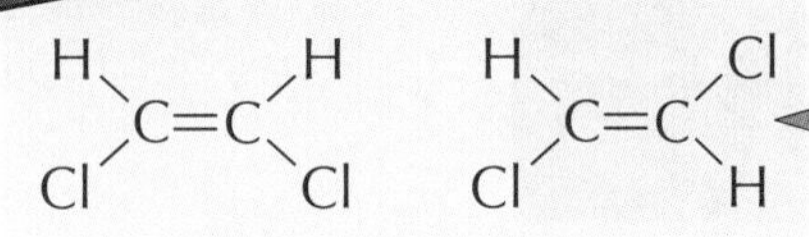

2) Atoms **can't rotate** around C=C double bonds like they can around single bonds.
The two substances on the left are **different** — because nothing can rotate around that **double bond**.
In fact, double bonds are fairly **rigid** — they don't bend much either.

3) Even though atoms can't rotate about **double bonds**, things can still rotate about any **single bonds** in the molecule — like in this molecule of pent-2-ene.
4) The **restricted rotation** around C=C double bonds is what causes **E/Z isomerism**.

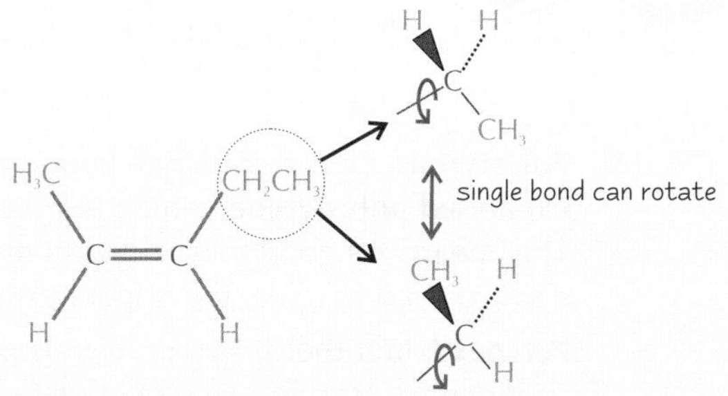

E/Z isomerism** is a Type of **Stereoisomerism

1) **Stereoisomers** have the same structural formula but a **different arrangement** in space.
(Just bear with me for a moment... that will become clearer, I promise.)
2) Because of the **lack of rotation** around the double bond, some **alkenes** can have stereoisomers.
This happens when the two double-bonded carbon atoms each have **different atoms** or **groups** attached to them. Then you get an '**E-isomer**' and a '**Z-isomer**'.
For example, the double-bonded carbon atoms in but-2-ene each have an **H** and a **CH_3** group attached.

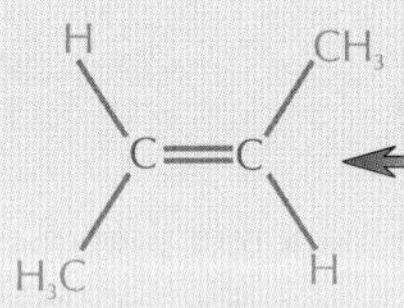
E-isomer

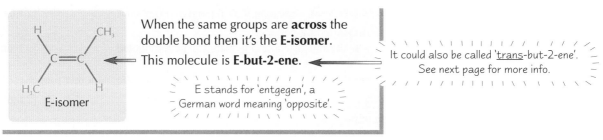

When the same groups are **across** the double bond then it's the **E-isomer.**
This molecule is **E-but-2-ene.**

E stands for 'entgegen', a German word meaning 'opposite'.

It could also be called 'trans-but-2-ene'. See next page for more info.

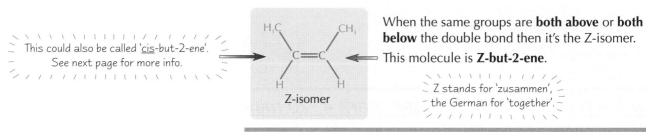

This could also be called 'cis-but-2-ene'. See next page for more info.

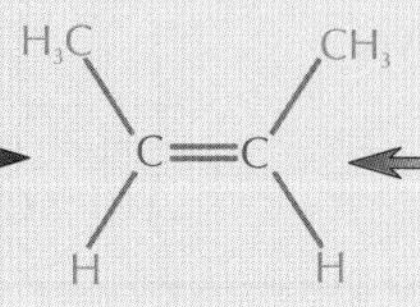
Z-isomer

When the same groups are **both above** or **both below** the double bond then it's the Z-isomer.
This molecule is **Z-but-2-ene.**

Z stands for 'zusammen', the German for 'together'.

E/Z Isomerism

E/Z Isomers Can Sometimes Be Called Cis-Trans Isomers

1) E/Z isomerism is sometimes called **cis-trans isomerism**, where...
   (i) '**cis**' means the **Z-isomer**, and
   (ii) '**trans**' means the **E-isomer**.

   So E-but-2-ene can be called trans-but-2-ene, and Z-but-2-ene can be called cis-but-2-ene.

   We're talking Latin this time... 'Cis' means 'on the same side', while 'trans' means 'across'.

   Here's another example:
   The **Br** atom and the **CH_3** group are on **opposite** sides of the double bond, so this is **trans-1-bromopropene**.
   No problems there.

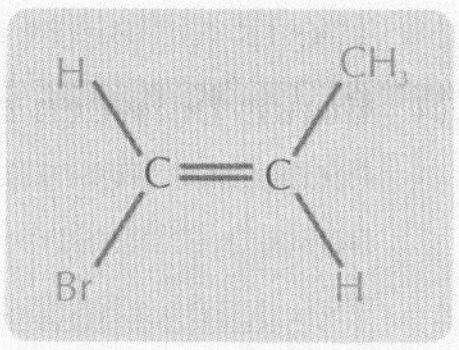

2) But if each carbon atom has totally **different** groups attached to it, the cis-trans naming system can't cope.

   Oh dear. This could be **trans-1-bromo-1-fluoropropene**, because the **Br** and **CH_3** are on **opposite** sides, or it could be **cis-1-bromo-1-fluoropropene**, because the **F** and **CH_3** are on the same side...

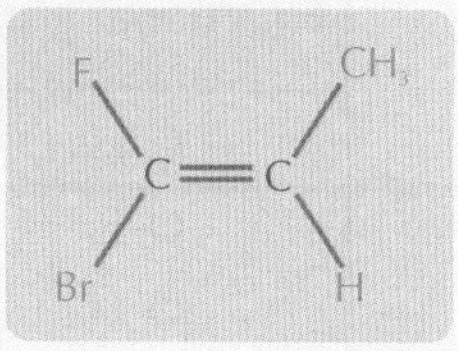

3) The E/Z system keeps on working though. This is because each of the groups linked to the double-bonded carbons is given a **priority**.

   If the two carbon atoms have their 'higher priority group' on **opposite** sides, then it's an **E isomer**.
   If the two carbon atoms have their 'higher priority group' on the **same** side, then it's a **Z isomer**.

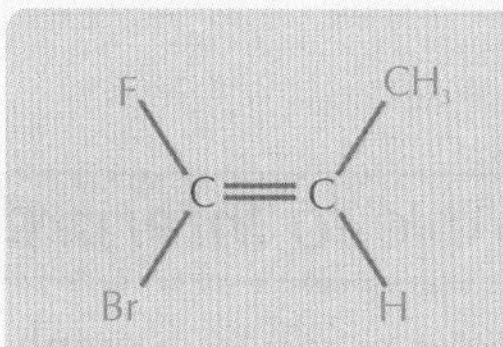

E-1-bromo-1-fluoropropene

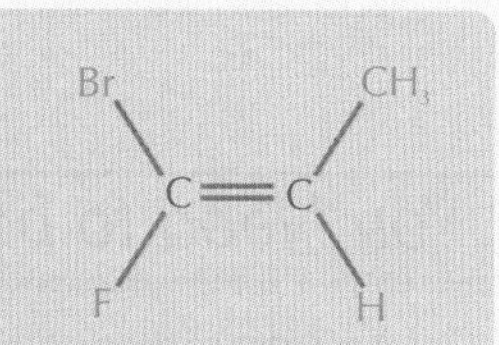

Z-1-bromo-1-fluoropropene

4) In the E/Z system:
   - Br has a **higher priority** than F, and
   - CH_3 has a higher priority than H.

   So the names depend on where the Br atom is in relation to the CH_3 group.

You don't need to know the rules for deciding the order of these priorities.

Practice Questions

Q1 Which of the following is the Z-isomer of but-2-ene?

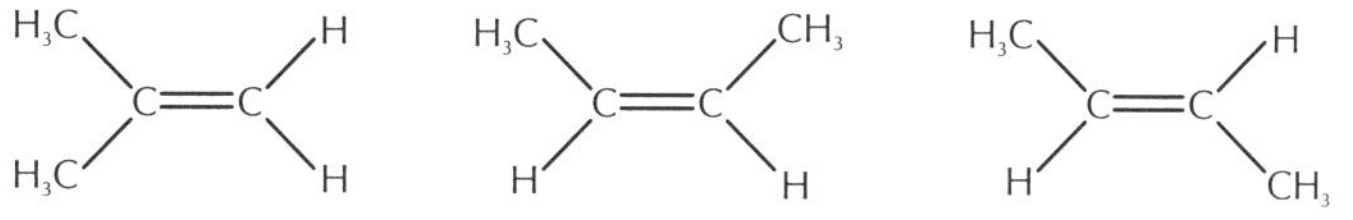

Q2 Define the term 'stereoisomers'.

Q3 Which corresponds to the 'cis-isomer,' the E-isomer or Z-isomer?

Exam Questions

Q1 a) Draw and name the E/Z isomers of pent-2-ene. [4 marks]
   b) Explain why alkenes can have E/Z isomers but alkanes cannot. [2 marks]

Q2 An alkene has 4 different groups attached: A, B, X and Y.
   Which of the following is the E-isomer if A and X have priority?

1.
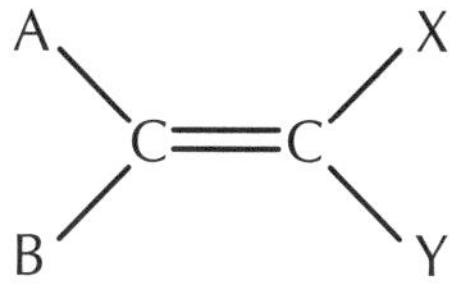

2.
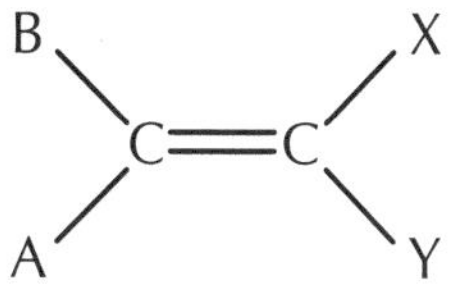

[1 mark]

And there you have it, folks — two E/Z pages in an AS Chemistry book...

Cis and trans are fairly easy to remember... 'cis' — think of sisters standing next to each other, while 'trans' means 'across' in things like transmit, transfer, and the Trans-Siberian Railway. And for E/Z isomers, remember that Z-isomers are the ones with the groups on 'ze zame zide'. Or if you prefer, you could learn to speak German...

Infrared Spectroscopy

If you've got some stuff and don't know what it is, don't taste it. Stick it in an infrared spectrometer instead. Infrared spectroscopy produces scary looking graphs. But just learn the basics, and you'll be fine.

Infrared Spectroscopy *Helps You* ***Identify Organic Molecules***

1) In infrared (IR) spectroscopy, a beam of **IR radiation** is passed through a sample of a chemical.
2) The IR radiation is absorbed by the **covalent bonds** in the molecules, increasing their **vibrational** energy (see p87).
3) **Bonds between different atoms** absorb **different frequencies** of IR radiation. Bonds in different **places** in a molecule absorb different frequencies too — so the O–H group in an **alcohol** and the O–H in a **carboxylic acid** absorb different frequencies.
4) This table shows what **frequencies** different bonds absorb —

Functional group	Where it's found	Frequency/ Wavenumber (cm^{-1})	Type of absorption
C–H	most organic molecules	2800 - 3100	strong, sharp
O–H	alcohols	3200 - 3550	strong, broad
O–H	carboxylic acids	2500 - 3300	medium, broad
C=O	aldehydes, ketones, carboxylic acids	1680 - 1750	strong, sharp

This tells you what the peak on the graph will look like.

You don't need to learn this data, but you do need to understand how to use it.

You Need to be Able to ***Interpret*** *an* ***Infrared Spectrum***

1) An infrared spectrometer produces a **graph** that shows you what frequencies of radiation the molecules are absorbing. So you can use it to identify the **functional groups** in a molecule:

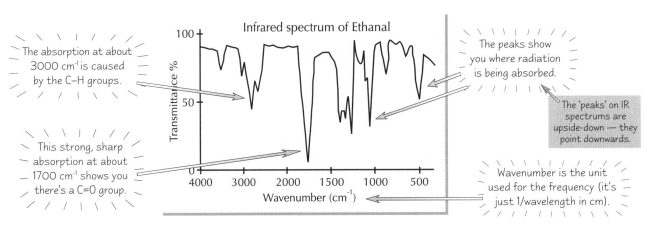

The absorption at about 3000 cm^{-1} is caused by the C–H groups.

This strong, sharp absorption at about 1700 cm^{-1} shows you there's a C=O group.

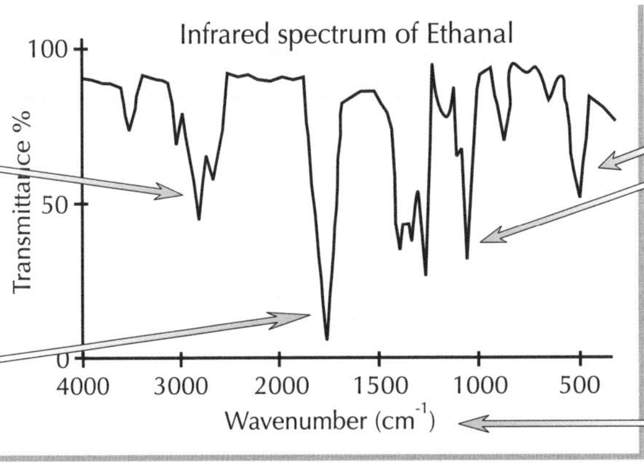

The peaks show you where radiation is being absorbed.

The 'peaks' on IR spectrums are upside-down — they point downwards.

Wavenumber is the unit used for the frequency (it's just 1/wavelength in cm).

2) This also means that you can tell if a functional group has **changed** during a reaction. For example, if you **oxidise** an **alcohol** to an **aldehyde** you'll see the O–H absorption **disappear** from the spectrum, and a C=O absorption **appear**.

Example: A chemical was suspected to be a pure sample of an unknown aldehyde. When the chemical was tested using infrared spectroscopy, the spectrum below was obtained. Is the chemical an aldehyde? Explain your answer.

1) If the chemical was an **aldehyde**, it would contain a **carbonyl** group (a **C=O** functional group — see p97).
2) In infrared spectroscopy, a carbonyl group would show a **strong, sharp peak** at about **1680-1750 cm^{-1}**.
3) The spectrum on the right doesn't have a strong peak at this frequency, and so is **not** an **aldehyde** (or a ketone or a carboxylic acid).

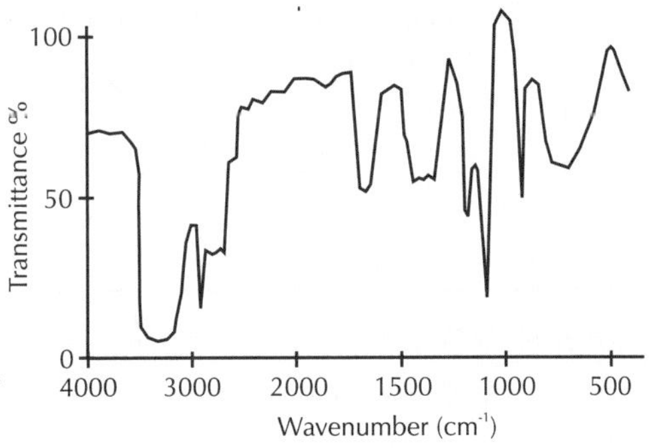

Actually, this is the infrared spectrum of ethanol.

Infrared Spectroscopy

The **Fingerprint** Region **Identifies** a Molecule

1) The region between **1000 cm^{-1} and 1550 cm^{-1}** on the spectrum is called the **fingerprint** region. It's **unique** to a **particular compound**.
2) You can check this region of an unknown compound's IR spectrum against those of known compounds. If it **matches up** with one of them, hey presto — you know what the molecule is.

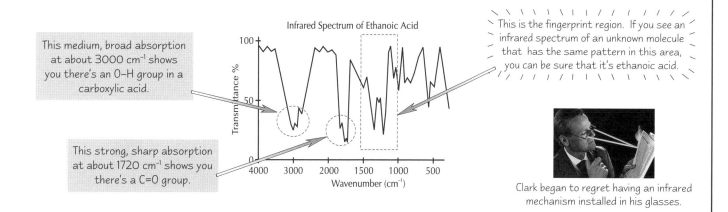

This medium, broad absorption at about 3000 cm^{-1} shows you there's an O–H group in a carboxylic acid.

This strong, sharp absorption at about 1720 cm^{-1} shows you there's a C=O group.

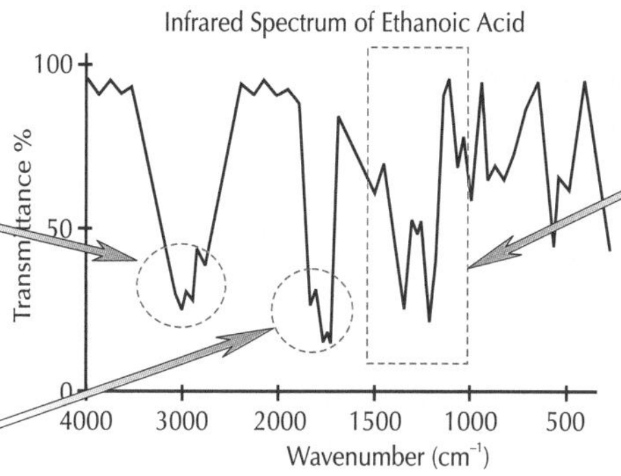

This is the fingerprint region. If you see an infrared spectrum of an unknown molecule that has the same pattern in this area, you can be sure that it's ethanoic acid.

Clark began to regret having an infrared mechanism installed in his glasses.

Practice Questions

Q1 Which parts of a molecule absorb infrared energy?

Q2 Why do most infrared spectra of organic molecules have a strong, sharp peak at around 3000 cm^{-1}?

Q3 On an infrared spectrum, what is meant by the 'fingerprint region'?

Exam Question

Q1 A molecule with a molecular mass of 74 produces the following IR spectrum.

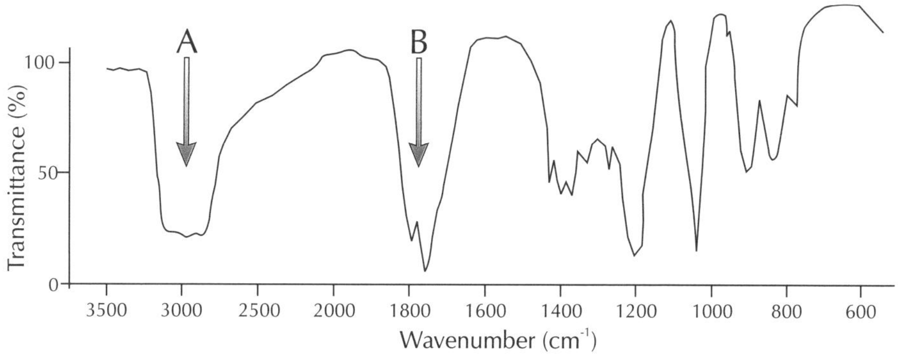

Use the infrared absorption data on the opposite page.

a) Which functional groups are responsible for peaks A and B? [2 marks]

b) Suggest the molecular formula and name of this molecule. Explain your answer. [3 marks]

I wonder what the infrared spectrum of a fairy cake would look like...

I don't suppose I'll ever know. Very squiggly I imagine. Luckily you don't have to be able to remember what any of the infrared spectrum graphs look like. But you definitely need to know how to interpret them, because sure as eggs are eggs it'll turn up in the exam. And there's only one thing to do to make sure you know how — it's those evil practice questions again...

Practical and Investigative Skills

You're going to have to do some practical work too — and once you've done it, you have to make sense of your results...

Make it a **Fair Test** — Control your **Variables**

You probably know this all off by heart but it's easy to get mixed up sometimes. So here's a quick recap:

Variable — A variable is a **quantity** that has the **potential to change**, e.g. mass. There are two types of variable commonly referred to in experiments:

- **Independent variable** — the thing that you **change** in an experiment.
- **Dependent variable** — the thing that you **measure** in an experiment.

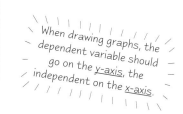

When drawing graphs, the dependent variable should go on the y-axis, the independent on the x-axis.

So, if you're investigating the effect of **temperature** on rate of reaction using the apparatus on the right, the variables will be:

Independent variable	Temperature
Dependent variable	Amount of oxygen produced — you can measure this by collecting it in a gas syringe
Other variables — you MUST keep these the same	Concentration and volume of solutions, mass of solids, pressure, the presence of a catalyst and the surface area of any solid reactants

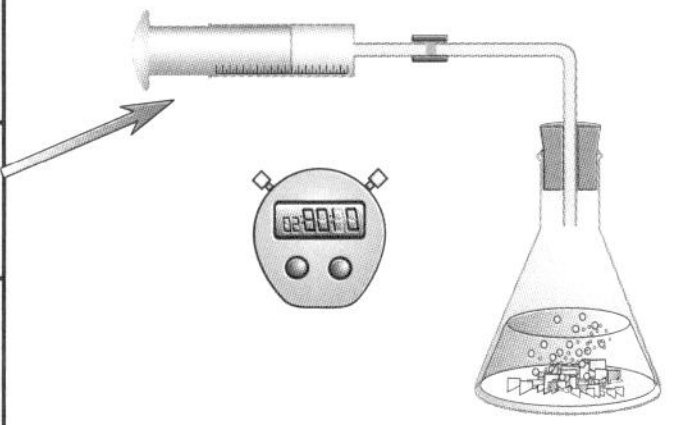

Organise Your Results in a **Table** — And Watch Out For **Anomalous** Ones

Before you start your experiment, make a **table** to write your results in.
You'll need to repeat each test at least three times to check your results are reliable.

This is the sort of table you might end up with when you investigate the effect of **temperature** on **reaction rate**. (You'd then have to do the same for **different temperatures**.)

Temperature	Time (s)	Volume of gas evolved (cm^3) Run 1	Volume of gas evolved (cm^3) Run 2	Volume of gas evolved (cm^3) Run 3	Average volume of gas evolved (cm^3)
20 °C	10	8	7	8	7.7
	20	17	19	20	18.7
	30	28	20	30	29

Find the average of each set of repeated values.
You need to add them all up and divide by how many there are.
E.g.: (8 + 7 + 8) ÷ 3 = 7.7 cm^3

Watch out for **anomalous results**. These are ones that don't fit in with the other values and are likely to be wrong. They're likely to be due to random errors — here the syringe plunger may have got stuck.

Ignore anomalous results when you calculate the average.

Know Your Different Sorts of **Data**

Experiments always involve some sort of measurement to provide **data**.
There are different types of data —

Discrete — you get discrete data by **counting**. E.g. the number of bubbles produced in a reaction would be discrete. You can't have 1.25 bubbles. That'd be daft. Shoe size is another good example of a discrete variable.

Continuous — a continuous variable can have **any value** on a scale. For example, the volume of gas produced or the mass of products from a reaction. You can never measure the exact value of a continuous variable.

Categoric — a categoric variable has values that can be sorted into **categories**. For example, the colours of solutions might be blue, red and green. Or types of material might be wood, steel, glass.

Ordered (ordinal) — Ordered data is similar to categoric, but the categories can be **put in order**. For example, if you classify reactions as 'slow', 'fairly fast' and 'very fast' you'd have ordered data.

Practical and Investigative Skills

Graphs: **Line, Bar or Scatter** — Use the **Best Type**

You'll usually be expected to make a **graph** of your results. Not only are graphs **pretty**, they make your data **easier to understand** — so long as you choose the right type.

Line graphs are best when you have **two sets of continuous data**. For example:

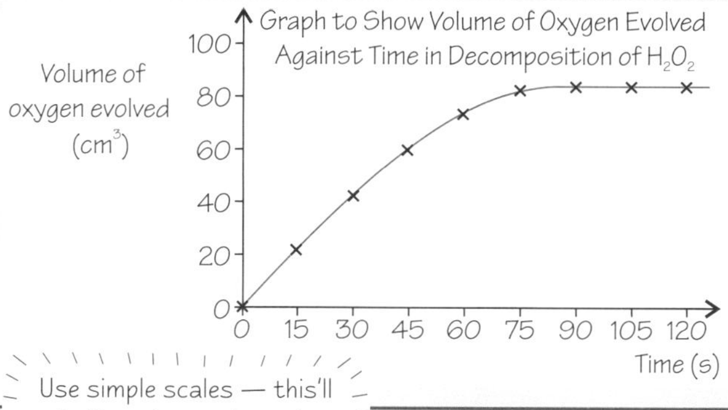

Use simple scales — this'll make it easier to plot points.

You should use a bar chart when one of your data sets is **categoric or ordered data**. For example:

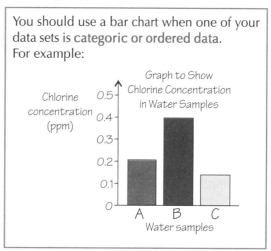

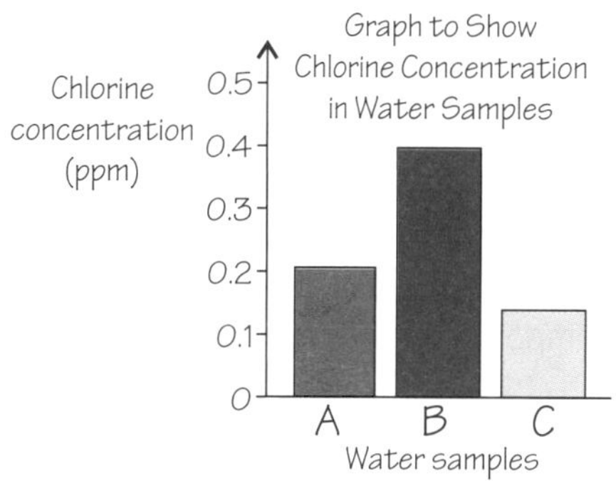

Scatter plots are great for showing how two sets of **discrete or continuous data** are related (or **correlated**).

Don't try to join all the points — draw a **line of best fit** to show the **trend**.

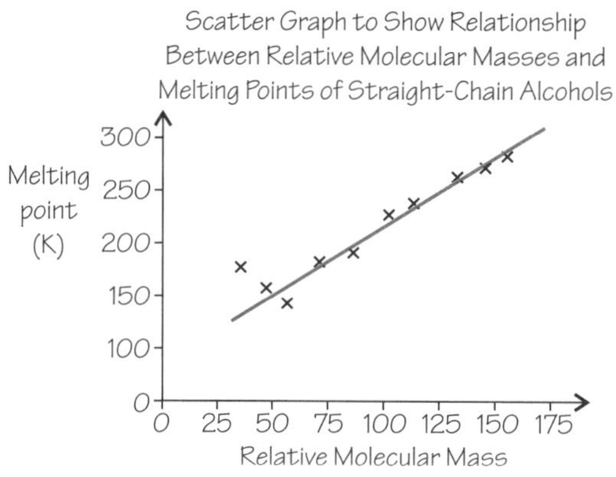

Scatter Graphs Show The Relationship Between Variables

Correlation describes the **relationship** between two variables — the independent one and the dependent one.

Data can show:

1) **Positive correlation** — as one variable **increases** the other **increases**. The graph on the left shows positive correlation.
2) **Negative correlation** — as one variable **increases** the other **decreases**.
3) **No correlation** — there is **no relationship** between the two variables.

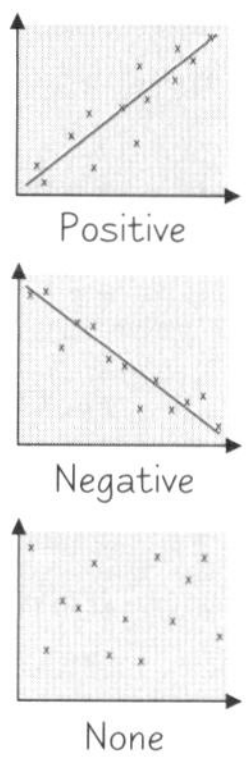

There's also pie charts. These are normally used to display categoric data.

Whatever type of graph you make, you'll ONLY get full marks if you:

- Choose a sensible scale — don't do a tiny graph in the corner of the paper.
- Label both axes — including units.
- Plot your points accurately — using a sharp pencil.

Correlation **Doesn't** Mean **Cause** — Don't Jump to Conclusions

1) Ideally, only **two** quantities would **ever** change in any experiment — everything else would remain **constant**.
2) But in experiments or studies outside the lab, you **can't** usually control all the variables. So even if two variables are correlated, the change in one may **not** be causing the change in the other. Both changes might be caused by a **third variable**.

Watch out for bias too — for instance, a bottled water company might point these studies out to people without mentioning any of the doubts.

Example

For example: Some studies have found a correlation between **drinking chlorinated tap water** and the risk of developing certain cancers. So some people argue that this means water shouldn't have chlorine added.

BUT it's hard to control all the variables between people who drink tap water and people who don't. It could be many lifestyle factors.

Or, the cancer risk could be affected by something else in tap water — or by whatever the non-tap water drinkers drink instead...

Practical and Investigative Skills

Don't Get **Carried Away** When Drawing Conclusions

The **data** should always **support** the conclusion. This may sound obvious but it's easy to **jump** to conclusions. Conclusions have to be **specific** — not make sweeping generalisations.

Example

The rate of an enzyme-controlled reaction was measured at **10 °C, 20 °C, 30 °C, 40 °C, 50 °C and 60 °C**. All other variables were kept constant, and the results are shown in this graph.

A science magazine **concluded** from this data that enzyme X works best at **40 °C**. The data **doesn't** support this.

The enzyme **could** work best at 42 °C or 47 °C but you can't tell from the data because **increases** of **10 °C** at a time were used. The rate of reaction at in-between temperatures **wasn't** measured.

All you know is that it's faster at **40 °C** than at any of the other temperatures tested.

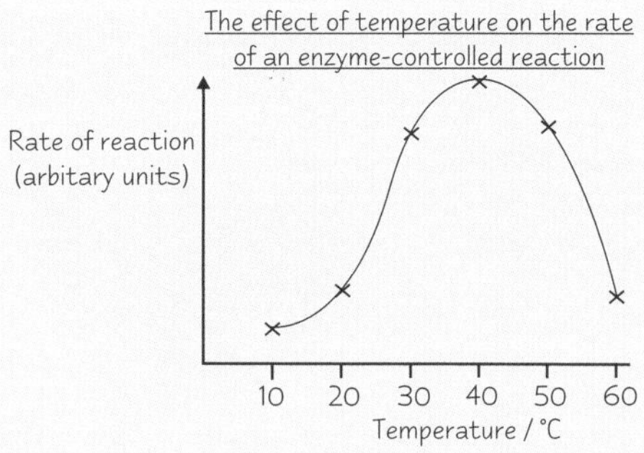

Example

The experiment above **ONLY** gives information about this particular enzyme-controlled reaction. You can't conclude that **all** enzyme-controlled reactions happen faster at a particular temperature — only this one. And you can't say for sure that doing the experiment at, say, a different constant pressure, wouldn't give a different optimum temperature.

You need to Look **Critically** at Your Results

There are a few bits of lingo that you need to understand. They'll be useful when you're evaluating your results.

1) **Valid results** — Valid results answer the original question. For example, if you haven't **controlled all the variables** your results won't be valid, because you won't be testing just the thing you wanted to.

2) **Accurate** — Accurate results are those that are **really close** to the **true** answer.

3) **Precise results** — These are results taken using **sensitive instruments** that measure in **small increments**, e.g. pH measured with a meter (pH 7.692) will be **more precise** than pH measured with paper (pH 7).

It's possible for results to be precise **but not** accurate, e.g. a balance that weighs to 1/1000 th of a gram will give precise results but if it's not **calibrated** properly the results won't be accurate.

You may have to calculate the **percentage uncertainty** of a measurement — that's how much error it might have. E.g. the uncertainty associated with a pipette is 0.06 cm³. If you measure 25 cm³ with it, the percentage uncertainty is:

$$\text{percentage uncertainty} = \frac{\text{uncertainty}}{\text{reading}} \times 100 = \frac{0.06}{25} \times 100 = \mathbf{0.24\%}$$

Watch out when you're using burettes in titrations though. You take two readings, an initial one and a final one — the titre is the final volume minus the initial volume. If each reading has an uncertainty of 0.05 cm³ associated with it, the **overall uncertainty** for the titre is 0.05 × 2 = 0.1 cm³.

4) **Reliable results** — **Reliable** means the results can be **consistently reproduced** in independent experiments. And if the results are reproducible they're more likely to be **true**. If the data isn't reliable for whatever reason you **can't draw** a valid **conclusion**.

For experiments, the **more repeats** you do, the **more reliable** the data. If you get the **same result** twice, it could be the correct answer. But if you get the same result **20 times**, it'd be much more reliable. And it'd be even more reliable if everyone in the class got about the same results using different apparatus.

Work **Safely** and **Ethically** — Don't Blow Up the Lab or Harm Small Animals

In any experiment you'll be expected to show that you've thought about the **risks and hazards**. It's generally a good thing to wear an apron and goggles, but you may need to take additional safety measures, depending on the experiment. For example, anything involving nasty gases will need to be done in a fume cupboard.

You need to make sure you're working **ethically** too. This is most important if there are other people or animals involved. You have to put their welfare first.

Answers

Unit 1: Module 1 — The Elements of Life

Page 5 — The Atom

1) a) *Similarity — They've all got the same number of protons/electrons. [1 mark]*
Difference — They all have different numbers of neutrons. [1 mark]
b) *1 proton [1 mark], 1 neutron (2 – 1) [1 mark], 1 electron [1 mark].*
c) *^{3}H. [1 mark]*
Since tritium has 2 neutrons in the nucleus and also 1 proton, it has a mass number of 3. You could also write $^{3}_{1}H$ but you don't really need the atomic number.

2) a) *(i) Same number of electrons. [1 mark]*
$^{32}_{16}S^{2-}$ has 16 + 2 = 18 electrons. $^{40}_{18}Ar$ has 18 electrons too. [1 mark]
(ii) Same number of protons. [1 mark].
Each has 16 protons (the atomic number of S must always be the same) [1 mark].
(iii) Same number of neutrons. [1 mark]
$^{40}_{18}Ar$ has 40 – 18 = 22 neutrons. $^{42}_{20}Ca$ has 42 – 20 = 22 neutrons. [1 mark]
b) ***A** and **C**. [1 mark] They have the same number of protons but different numbers of neutrons. [1 mark].*
It doesn't matter that they have a different number of electrons because they are still the same element.

Page 7 — Atomic Models

1) a) *Bohr knew that if an electron was freely orbiting the nucleus it would spiral into it, causing the atom to collapse [1 mark]. His model only allowed electrons to be in fixed shells and not in between them [1 mark].*
b) *When an electron moves from one shell to another electromagnetic radiation is emitted or absorbed [1 mark].*
c) *Atoms react in order to gain full shells of electrons [1 mark]. Noble gases have full shells and so do not react [1 mark]. (Alternatively: a full shell of electrons makes an atom stable [1 mark]; noble gases have full shells and do not react because they are stable [1 mark].)*

Page 9 — Relative Mass

1) a) *First multiply each relative abundance by the relative mass — 120.8 × 63 = 7610.4, 54.0 × 65 = 3510.0*
Next add up the products —
7610.4 + 3510.0 = 11 120.4 *[1 mark]*
Now divide by the total abundance (120.8 + 54.0 = 174.8)

$$A_r(Cu) = \frac{11120.4}{174.8} \approx \mathbf{63.6} \qquad [1\ mark]$$

You can check your answer by seeing if A_r(Cu) is in between 63 and 65 (the lowest and highest relative isotopic masses).
b) *A sample of copper is a mixture of 2 isotopes of different abundances [1 mark]. The weighted average mass of these isotopes isn't a whole number [1 mark].*

2) a) *Mass spectroscopy. [1 mark]*
b) *You use pretty much the same method here as for question 1)a).*
93.11 × 39 = 3631.29, 0.12 × 40 = 4.8, 6.77 × 41 = 277.57
3631.29 + 4.8 + 277.57 = 3913.66 *[1 mark]*
This time you divide by 100 because they're percentages.

$$A_r(K) = \frac{3913.66}{100} \approx \mathbf{39.14} \qquad [1\ mark]$$

Again check your answer's between the lowest and highest relative isotopic masses, 39 and 41. A_r(K) is closer to 39 because most of the sample (93.11%) is made up of this isotope.

Page 11 — Nuclear Radiation

1)
$$^{216}_{84}Po \rightarrow {}^{212}_{82}Pb + {}^{4}_{2}He \text{ or } {}^{4}_{2}\alpha$$
(216 – 212 = 4; 84 – 82 = 2)
[1 mark]

$$^{212}_{82}Pb \rightarrow {}^{212}_{83}Bi + {}^{0}_{-1}e$$
(212 – 0 = 212; 82 – (-1) = 83)
[1 mark]

2) a) *Atomic number = 12 [1 mark]*
Name is magnesium [1 mark]
Mass number = 24 [1 mark]
In beta decay the atomic number increases by 1, but the mass number does not change. The atomic number tells you the name of the isotope.
b) *800 to 50 involves 4 half-lives [1 mark]*
4 × 15 hours = 60 hours [1 mark]

3) *Gamma radiation is able to pass through body materials easily so it can be detected outside the body, whereas alpha radiation can't [1 mark]. Gamma radiation is far less ionising than alpha radiation so it causes far less damage [1 mark].*

Page 13 — The Mole and Equations

1) *M of C_2H_5Cl = (2 × 12) + (5 × 1) + (1 × 35.5) = 64.5 g mol^{-1} [1 mark]*

Number of moles of $C_2H_5Cl = \frac{258}{64.5}$ = 4 moles *[1 mark]*

From the equation, 1 mole C_2H_5Cl is made from 1 mole C_2H_4
so, 4 moles C_2H_5Cl is made from 4 moles C_2H_4. *[1 mark]*
M of C_2H_4 = (2 × 12) + (4 × 1) = 28 g
*so, the mass of 4 moles C_2H_4 = 4 × 28 = **112 g*** *[1 mark]*

2) *M of $CaCO_3$ = 40 + 12 + (3 × 16) = 100 g*

Number of moles of $CaCO_3 = \frac{10.5}{84}$ = 0.125 moles

From the equation, 1 mole $CaCO_3$ produces 1 mole CaO
so, 0.15 moles of $CaCO_3$ produces 0.15 moles of CaO. *[1 mark]*
M of CaO = 40 + 16 = 56 g *[1 mark]*
*so, mass of 0.15 moles of CaO = 56 × 0.15 = **8.4 g*** *[1 mark]*

3) *On the LHS, you need 2 each of K and I, so use 2KI*
*This makes the final equation: **$2KI + Pb(NO_3)_2 \rightarrow PbI_2 + 2KNO_3$*** *[1 mark]*
In this equation, the NO_3 group remains unchanged, so it makes balancing much easier if you treat it as one indivisible lump.

Page 15 — Empirical and Molecular Formulas

1) *Assume you've got 100 g of the compound so you can turn the % straight into mass.*

No. of moles of C = $\frac{92.3}{12}$ = 7.69 moles

No. of moles of H = $\frac{7.7}{1}$ = 7.7 moles *[1 mark]*

Divide both by the smallest number, in this case 7.69.
So ratio C : H = 1 : 1
So, the empirical formula = CH *[1 mark]*

The mass of the atoms in the empirical formula = 12 + 1 = 13

No. of empirical units in molecule = $\frac{78}{13}$ = 6

*So the molecular formula = **C_6H_6*** *[1 mark]*

2) *The magnesium is burning, so it's reacting with oxygen and the product is magnesium oxide.*
First work out the number of moles of each element.

No. of moles Mg = $\frac{1.2}{24}$ = 0.05 moles

Mass of O is everything that isn't Mg: 2 – 1.2 = 0.8 g

No. of moles O = $\frac{0.8}{16}$ = 0.05 moles *[1 mark]*

Ratio Mg : O = 0.05 : 0.05
Divide both by the smallest number, in this case 0.05.
So ratio Mg : O = 1 : 1
*So the empirical formula is **MgO*** *[1 mark]*

Answers

3) First calculate the no. of moles of each product and then the mass of C and H:

No. of moles of $CO_2 = \frac{33}{44} = 0.75$ moles

Mass of C = 0.75 × 12 = 9 g

No. of moles of $H_2O = \frac{10.8}{18} = 0.6$ moles

0.6 moles H_2O = 1.2 moles H
Mass of H = 1.2 × 1 = 1.2 g [1 mark]

Organic acids contain C, H and O, so the rest of the mass must be O.
Mass of O = 19.8 – (9 + 1.2) = 9.6 g

No. of moles of O = $\frac{9.6}{16}$ = 0.6 moles [1 mark]

Mole ratio = C : H : O = 0.75 : 1.2 : 0.6
Divide by smallest 1.25 : 2 : 1
The carbon part of the ratio isn't a whole number, so you have to multiply them all up until it is. As its fraction is ¼, multiply them all by 4.
So, mole ratio = C : H : O = 5 : 8 : 4
Empirical formula = $\mathbf{C_5H_8O_4}$ [1 mark]
Empirical mass = (12 × 5) + (1 × 8) + (16 × 4) = 132 g
This is the same as what we're told the molecular mass is, so the molecular formula is also $\mathbf{C_5H_8O_4}$. [1 mark]

Page 17 — Electron Shells and Atomic Spectra

1) $\Delta E = h\nu = (6.626 \times 10^{-34}) \times (4.57 \times 10^{14}) = \mathbf{3.03 \times 10^{-19}\ J}$
[1 mark for correct number, and 1 mark for correct unit]

2) a) The movement of electrons/an electron [1 mark] from lower to higher energy levels [1 mark].
b) Line E (because it is at the highest frequency) [1 mark].
c) i) It would consist of bright, not dark, lines [1 mark].
ii) The lines would be at the same frequencies [1 mark].
d) Because the energy levels get closer together with increasing energy [1 mark].

3) a) Use $E = h\nu$: $E = (6.626 \times 10^{-34}) \times (5.1 \times 10^{14}) = \mathbf{3.38 \times 10^{-19}\ J}$
[1 mark for correct number, and 1 mark for correct unit]

Page 19 — Ionic Bonding

1) a)

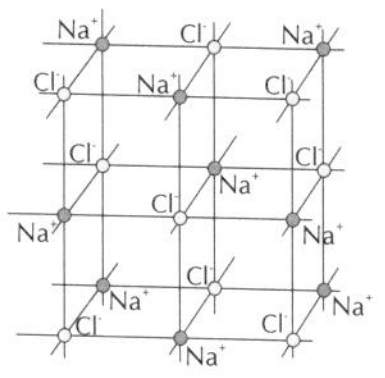

Your diagram should show the following —
- cubic structure with ions at corners [1 mark]
- sodium ions and chloride ions labelled [1 mark]
- alternating sodium ions and chloride ions [1 mark]

b) giant ionic/crystal (lattice) [1 mark]
c) You'd expect it to have a high melting point [1 mark]. Because there are strong bonds between the ions [1 mark] due to the electrostatic forces [1 mark]. A lot of energy is required to overcome these bonds [1 mark].

2) a) Electrons move from one atom to another [1 mark].
Any correct examples of ions, one positive, one negative.
E.g. Na^+, Cl^-. [1 mark for each.]
b) In a solid, ions are held in place by strong ionic bonds [1 mark]. When the solid is heated to melting point, the ions gain enough energy [1 mark] to overcome the forces of attraction [1 mark] enough to become mobile [1 mark] and so can carry charge (and hence electricity) through the substance [1 mark].

Page 21 — Covalent Bonding

1) a)

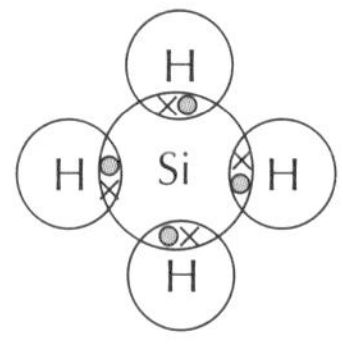

[1 mark for showing a covalently bonded molecule, 1 mark for all bonds shown correctly]
Because Si is in the same group as carbon, it will often form very similar compounds.

b) E.g. Non-conductor of electricity (no free electrons) [1 mark]
Low melting point (simple molecular, non-polar molecule — like methane) [1 mark].

2) Methane is a simple molecular substance [1 mark]. When it melts only weak intermolecular forces are overcome [1 mark].
Magnesium oxide is ionic [1 mark], so to melt it the strong electrostatic attractions must be broken, which requires more energy/higher temperatures [1 mark].

3) a)

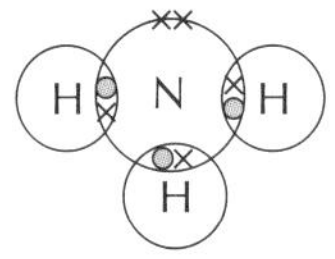

[1 mark for nitrogen and hydrogens covalently bonded. 1 mark for nitrogen's lone pair shown.]

b)

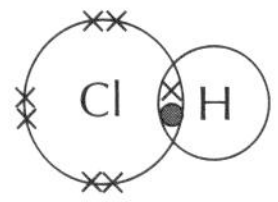

[1 mark for covalent bond. 1 mark for three lone pairs.]

c)

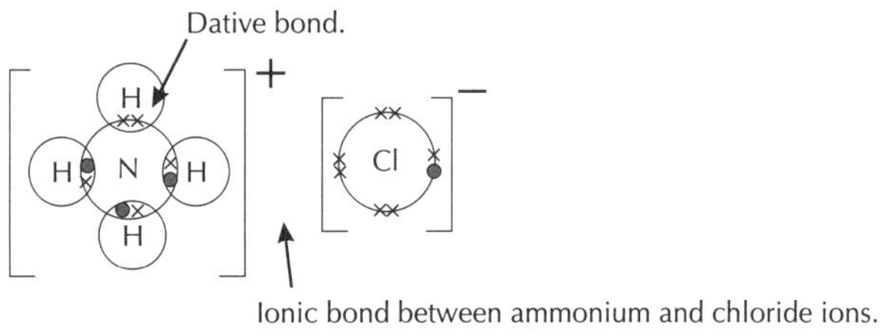

[1 mark for dative bond in ammonium ion, 1 mark for negative chloride ion, 1 mark for positive ammonium ion.]

d) Ammonium chloride is likely to be soluble in water [1 mark].
The polar water molecules can break apart an ionic lattice [1 mark].

Page 23 — Giant Covalent and Metallic Structures

1) a)

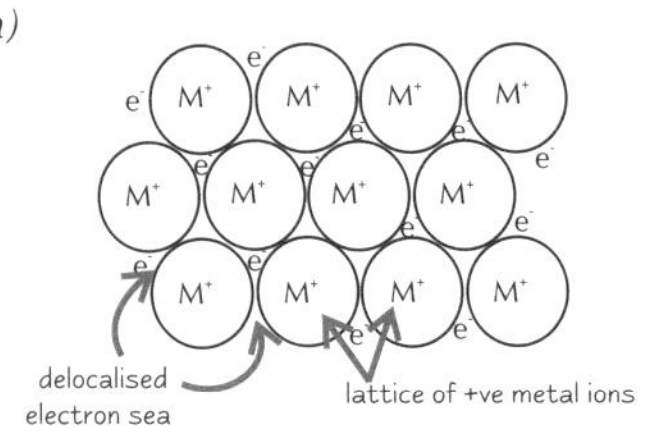

[1 mark for showing any closely packed metal ions and 1 mark for sea of delocalised electrons]
Metallic bonding results from the attraction between positive metal ions [1 mark] and a sea of delocalised electrons between them [1 mark].

b) Calcium (Ca^{2+}) has two delocalised electrons per atom [1 mark], while potassium (K^+) has only one delocalised electron per atom [1 mark]. So calcium has more delocalised electrons and therefore stronger metallic bonding [1 mark].

Answers

2) Carbon dioxide is a simple molecular substance *[1 mark]*. Covalent bonds between carbon and oxygen are strong but when carbon dioxide sublimes it is the weak intermolecular forces that are overcome *[1 mark]*. Silicon dioxide has a giant covalent lattice structure *[1 mark]*, so to melt it the strong covalent bonds must be broken, which requires more energy/higher temperatures *[1 mark]*.

3) Graphite consists of sheets of carbon atoms *[1 mark]*, where each carbon atom is bonded to three others *[1 mark]*. This means that each atom has one free electron not involved in bonds, and it is these free electrons that allow graphite to conduct electricity *[1 mark]*.

4) Copper is metallically bonded and so delocalised electrons are free to move (carry electric current) *[1 mark]*. Oxygen and sulfur form copper oxide/sulfide, fixing some electrons (as anions) *[1 mark]*. This prevents them from moving and carrying charge *[1 mark]*.

5) a) Giant covalent *[1 mark]*

b) High melting point / electrical non-conductor (insulator) / insoluble. *[Any two. 1 mark for each.]*

Page 25 — Shapes of Molecules

1) a) NCl_3 *[1 mark]* BCl_3 *[1 mark]*

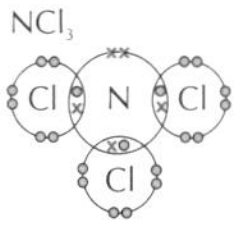

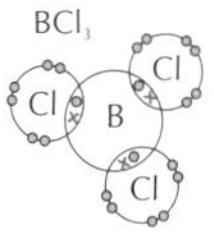

b) NCl_3 *[1 mark]*

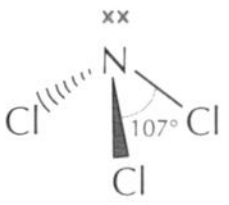

shape: trigonal pyramidal *[1 mark]*,
bond angle: 107° (accept 105° to 109°) *[1 mark]*

BCl_3 *[1 mark]*

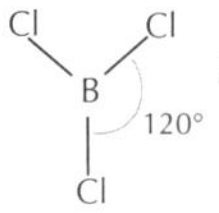

(It must be a reasonable "Y" shaped molecule.)
shape: trigonal planar *[1 mark]*,
bond angle: 120° exactly *[1 mark]*

c) BCl_3 has three electron pairs only around B. *[1 mark]*
NCl_3 has four electron pairs around N *[1 mark]*, including one lone pair. *[1 mark]*

Page 27 — The Periodic Table

1) a) Aluminium has metallic bonding consisting of positively charged particles in a regular lattice structure surrounded by free delocalised electrons *[1 mark]*. These metallic bonds are relatively strong in aluminium because there are 3 delocalised electrons per atom, which makes for strong forces of attraction *[1 mark]*.
These electrons are free to carry an electric current *[1 mark]*.

b) Sulfur consists of simple molecules (S_8) *[1 mark]*. The forces of attraction between the S_8 molecules are weak, and so sulfur has a relatively low melting point *[1 mark]*. There are no free electrons, and so it is a non-conductor of electricity *[1 mark]*.

2) a) Cl_2 *[1 mark]*
b) Si *[1 mark]*
c) Al *[1 mark]*
d) S or P *[1 mark]*

Page 29 — Group 2

1) a) Ca^{2+} *[1 mark]*

b) $CaCO_3(s) \rightarrow CaO(s) + CO_2(g)$
[1 mark for correct equation, and 1 mark for state symbols.]

c) Calcium has a higher charge density than barium *[1 mark]*, and so it has greater polarising power *[1 mark]*. The greater polarising power of the calcium ion distorts the electron cloud around the carbonate ion *[1 mark]* (making it less thermally stable).

2) a) $Mg(OH)_2 + 2HCl \rightarrow MgCl_2 + 2H_2O$
[1 mark for correct reactants and products, plus 1 mark if equation correctly balanced.]

b) $CaO + H_2O \rightarrow Ca^{2+}(aq) + 2OH^-(aq)$
or $CaO + H_2O \rightarrow Ca(OH)_2(aq)$
[1 mark for correct reactants and products, plus 1 mark if equation correctly balanced.]

c) Calcium hydroxide is more soluble in water than magnesium hydroxide *[1 mark]*, and so dissociation produces a higher concentration of hydroxide ions in solution *[1 mark]*.

Unit 1: Module 2 — Developing Fuels

Page 31 — Gas Volumes and Entropy

1) There would be an increase in entropy *[1 mark]*.
The reactants contain a solid (Na) while the products contain a gas (H_2). *[1 mark]*
Gases have a higher entropy than solids. *[1 mark]*
Entropy just means 'how disordered the particles are'.

2) a) The equation for the reaction is:
$CaCO_3 + 2HCl \rightarrow CaCl_2 + H_2O + CO_2$ *[1 mark]*

b) M of $CaCO_3 = 40 + 12 + (3 \times 16) = 100$ g.
So 10 g of calcium carbonate is 0.1 moles *[1 mark]*.
From the equation, 1 mole of $CaCO_3$ reacting with excess HCl will give off 1 mole of CO_2, so 0.1 mole of $CaCO_3$ will produce 0.1 mole of CO_2 *[1 mark]*.
At r.t.p., 0.1 mole of gas has a volume of $24 \times 0.1 = 2.4$ dm^3 *[1 mark]*.

3) One mole of reactants turns into two moles of products, meaning an increase in entropy *[1 mark]*. In addition, one of the products is a gas, meaning the molecules move with greater speed and disorder, and therefore greater entropy *[1 mark]*.

Page 33 — Enthalpy Changes

1) The negative charge density *[1 mark]* between carbon and oxygen in C=O is greater than in C–O *[1 mark]*.
Attraction between the positive nuclei *[1 mark]* of carbon and oxygen for this electron density is stronger for C=O. *[1 mark]*.
So the bond enthalpy of C=O is higher *[1 mark]* and the atoms are closer together in C=O *[1 mark]*, giving a shorter bond length.

Page 35 — Hess's Law

1) $\Delta H_r^\ominus$ = sum of $\Delta H_f^\ominus$(products) – sum of $\Delta H_f^\ominus$(reactants) *[1 mark]*
$= [0 + (3 \times -602)] - [-1676 + (3 \times 0)]$ *[1 mark]*
$=$ **-130 kJ mol^{-1}** *[1 mark]*
Don't forget the units. It's a daft way to lose marks.

2) a) $C_3H_8(g) + 5O_2(g) \rightarrow 3CO_2(g) + 4H_2O(l)$
[1 mark for the correct formulas for both reactants and products, 1 mark for correctly balancing the equation, 1 mark for the correct state symbols.]

b)

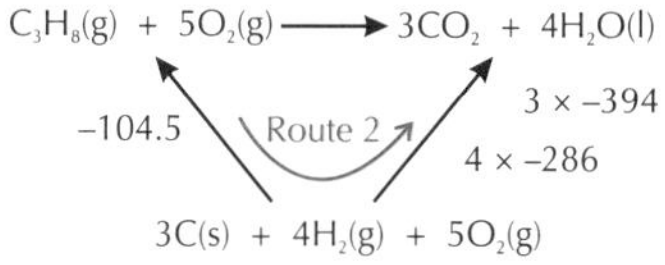

[1 mark for correct substances in Hess cycle, 1 mark for correct balancing.]
By Hess's law the enthalpy of combustion is found by using the values in "Route 2" of the Hess cycle:
$+104.5 + (3 \times (-394) + (4 \times (-286)) = -2221.5$ kJ/mol
[1 mark for value, 1 mark for units]

3)

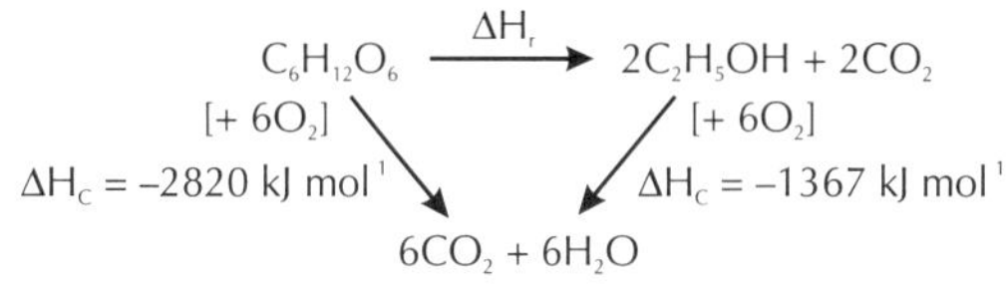

ΔH_r = $\Delta H_c^\ominus$(glucose) – $\Delta H_c^\ominus$(ethanol) *[1 mark]*
$= [-2820] - [-1367]$ *[1 mark]*
$=$ **-1453 kJ mol^{-1}** *[1 mark]*

Answers

Page 37 — Measuring Enthalpy Changes

1) $\Delta T = 25.5 - 19 = 6.5\ °C$ *[1 mark]*
$m = 25 + 25 = 50\ cm^3$ of solution, which has a mass of 50 g (assume density to be $1.0\ g\ cm^{-3}$) *[1 mark]*.
Heat produced by reaction $= mc\Delta T$
$= 50 \times 4.18 \times 6.5 = 1358.5\ J$ *[1 mark]*

No. of moles of HCl $= \dfrac{1 \times 25}{1000} = 0.025$ moles *[1 mark]*

0.025 moles of HCl produces 1358.5 J of heat, therefore 1 mole of HCl produces $\dfrac{1358.5}{0.025}$ *[1 mark]* $= 54\ 340\ J \approx 54.3\ kJ$

So the enthalpy change is $-54.3\ kJ\ mol^{-1}$ (you need the minus sign because it's exothermic)
[1 mark for correct number, 1 mark for minus sign].

2) a) No. of moles of $CuSO_4$ $= \dfrac{0.2 \times 50}{1000} = 0.01$ moles *[1 mark]*
From the equation, 1 mole of $CuSO_4$ reacts with 1 mole of Zn.
So, 0.01 moles of $CuSO_4$ reacts with 0.01 moles of Zn *[1 mark]*.
Heat produced by reaction $= mc\Delta T$
$= 50 \times 4.18 \times 2.6 = 543.4\ J$ *[1 mark]*
0.01 moles of zinc produces 543.4 J of heat, therefore 1 mole of zinc produces $\dfrac{543.4}{0.01}$ *[1 mark]* $= 54\ 340\ J \approx 54.3\ kJ$
So the enthalpy change is **$-54.3\ kJ\ mol^{-1}$** (you need the minus sign because it's exothermic) *[1 mark for correct number, 1 mark for minus sign]*.
It'd be dead easy to work out the heat produced by the reaction, breathe a sigh of relief and sail on to the next question. But you need to find out the enthalpy change when 1 mole of zinc reacts. It's always a good idea to reread the question and check you've actually answered it.

b) E.g. Some heat is absorbed by the beaker / Some heat is lost to the surroundings *[1 mark]*. The experimental temperature increase/ enthalpy change will be smaller than the true value (the enthalpy change will be less negative) *[1 mark]*.

Page 39 — Catalysts

1) a) $V_2O_5(s)$ is classed as a heterogeneous catalyst, as it is in a different phase/state from the reactants *[1 mark]*.
b) Find the mass of the $V_2O_5(s)$ before and after the reaction — if it is acting as a catalyst, they will be the same *[1 mark]*.
c) The arsenic probably clings to the surface of the platinum *[1 mark]* and stops it getting involved in the reaction *[1 mark]*.
Vanadium(V) oxide's solid, but the reactants are gases — so it's a heterogeneous catalyst. This is how they're normally poisoned.

Page 41 — Organic Groups

1) a)

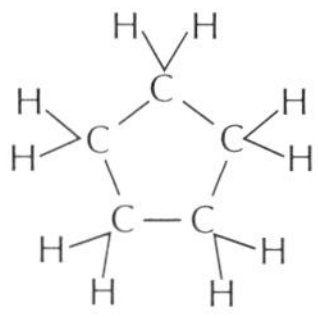

[2 marks. Allow 1 mark for other correctly drawn cycloalkanes.]

b)

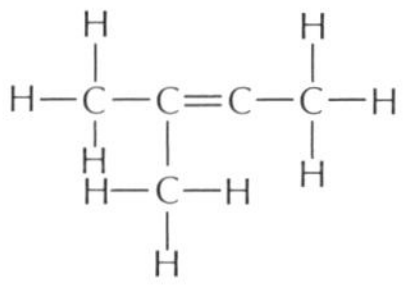

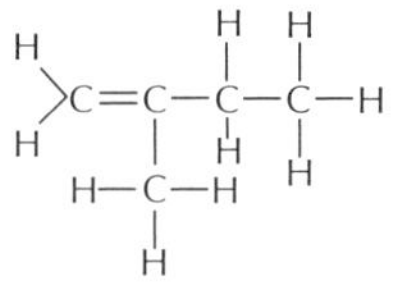

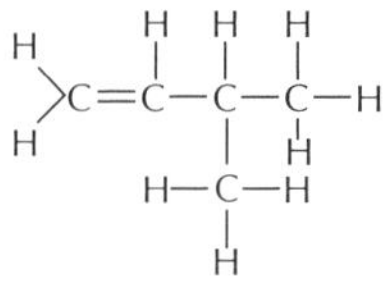

[2 marks for any of the above structures. 1 mark for correctly drawn branched alkene with a different molecular formula.]

c)

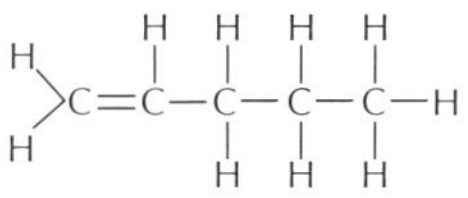

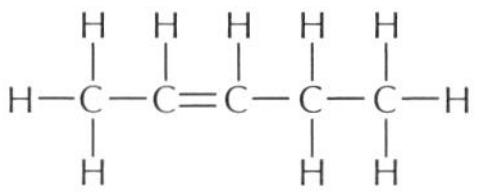

[2 marks for either of the above structures. 1 mark for correctly drawn unbranched alkene with a different molecular formula.]

2) a) ether

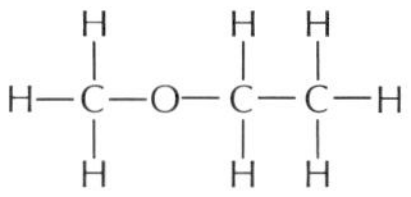

[1 mark]

b) alcohol

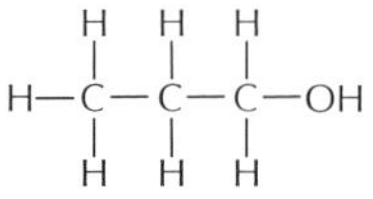

or

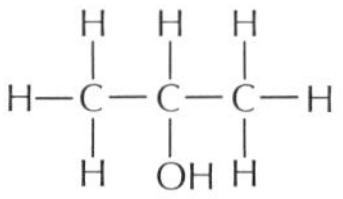

[1 mark]

Page 43 — Isomerism

1)

butan-1-ol

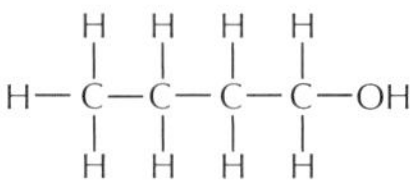

[1 mark for name, 1 mark for structure]

butan-2-ol

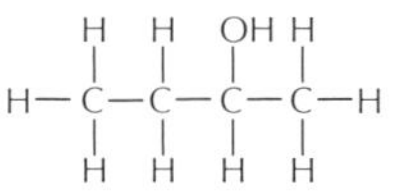

[1 mark for name, 1 mark for structure]

2-methylpropan-1-ol

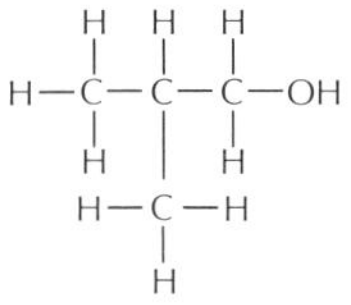

[1 mark for name, 1 mark for structure]

2-methylpropan-2-ol

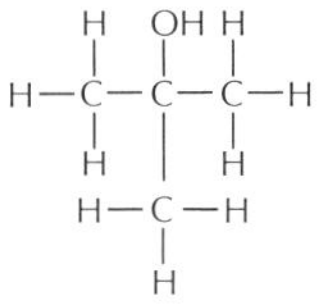

[1 mark for name, 1 mark for structure]

Answers

2) a) 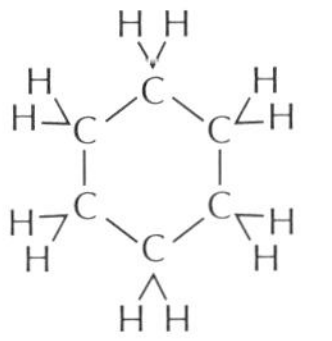 and 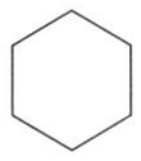 *[1 mark for each]*

b) 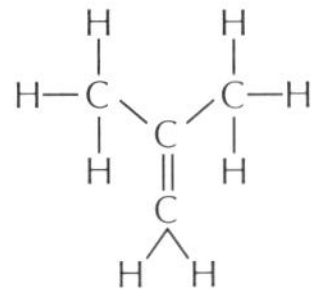 and  *[1 mark for each]*

3) a) *propan-1-ol* *[1 mark]*
b) *2-methylbutane* *[1 mark]*

Page 45 — Shapes of Organic Molecules

1) a)

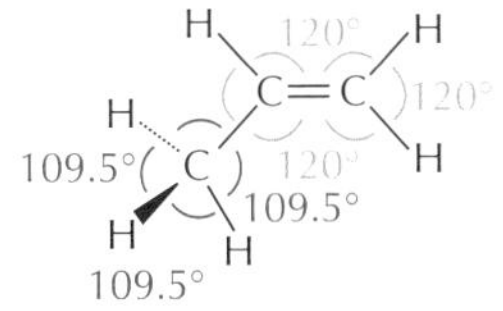

[1 mark for the structure shown correctly, plus 1 mark for an angle of 109.5° labelled, and 1 mark for an angle of 120° labelled.]

b)

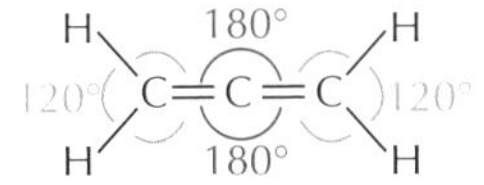

[1 mark for an angle of 180° labelled, and 1 mark for an angle of 120° labelled.]

2) a) CH_3OH *[1 mark]*

b) i) and ii)

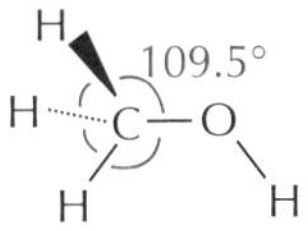

[1 mark for structure, 1 mark for showing any of the marked angles.]

3) a)

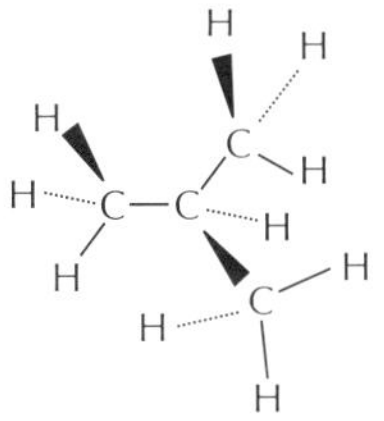

[2 marks for all four carbons shown with four tetrahedral bond angles, or 1 mark for at least one carbon shown with four tetrahedral bonds.]

b) *Electron pairs repel each other [1 mark]. This shape allows the electron pairs to be as far apart as possible [1 mark].*

Page 47 — Catalysts and Petroleum

1) a) (i) *There's greater demand for smaller fractions [1 mark] for motor fuels [1 mark]. Or alternatively: There's greater demand for alkenes [1 mark] to make petrochemicals/polymers [1 mark].*

(ii) *E.g.* $C_{12}H_{26} \rightarrow C_2H_4 + C_{10}H_{22}$ *[1 mark].*

There are loads of possible answers — just make sure the C's and H's balance and there's an alkane and an alkene.

b) (i) *A measure of the tendency of the petrol to auto-ignite [1 mark] — the higher the number, the lower the tendency [1 mark].*

(ii) *Branched- alkanes, cycloalkanes and arenes [1 mark for each].*
They promote efficient combustion/reduce knocking [1 mark].

(iii)

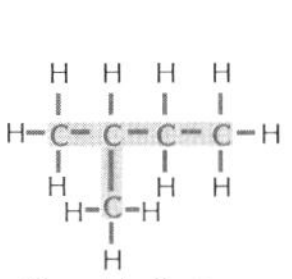

2-methylbutane

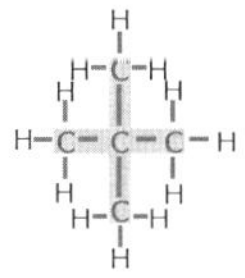

2, 2-dimethylpropane

[1 mark for each structure, 1 mark for each name]
2,2-dimethylpropane will increase the octane rating most [1 mark].
This is cos shorter, more branched alkanes increase the octane rating more. Don't worry about why — just remember that they do.

Page 49 — Fuels

1) a) $2C_8H_{18} + 25O_2 \rightarrow 16CO_2 + 18H_2O$
or $C_8H_{18} + 12\frac{1}{2}O_2 \rightarrow 8CO_2 + 9H_2O$
[1 mark for correct reactants and products. 1 mark for correct balancing.]

b) *If there is not enough oxygen to allow the fuel to burn fully, then incomplete combustion takes place. One of the products of incomplete combustion is carbon monoxide (CO) [1 mark], which is poisonous [1 mark].*

2) a) (i) *Oxides of nitrogen (NO_x) are produced when nitrogen and oxygen atoms in the air react together as a result of the high temperature and pressure in an engine [1 mark]. Unburnt hydrocarbons [1 mark] and these nitrogen oxides react in the presence of sunlight [1 mark] to form ground-level ozone (O_3), which is a major component of smog [1 mark].*

(ii) *E.g. catalytic converters on cars can remove unburnt hydrocarbons and oxides of nitrogen from the exhaust. [1 mark]*

b) *Acid rain is caused when sulfur dioxide [1 mark] and nitrogen dioxide [1 mark] escape into the atmosphere. The problem can be reduced by using calcium oxide to remove sulfur dioxide from power station flue gases [1 mark].*

c) *Any two from: change the law, tax pollution more highly, encourage people to change their behaviour.*
[1 mark each for any two types of measure]

Page 51 — Fuels of the Future

1) a) *Continued use of fossil fuels means increasing amounts of carbon dioxide being emitted, which could lead to problems with climate change [1 mark]. Fossil fuels are also non-renewable, and so they will eventually run out, leading to problems if we do not have alternatives [1 mark].*

b) (i) *E.g. wind power does not emit carbon dioxide into the atmosphere [1 mark] (although CO_2 will be emitted during the manufacture of wind turbines). However, wind power is not completely reliable [1 mark], and it takes a lot of wind turbines to generate the same amount of power as can be produced by a fossil-fuel power station [1 mark].*

(ii) *E.g. nuclear power itself does not emit CO_2 [1 mark] (although the process of producing nuclear fuel does). Nuclear power produces radioactive waste [1 mark], which can be difficult to deal with.*

(iii) *E.g. hydrogen is a 'clean' fuel whose only waste product is water [1 mark]. It takes energy to extract hydrogen from seawater [1 mark]. It is difficult to transport and store hydrogen [1 mark].*

2) *Burning biofuels does produce carbon dioxide [1 mark], although it is CO_2 that the plants the biofuel is made from absorbed while they were growing [1 mark]. This is why biofuels are often considered to be carbon neutral [1 mark]. However, CO_2 is also given out while refining and transporting the fuel [1 mark].*

Answers

Unit 2: Module 1 — Elements from the Sea

Page 53 — More Calculations

1) M of C_3H_7Br = (3 × 12) + (7 × 1) + (1 × 80) = 123 g [1 mark]

Number of moles of C_3H_7Br = $\frac{49.2}{123}$ = 0.4 moles [1 mark]

From the equation, 1 mole C_3H_7Br is made from 1 mole C_3H_6
so, 0.4 moles C_3H_7Br is made from 0.4 moles C_3H_6. [1 mark]
M of C_3H_6 = (3 × 12) + (6 × 1) = 42 g
so, the mass of 0.4 moles C_3H_6 = 0.4 × 42 = **16.8 g** [1 mark]

2) a) M of $MgCO_3$ = 24 + 12 + (3 × 16) = 84 g

Number of moles of $MgCO_3$ = $\frac{10.5}{84}$ = 0.125 moles [1 mark]

From the equation, 1 mole $MgCO_3$ produces 1 mole MgO
so, 0.125 moles of $MgCO_3$ produces 0.125 moles of MgO. [1 mark]
M of MgO = 24 + 16 = 40 g
so, mass of 0.125 moles of MgO = 40 × 0.125 = **5 g** [1 mark]

b) From the equation, 1 mole $MgCO_3$ produces 1 mole CO_2
so, 0.125 moles of $MgCO_3$ produces 0.125 moles of CO_2. [1 mark]
1 mole gas occupies 24 dm^3, [1 mark]
so, 0.125 moles occupies = 24 × 0.125 = **3 dm³** [1 mark]

3) a) Moles of $BaCl_2(aq)$ = volume (in dm^3) × molarity
= (25/1000) × 1 = 0.025 moles [1 mark]

b) From the equation, the number of moles of barium sulfate formed equals the number of moles of barium chloride that react.
Since all other substances are in excess, 0.025 moles of $BaSO_4(s)$ are formed [1 mark].
The relative formula mass of $BaSO_4$ = 137 + 32 + (4 × 16)
= 233 [1 mark]
So theoretical yield = 0.025 × 233 = 5.83 g [1 mark]

c) Percentage yield = (actual yield ÷ theoretical yield) × 100%
= (5.20 ÷ 5.83) × 100% = 89.2% [1 mark]

Page 55 — Titrations

1) First write down what you know —

CH_3COOH	+	NaOH	→	CH_3COONa	+	H_2O
25.4 cm^3		14.6 cm^3				
?		0.5 M				

Number of moles of NaOH = $\frac{0.5 \times 14.6}{1000}$ = 0.0073 moles [1 mark]

From the equation, you know 1 mole NaOH neutralises 1 mole of CH_3COOH, so if you've used 0.0073 moles NaOH you must have neutralised 0.0073 moles CH_3COOH. [1 mark]

Concentration of CH_3COOH = $\frac{0.0073 \times 1000}{25.4}$ = **0.287 M** [1 mark]

2) First write down what you know again —
$CaCO_3 + H_2SO_4 \rightarrow CaSO_4 + H_2O + CO_2$
0.75 g 0.25 M

M of $CaCO_3$ = 40 + 12 + (3 × 16) = 100 g mol^{-1} [1 mark]

Number of moles of $CaCO_3$ = $\frac{0.75}{100}$ = 7.5 x 10^{-3} moles [1 mark]

From the equation, 1 mole $CaCO_3$ reacts with 1 mole H_2SO_4
so, 7.5 x 10^{-3} moles $CaCO_3$ reacts with 7.5 x 10^{-3} moles H_2SO_4. [1 mark]

The volume needed is = $\frac{(7.5 \times 10^{-3}) \times 1000}{0.25}$ = 30 cm^3 [1 mark]

If the question mentions concentration or molarities, you can bet your last clean pair of underwear that you'll need to use the formula

number of moles = $\frac{\text{concentration} \times \text{volume}}{1000}$

Just make sure the volume's in cm^3 though.

Page 58 — Electronic Structure

1) a) $1s^2\ 2s^2\ 2p^6\ 3s^2\ 3p^6\ 4s^1$ [1 mark]

b)

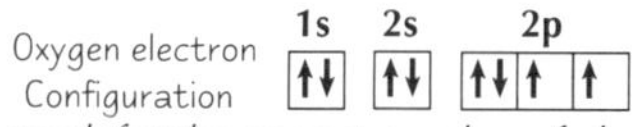

[1 mark for the correct number of electrons in each sub-shell.
1 mark for having spin-pairing in one of the p orbitals and parallel spins in the other two p orbitals.]
A box filled with 2 arrows is spin-pairing — 1 up and 1 down. If you've put the four p electrons into just 2 orbitals, it's wrong.

c) The outer shell electrons in potassium and oxygen can get close to the outer shells of other atoms so they can be transferred or shared [1 mark]. The inner shell electrons are tightly held and shielded from the electrons in other atoms/molecules [1 mark].

2) a) $1s^2\ 2s^2\ 2p^6\ 3s^2\ 3p^6\ 3d^5\ 4s^2$. [1 mark]

b) Germanium ($1s^2\ 2s^2\ 2p^6\ 3s^2\ 3p^6\ 3d^{10}\ 4s^2\ 4p^2$). [1 mark].
The 4p sub-shell is partly filled so it must be a p block element.

c)

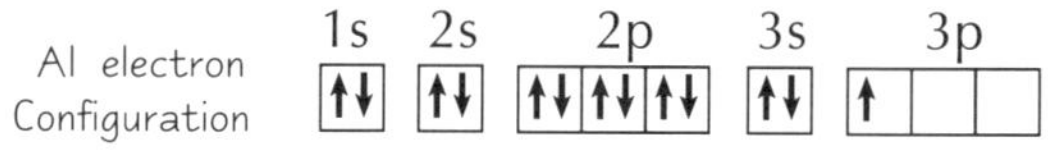

[1 mark for the correct number of electrons in each sub-shell.
1 mark for one arrow in each box pointing up, and one pointing down.]

d) Ar (atom) [1 mark], K^+ (positive ion) [1 mark], Cl^- (negative ion) [1 mark]. You also could have suggested Ca^{2+}, S^{2-} or P^{3-}.

Page 61 — Oxidation and Reduction

1) a) $H_2SO_4\ (aq) + 8HI\ (aq) \rightarrow H_2S\ (g) + 4I_2\ (s) + 4H_2O\ (l)$ [1 mark]

b) Ox. state of S in H_2SO_4 = +6 [1 mark]
Ox. state in H_2S = –2 [1 mark]

c) Iodide [1 mark] — it donates electrons / its oxidation number increases [1 mark]

d) $2I^- \rightarrow I_2 + 2e^-$ [1 mark]

e) $H_2SO_4 + 8H^+ + 8e^- \rightarrow H_2S + 4H_2O$
[all species correct — 1 mark, balancing — 1 mark]
The ionic equations here are pretty tricky. Use the equation you're given as much as possible. For part e), sulphur is being reduced from +6 to –2, so it's gaining 8 electrons. You also need to add H^+s and H_2O's to balance it. With ionic equations, always make sure the charges balance. E.g. in part e), charge on left = +8 – 8 = 0 = right-hand side.

Page 63 — Electronegativity

1) a) The power of an atom to withdraw electron density [1 mark] from a covalent bond [1 mark] OR the ability of an atom to attract the bonding electrons [1 mark] in a covalent bond [1 mark].

b) (i) Br — Br
non-polar
(or no dipole)

(ii)

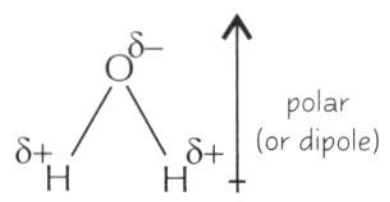

(iii)

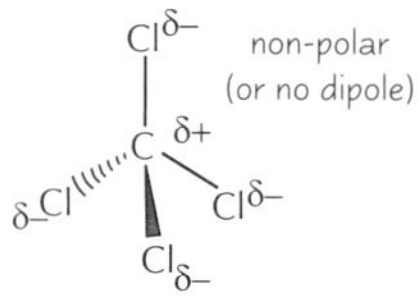

(iv)

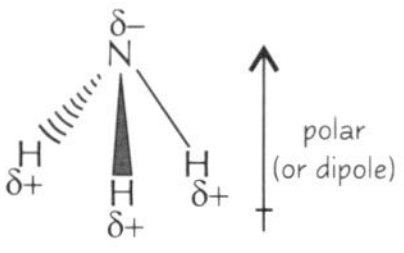

[1 mark each for correct shape and bond polarities, 1 mark each for correct overall polarity].
To help you decide if the molecule's polar or not, imagine the atoms are having a tug of war with the electrons. If they're all pulling the same amount in different directions, the electrons aren't going to go anywhere.

c) The lone pair of electrons on nitrogen [1 mark] cancels out the dipole or polarity [1 mark].
This can't happen with NH_3 because the dipole's in the opposite direction.

Answers

2) a) 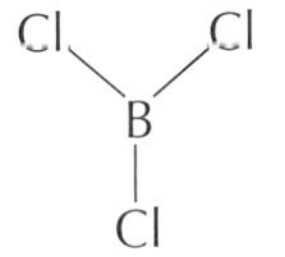

b) 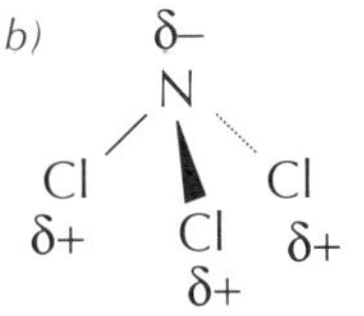

[1 mark for each molecule's shape, 1 mark for no dipoles in BCl_3, 1 mark for the correct dipoles shown in NCl_3.]

Page 65 — Intermolecular Forces

1) Pentane is the most linear molecule [1 mark] and has the greatest surface area [1 mark]. This gives it a greater exposed surface area, and so a greater ability for temporary dipoles to be induced in adjacent molecules [1 mark], meaning stronger intermolecular forces [1 mark]. The surface area of 2-methylbutane is less than that of pentane and that of 2,2-dimethylpropane is smaller still [1 mark], meaning that these substances have weaker intermolecular forces [1 mark].

Page 67 — Ionisation Enthalpies

1) a) There's an increasing attraction between the outer shell electrons and the nucleus. This is due to an increase in nuclear charge since there are more protons [1 mark]. Also, shielding is roughly constant since each additional electron is added to the same shell. [1 mark]

b) For Li and Be, the 2s sub-shell is filling [1 mark]. For B to N, the 2p sub-shell is half filling. This sub-shell is further out so it's easier to remove electrons [1 mark]. For O to Ne, the electrons begin spin-pairing in the 2p sub-shell. There's extra repulsion between the electrons, so they're easier to remove [1 mark]. This 2, 3, 3 pattern of first ionisation energies shows the sub-shell structure.

Page 69 — Group 7 — The Halogens

1) a) $I_2 + 2At^- \rightarrow 2I^- + At_2$ [1 mark]

b) The (sodium) astat<u>ide</u> [1 mark]

2) a) The chlorine atoms gain electrons, meaning they are reduced. The bromide ions lose electrons, meaning they are oxidised. [1 mark].

b) Chlorine [1 mark]

c) Fluorine [1 mark]

Page 71 — More About The Halogens

1) a) Chlorine is very reactive/highly oxidising [1 mark]. It is dangerous to humans / is toxic / corrosive [1 mark]. It is difficult/expensive to store safely / transport in large quantities [1 mark].

b) E.g. PVC/polyvinyl chloride, for insulating electrical wiring [1 mark], bleach/sodium chlorate(I), for water treatment [1 mark].

c) $2Cl^- \rightarrow Cl_2 + 2e^-$
[1 mark for Cl– discharged, 1 mark for Cl_2 produced with correct balancing]
$2H^+ + 2e^- \rightarrow H_2$
[1 mark for H^+ discharged, 1 mark for H_2 produced with correct balancing]

2) a) At the anode: $2Br^-(aq) \rightarrow Br_2(aq) + 2e^-$
At the cathode: $2H^+(aq) + 2e^- \rightarrow H_2(g)$
[1 mark for each correct equation]

b) Bromine is a toxic substance [1 mark], and it's safer to transport it as a compound [1 mark].

Page 73 — The Chemical Industry

1) a) Addition reactions produce no waste products / avoid waste disposal [1 mark]. They also make better use of resources [1 mark].

b) E.g. Not all the starting material reacts / Side reactions may occur / some reactants/products may be lost [1 mark].

c) You would expect to find an ethanol plant near an oil refinery [1 mark] so that ethene produced at the refinery can be easily transported to the ethanol plant [1 mark].

2) a) $(250 \div 300) \times 100$ [1 mark] = 83.3% [1 mark]

b) E.g. Advantage: lower labour costs/process can be automated/can make large quantities non-stop/less variation in quality [1 mark].
Disadvantage: More expensive to build plant / Expensive to run plant below full capacity / Inefficient to make small amounts / Can't use equipment to make other products [1 mark].

Page 75 — Halogenoalkanes

1) 1-bromo,1-chloro,2,2,2-trifluoroethane or 2-bromo,2-chloro,1,1,1-trifluoroethane (allow 2,2,2-trifluoro,1-bromo,1-chloroethane or 1,1,1-trifluoro,2-bromo,2-chloroethane) [1 mark]

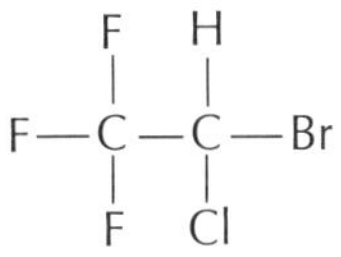

[1 mark]

2) Tube A = 1-bromopropane, Tube B = 1-chloropropane, Tube C = 1-iodopropane [1 mark for all correct]
The larger/greater mass/more electrons the halogen has [1 mark] the stronger the van der Waals forces [1 mark] and the more energy required to overcome them [1 mark].

Page 77 — More About Haloalkanes

1) a) (i) hydrolysis / nucleophilic substitution [1 mark]
(ii) propan-2-ol [2 marks for correct answer. Allow 1 mark for just propanol.]

b) The reaction would be faster with 2-iodopropane [1 mark]. This is because the C-I bond is weaker than the C-Br bond [1 mark].

c) 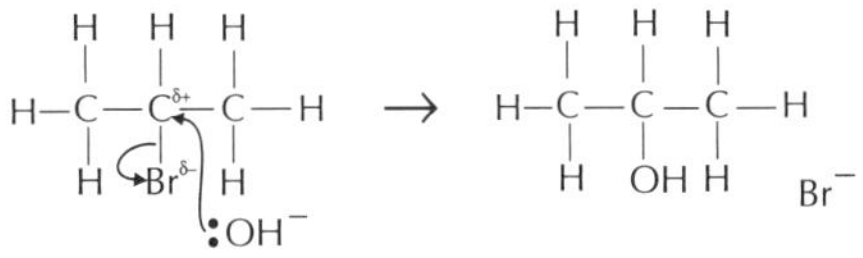

[1 mark for each curly arrow – one must start on C-Br bond and go to Br. The other must start on lone pair on O and go towards correct C. 1 mark for correct structures of reactants and product, including charge on OH.]
There is a different mechanism that also occurs (the S_N1 mechanism), but you don't need to know that one.

Unit 2: Module 2 — The Atmosphere

Page 79 — Giant Structures

1) a) It is covalently bonded [1 mark] — its non-conductivity as a liquid / its insolubility in water suggests there are no free electrons / free ions [1 mark].
It has a giant network/lattice structure [1 mark] — its very high melting/sublimation point means particles must be held together by strong covalent bonds that need to be overcome rather than weak intermolecular forces [1 mark].

b) i) Covalent [1 mark], simple molecular [1 mark]

ii) In boron(III) chloride, only weak instantaneous dipole – induced dipole forces need to be overcome [1 mark]. In boron nitride, strong covalent bonds must be overcome [1 mark]. This takes more energy [1 mark].

Page 81 — Reaction Rates

1) The molecules don't always have enough energy [1 mark]. Collisions don't always happen in the right orientation (the molecules mightn't be facing each other in the best way and will just bounce off each other) [1 mark].

2) The particles in a liquid move freely and all of them are able to collide with the solid particles [1 mark]. Particles in solids just vibrate about fixed positions, so only those on the touching surfaces between the two solids will be able to react. [1 mark]

3) a) Y [1 mark]
The same amount of hydrogen peroxide is decomposed, so the same amount of oxygen will be evolved (so it can't be curve X) [1 mark]. Curve Y shows that oxygen is evolved more slowly [1 mark]. Reaction rates are slower at lower temperatures [1 mark].

Answers

Page 83 — More On Reaction Rates

1) The homogeneous catalyst forms intermediate compounds [1 mark]. The activation enthalpy needed to form the intermediates (and to form the products from the intermediates) is lower than that needed to make the products directly from the reactants [1 mark].

2)

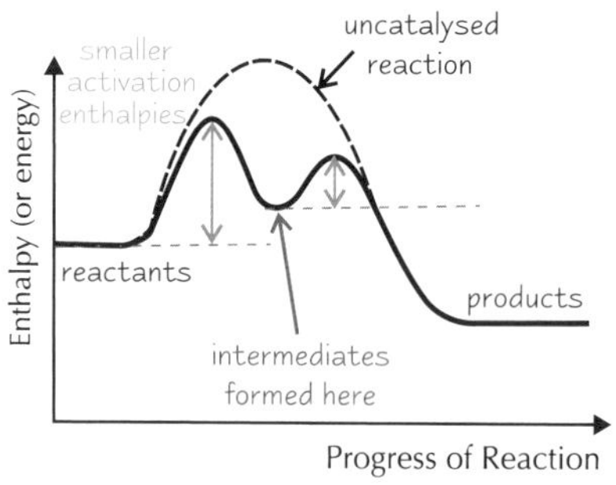

Curve for uncatalysed reaction. [1 mark]
Curve for catalysed reaction with lower activation enthalpy. [1 mark]
Two humps and label for intermediate. [1 mark]
Both axes correctly labelled. [1 mark]

3) The catalyst is reformed by the time the products form. It is chemically unchanged at the end of the process [1 mark].

Page 85 — Reversible Reactions

1) a) If a reaction at equilibrium is subjected to a change in concentration, pressure or temperature, the equilibrium will shift to try to oppose (counteract) the change. [1 mark].
Examiners are always asking for definitions so learn them — they're easy marks.

b) (i) There's no change [1 mark]. There's the same number of molecules/moles on each side of the equation [1 mark].
(ii) Reducing temperature removes heat. So the equilibrium shifts in the exothermic direction to release heat [1 mark]. The reverse reaction is exothermic (since the forward reaction is endothermic). So, the position of equilibrium shifts left [1 mark].
(iii) Removing nitrogen monoxide reduces its concentration. The equilibrium position shifts right to try and increase the nitrogen monoxide concentration again [1 mark].

c) No effect [1 mark].
Catalysts don't affect the equilibrium position. They just help the reaction to get there sooner.

Page 87 — The Atmosphere

1) a) Visible light [1 mark] and infrared [1 mark]
b) Infrared [1 mark].
Molecules made up of identical atoms (e.g. N_2, O_2) are not affected [1 mark].

2) $E = h\nu$
$E = (6.63 \times 10^{-34}) \times (8.19 \times 10^{13})$ [1 mark]
$E = \mathbf{5.43 \times 10^{-20}\ J}$ [1 mark]

Page 89 — The Greenhouse Effect

1) a) Water vapour [1 mark], carbon dioxide [1 mark], methane [1 mark]
b) The molecules/bonds absorb infrared radiation [1 mark] and the bond's vibrational energy increases [1 mark].
Energy is transferred to other molecules by collision [1 mark].
The average kinetic energy of the molecules increases, so the temperature increases [1 mark].

2) a) E.g. Increased CO_2 levels in remote, unpolluted places / Oceans have become more acidic as more CO_2 dissolves (forming carbonic acid) / Lower levels of CO_2 found in air trapped for many years in polar ice [1 mark]
b) E.g. Capturing CO_2 and storing it in underground rock formations / storing it deep in the ocean / converting it to stable minerals / developing alternative fuels / increasing photosynthesis e.g. by increasing growth of phytoplankton [1 mark each method, up to a maximum of 2 marks].

Page 91 — Halogenoalkanes and CFCs

1) a) 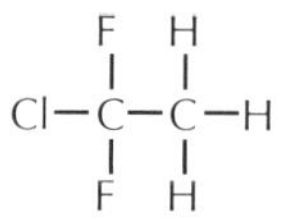 [1 mark]

b) $CH_3CF_2Cl \rightarrow CH_3CF_2\bullet + Cl\bullet$ [1 mark for each correct radical]

2) a) Coolants in fridges / aerosol propellants / fire extinguishers / foaming plastics [1 mark each use, up to a maximum of 3 marks]
b) They are unreactive/chemically stable. They are non-flammable. They are non-toxic. They are volatile. [1 mark each, up to a maximum of 3 marks]
c) Because they were destroying the ozone layer. [1 mark]
d) E.g. HCFCs [1 mark] — still damage the ozone layer OR are greenhouse gases [1 mark]
HFCs [1 mark] — are greenhouse gases [1 mark]
Hydrocarbons [1 mark] — are greenhouse gases [1 mark]

Page 93 — Ozone

1) a) Ozone is formed by the effect of UV radiation from the Sun on oxygen molecules [1 mark]. The oxygen molecules split to form oxygen free radicals [1 mark] which react with more oxygen molecules to form ozone [1 mark].
b) The ozone layer prevents most harmful UV radiation from the Sun from reaching the Earth's surface [1 mark].
c) The ozone molecules interact with UV radiation to form an oxygen molecule and a free oxygen radical ($O_3 + h\nu \rightarrow O_2 + O\bullet$) [1 mark]. The radical produced then forms more ozone with an O_2 molecule ($O_2 + O\bullet \rightarrow O_3$) [1 mark].

2) a) E.g. It is toxic to humans [1 mark]
b) Ground-level ozone forms as a result of sunlight acting on mixtures of nitrogen dioxide and hydrocarbons [1 mark], which are emitted by power stations / vehicles [1 mark].

Unit 2: Module 3 — The Polymer Revolution

Page 96 — Addition Reactions of Alkenes

1) a) Unsaturated hydrocarbons contain one or more double (or triple) carbon-carbon bonds [1 mark].

b) Cyclohexane:

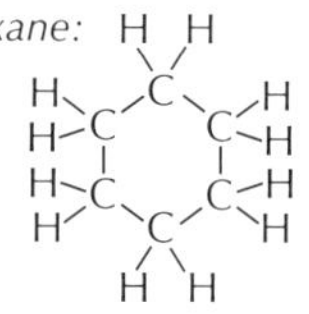

Hex-1-ene:

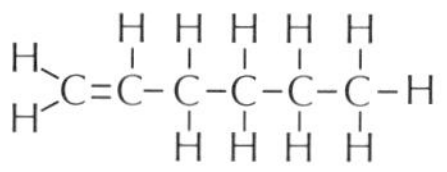

[1 mark for each]

c) Add bromine water to samples of each substance [1 mark].
With cyclohexane, the solution will remain orange [1 mark].
With hex-1-ene, the solution will become colourless [1 mark].

2) a) $CH_3CH_2CH_2CH{=}CH_2$ (or $CH_2{=}CHCH_2CH_2CH_3$) pent-1-ene [1 mark]
$CH_3CH_2CH{=}CHCH_3$ (or $CH_3CH{=}CHCH_2CH_3$) pent-2-ene [1 mark]
You don't need to show the double bond as long as the number of hydrogen atoms on each carbon is correct.
b) $CH_3CH_2CH_2CH{=}CH_2 + H_2 \rightarrow CH_3CH_2CH_2CH_2CH_3$ [1 mark]

3) a) concentrated sulfuric acid [1 mark]
b) The ethene reacts with the sulfuric acid to form ethyl hydrogen sulfate [1 mark].
The ethyl hydrogen sulfate then reacts with water to form ethanol [1 mark].

Answers

Page 99 — Alcohols and Other Organic Compounds

1) a) *butan-1-ol [1 mark], a primary alcohol [1 mark]*
   b) *methylpropan-2-ol [1 mark], a tertiary alcohol [1 mark]*
   c) *butan-2-ol [1 mark], a secondary alcohol [1 mark]*

2) a) *Alcohol A (propan-1-ol) [1 mark]. Propanoic acid [1 mark].*
   b) *Oxidising agent (e.g. acidified potassium dichromate(VI) [1 mark]. This then needs to be heated under reflux [1 mark].*

3) a)

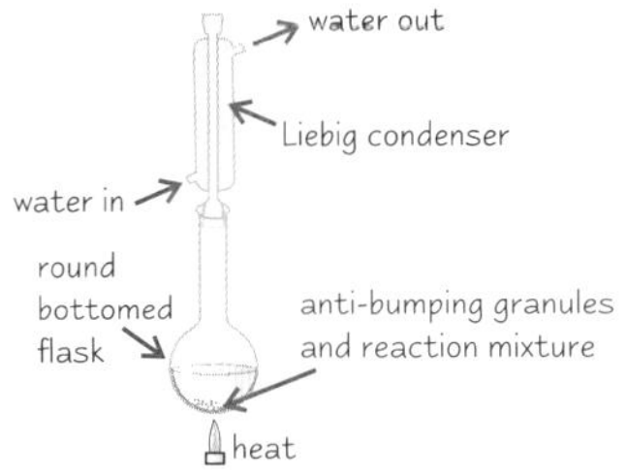

[1 mark for diagram]
The reflux apparatus means that the reaction can be heated to boiling point [1 mark] without losing any materials/reactants/products OR that vapour will condense and drip back into the flask [1 mark]

b) (i) *Carboxylic acid [1 mark]*
(ii) *$CH_3CH_2CH_2OH + [O] \rightarrow CH_3CH_2CHO + H_2O$ [1 mark]*
$CH_3CH_2CHO + [O] \rightarrow CH_3CH_2COOH$ [1 mark]
(iii) *Distillation [1 mark]. This is so aldehyde is removed immediately as it forms [1 mark].*
If you don't get the aldehyde out quick-smart, it'll be a carboxylic acid before you know it.

c) (i)

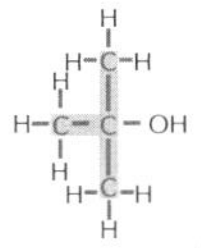

[1 mark]

(ii) *2-methylpropan-2-ol is a tertiary alcohol (which is more stable) [1 mark].*

Page 101 — Hydrogen Bonding

1) *A: Ammonia will have the higher boiling point [1 mark].*
B: Water will have the higher boiling point [1 mark].
C: Propan-1-ol will have the higher boiling point [1 mark].
The molecules of these substances can form hydrogen bonds [1 mark]. These are stronger/take more energy to overcome [1 mark] than the intermolecular forces between the other types molecules [1 mark].

2) *Ethan-1,2-diol has stronger intermolecular forces of attraction [1 mark]. The two alcohol groups in ethan-1,2-diol can form twice as many hydrogen bonds [1 mark].*

Page 103 — Polymers

1) a)

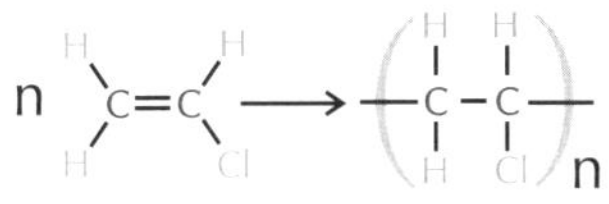

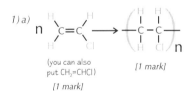

(you can also put CH_2=CHCl)
[1 mark]

[1 mark]

b) *Thermosoftening polymers have weak forces between the chains [1 mark]. These are easily overcome by heat and the polymer melts [1 mark]. If it is allowed to cool in a mould, the forces reform and the polymer retains the new shape [1 mark].*

2) a) *propene:*

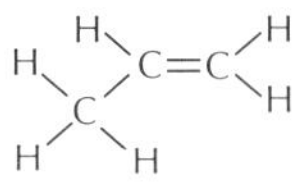

[1 mark]

repeat unit of poly(propene):

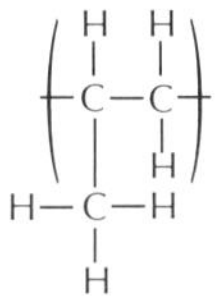

[1 mark]

b) *methylpropene [1 mark]*

Page 105 — E/Z Isomerism

1) a)

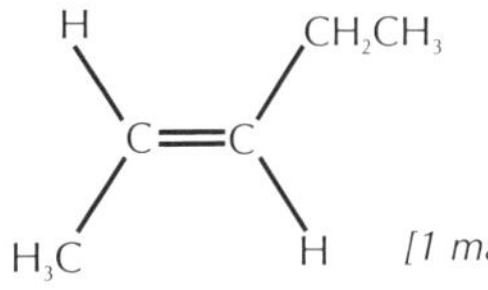

[1 mark]

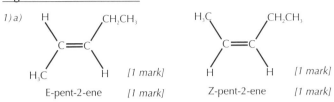

E-pent-2-ene *[1 mark]*

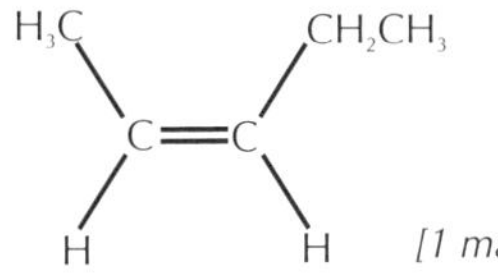

[1 mark]

Z-pent-2-ene *[1 mark]*

b) *E/Z isomers occur because atoms can't rotate about C=C double bonds [1 mark]. Alkenes contain C=C double bonds and alkanes don't, so alkenes can form E/Z isomers and alkanes can't [1 mark].*

2) *2 [1 mark]*

Page 107 — Infrared Spectroscopy

1 a) *A's due to an O–H group in a carboxylic acid [1 mark].*
B's due to a C=O as in an aldehyde, ketone, acid or ester [1 mark].
b) *The spectrum suggests it's a carboxylic acid — it's got a COOH group [1 mark]. This group has a mass of 45, so the rest of the molecule has a mass of 29 (74 – 45), which is likely to be C_2H_5 [1 mark]. So the molecule could be C_2H_5COOH — propanoic acid [1 mark].*

Index

A
absorption spectra 16
accuracy 37, 110
acid rain 48
acids 54, 61
activation enthalpy 80-83
addition polymerisation 102
addition reactions 94-96
adsorption 39
alcohols 40, 74, 75, 96-99
aldehydes 97-99
aliphatic compounds 40
alkalis 54
alkanes 40, 46-48, 90, 94
alkenes 40, 94-96, 98, 102
alpha radiation 6, 10
alternative fuels 50, 89
amines 76
ammonia 20, 76, 91
ammonium ions 20
anthropogenic warming 89
A_r (relative atomic mass) 8
arenes 40, 47
aromatic compounds 40, 46, 47
astatine 68
atmosphere 86
atom economy 72
atomic (proton) number 4, 5
atomic models 6, 7
atomic radius 66, 74
atomic spectra 16, 17
atoms 4-7
auto-ignition 47
average bond enthalpies 32, 33
Avogadro's constant, L 12

B
balancing equations 12, 52
ball-and-stick model 45
bases 28
batch processes 72
benzene 40
beta radiation 10
biodiesel 50
bioethanol 50
Bohr model 7
boiling points 20, 46, 68, 74, 91, 100
bond angles 24, 44
bond enthalpies 32, 33, 35, 77
bond length 33
bond polarisation 21, 62, 77
bonding 18-23
British Antarctic Survey 92
bromine 68, 71, 90, 95
bromine water 94

C
calculating
  concentration 53, 54
  empirical formulas 14
  gas volumes 30, 52
  percentage yield 53
  reacting masses 13, 52
  solution volumes 55
calorimetry 36, 37
carbocations 95
carbon 22, 40, 41, 78
carbon capture and storage (CCS) 51, 89
carbon dioxide 48, 49, 79, 86-89, 91
carbon monoxide 38, 48
carbon neutral 50
carbon-14 11
carbonates 29
carbonyl compounds 97
carboxylic acids 97-99
catalysts 38, 39, 46, 47, 73, 82, 84, 94, 96
catalytic converters 38, 39, 48, 49
catalytic cracking 46
CFCs (chlorofluorocarbons) 86, 91-93
Chadwick, James 6
charge clouds 24, 44
chemical industry 72, 73
chemical properties 58
chlorine 62, 68, 71, 90, 93
chloroalkanes 74, 75
chloromethane 90
chromium 58
cis-trans isomerism 105
climate change 48, 51, 88, 89
collision theory 80-82
combustion 32, 48, 98
compound ions 60
concentration 53, 54, 82, 84, 85
conclusions 3, 110
conductivity 19, 20, 22, 23, 78
continuous processes 72
coordinate bonding 20
copolymers 102
copper 58
correlation 109
covalent bonding 20-22, 33, 62, 78
cows 88
cracking 46
cross-links 102
crude oil 46
curly arrows 95
cycloalkanes 40

D
ΔH 32
d block 57, 58
Dalton, John 6
data, types of 108
dative covalent bonding 20
dehydration of alcohols 98
delocalised electrons 23, 27, 40
desorption 39
diamond 78
dilute solutions 53
dipoles 62-64
dipole-dipole interactions 64
disorder 31
displacement reactions 69
displayed formulas 42
distillation 75, 99
dot-and-cross diagrams 18, 20, 21
double covalent bonds 44, 45, 94, 95, 104
dynamic equilibrium 84

E
E/Z isomerism 104, 105
electrolysis 70
electromagnetic radiation 86, 88
Electron Pair Repulsion Principle 24
electrons 4-7, 16, 17, 44, 56, 87
electron shielding 66
electronegativity 62, 68, 76, 100
electronic structure 16, 56-58
electrophiles 95
electrophilic addition 94-96
electrostatic attraction 18
elimination reactions 98
emission spectra 16
empirical formulas 14, 15
endothermic reactions 32, 85
energy levels 16, 17, 56, 87
energy security 51
enhanced greenhouse effect 88
enthalpy changes 32-36
enthalpy profile diagrams 80, 83
entropy 31
enzymes 82
equilibria 84, 85, 92
errors 37
ethanol 96, 98
ethene 96, 98
ethers 40, 41
exothermic reactions 32, 48, 85
experimental evidence 6

F
fingerprint region 107
first ionisation enthalpy 66, 67
fission 50
fluorine 68, 71, 100
fossil fuels 49, 88
fractional distillation 46
fragmentation patterns 9
free radicals 87, 90, 92, 93
free-radical substitution reactions 90
fuel cells 50
fuels 48-51
functional groups 41, 42, 97, 106
fusion 11

G
gamma radiation 10
gas volumes 30, 52
Geiger, Hans 6
general formulas 40, 42, 94, 97
giant covalent structures 22, 78, 79
giant ionic structures 19
giant metallic structures 23
global warming 88
graphite 22
greenhouse effect 88, 89
greenhouse gases 48, 50, 86-88, 91
Group 2 28, 29
Group 7 68, 69
groups of the Periodic Table 26

H
haemoglobin 48
half-equations 61
half-life 10
halides 68, 69, 70
halogenoalkanes 74-77, 90, 91, 93
halogens 68-71
HCFCs (hydrochlorofluorocarbons) 91
health and safety legislation 72
Hess's law 34, 35
heterogeneous catalysts 38, 39, 82
heterolytic fission 76, 90
hexane 68, 69
HFCs (hydrofluorocarbons) 91
homogeneous catalysts 82, 83, 93
homologous series 40, 97
homolytic fission 90
hydration (steam) 96
hydrocarbons 40, 91, 94
hydrogen 20, 94
hydrogen bonding 64, 100, 101
hydrogen halides 95
hydrolysis 96

I
ice 100
incomplete combustion 48
indicators 54
infrared radiation 48, 86-88, 106

Index

infrared spectroscopy 106, 107
initiation reactions 90
intermolecular forces 64, 65, 74, 100, 102
iodine 68, 71
ionic bonding 18, 19, 21, 33, 62
ionic equations 52, 61
ionisation enthalpies 66, 67
ions 4, 18
isomerisation 38, 46
isomers 40, 42, 43, 104, 105
isotopes 5, 8, 9, 10

K
ketones 97, 98
kinetic energy 80, 81

L
lattices 19, 22, 23, 78, 100
Le Chatelier's principle 84, 85
length of a bond 33
lone pairs 24, 25, 63

M
macromolecular structures 22, 78, 79
magnesium oxide 18
Marsden, Ernest 6
mass number 4, 5
mass spectrometry 8, 9, 89
Maxwell-Boltzmann distributions 80, 81
melting points 19, 20, 22, 23, 68, 78, 100
Mendeleev, Dmitri 26
metallic bonding 23
methane 86-88, 90
methyl orange 54
models 6, 7, 21, 45, 80
molar mass 12
molecular formulas 14, 15, 42
molecular shape 24, 25, 44
moles 12, 30
monomers 102
Montreal Protocol 91
Moseley, Henry 6, 26
M_r (relative molecular mass) 8

N
neutralisation 28, 54
neutrons 4-6
Newlands, John 26
nitrogen 86, 100
nitrogen oxides 48, 49, 93
noble gases 26
nomenclature 41, 74
non-renewable 49
nuclear equations 10
nuclear fusion 11
nuclear power 50
nuclear radiation 10, 11
nucleophiles 76
nucleophilic substitution reactions 76
nucleus 4, 6, 10

O
octane rating 47
OIL RIG 61
orbitals 56
organic chemistry 40, 41, 75
oxidation 32, 59, 60, 61, 98, 99
oxidation states (numbers) 59-61
oxides of nitrogen 38, 48, 86
oxidising agents 59, 68, 98
oxygen 59, 86, 100
ozone (ground level) 38, 48, 93
ozone layer 91-93

P
p block 57, 58
paddy fields 88
parts per million 86
Pauling scale 62
peer review 2, 6
penetrating power 10
percentage yield 53, 73
Periodic Table 26, 27, 57
periodic trends 27
permanent dipoles 63
Perspex™ 103
petrol 46, 47
petroleum 46
phenolphthalein 54
photochemical smog 48, 93
photodissociation 90
photosynthesis 32, 88
physical properties 19-23, 78, 79, 103
phytoplankton 89
Planck's constant 16, 87
plum pudding model 6
poisoning catalysts 39
polar bonds/molecules 62, 63
polarisation 29, 62
pollutants 38, 48-50, 72, 86
polymers 46, 101-103
  Perspex™ 103
  poly(chloroethene) 103
  poly(ethene) 102, 103
  poly(phenylethene) (polystyrene) 103
  poly(propene) 103
  poly(tetrafluoroethene) 103
potassium dichromate(VI) 98
pressure 82, 84, 85
principal quantum number 56
propagation reactions 90
proton (atomic) number 4, 5
protons 4-6
purification 75

Q
quantised levels 87
quantum model of the atom 7

R
radiation
  electromagnetic 86-88
  nuclear 10-11
radioactive decay 10
radioactive waste 50
radiocarbon dating 11
random errors 37
reaction rates 38, 73, 80-83
reactivity 68, 69, 77
redox reactions 59, 60, 68
reducing agents 59
reduction 59, 61
reflux 98, 99
reforming 38, 47
relative atomic mass (A_r) 5, 8, 9, 26
relative formula mass 8
relative isotopic abundance 8, 9
relative isotopic mass 8
relative molecular mass (M_r) 8, 12
reliable results 108
renewable fuels 50
reversible reactions 84, 85
Rutherford, Ernest 6

S
s block 57, 58
safety 73, 110
saturated hydrocarbons 40
scientific process 2, 3
shapes of molecules 24, 25, 44, 45
shells 16, 56-58
shielding 66, 68
silicon(IV) oxide (silicon dioxide) 22, 78, 79
silver nitrate 70, 77
skeletal formulas 42
skin cancer 92
smog 48, 93
sodium chloride 18, 19
sodium hydroxide 76
solar power 50
solubility 19-23, 28, 68, 78, 79, 101
soluble polymers 101
sparingly soluble 28
specific heat capacity 36
spectroscopy 106, 107
spin-pairing 56
standard conditions 32
standard enthalpy changes 34
state symbols 13
steam hydration 96
stereoisomers 104
structural formulas 42
structural isomers 42
sub-shells 56-58
sublimation 78
substitution reactions 90
successive ionisation enthalpies 66
sulfur dioxide 48, 49, 86
sulfuric acid 96, 98
sustainability 49, 50
systematic errors 37
systematic names 60

T
temporary dipoles 64
tentative nature of science 3
tetrahedral 22, 25, 44, 78
theoretical yield 53
thermal cracking 46
thermal decomposition 29, 32
thermoplastic polymers 102
thermosetting polymers 102
Thompson, J J 6
time-of-flight mass spectrometer 8
titrations 54, 55
tracers 10
transition metals 58

U
ultraviolet radiation 86-88, 90, 92, 93
unburnt hydrocarbons 38, 48
unsaturated hydrocarbons 40, 94

V
van der Waals forces 27, 64, 65, 68, 74, 100
variables 108, 109
volatility 68

W
water 28, 48, 76, 87
water vapour 86, 88
wavenumber 106

Y
yield 53, 73

The Periodic Table

Relative Atomic Mass (top of each box); Atomic number (bottom of each box)

Periods	Group I	Group II											Group III	Group IV	Group V	Group VI	Group VII	Group 0
1								1.0 H Hydrogen 1										4.0 He Helium 2
2	6.9 Li Lithium 3	9.0 Be Beryllium 4											10.8 B Boron 5	12.0 C Carbon 6	14.0 N Nitrogen 7	16.0 O Oxygen 8	19.0 F Fluorine 9	20.2 Ne Neon 10
3	23.0 Na Sodium 11	24.3 Mg Magnesium 12											27.0 Al Aluminium 13	28.1 Si Silicon 14	31.0 P Phosphorus 15	32.1 S Sulphur 16	35.5 Cl Chlorine 17	39.9 Ar Argon 18
4	39.1 K Potassium 19	40.1 Ca Calcium 20	45.0 Sc Scandium 21	47.9 Ti Titanium 22	50.9 V Vanadium 23	52.0 Cr Chromium 24	54.9 Mn Manganese 25	55.8 Fe Iron 26	58.9 Co Cobalt 27	58.7 Ni Nickel 28	63.5 Cu Copper 29	65.4 Zn Zinc 30	69.7 Ga Gallium 31	72.6 Ge Germanium 32	74.9 As Arsenic 33	79.0 Se Selenium 34	79.9 Br Bromine 35	83.8 Kr Krypton 36
5	85.5 Rb Rubidium 37	87.6 Sr Strontium 38	88.9 Y Yttrium 39	91.2 Zr Zirconium 40	92.9 Nb Niobium 41	95.9 Mo Molybdenum 42	98 Tc Technetium 43	101.1 Ru Ruthenium 44	102.9 Rh Rhodium 45	106.4 Pd Palladium 46	107.9 Ag Silver 47	112.4 Cd Cadmium 48	114.8 In Indium 49	118.7 Sn Tin 50	121.8 Sb Antimony 51	127.6 Te Tellurium 52	126.9 I Iodine 53	131.3 Xe Xenon 54
6	132.9 Cs Caesium 55	137.3 Ba Barium 56	138.9 La Lanthanum 57	178.5 Hf Hafnium 72	181.0 Ta Tantalum 73	183.9 W Tungsten 74	186.2 Re Rhenium 75	190.2 Os Osmium 76	192.2 Ir Iridium 77	195.1 Pt Platinum 78	197.0 Au Gold 79	200.6 Hg Mercury 80	204.4 Tl Thallium 81	207.2 Pb Lead 82	209.0 Bi Bismuth 83	209 Po Polonium 84	210 At Astatine 85	222 Rn Radon 86
7	223 Fr Francium 87	226.0 Ra Radium 88	227.0 Ac Actinium 89															

The Lanthanides	140.1 Ce Cerium 58	140.9 Pr Praseodymium 59	144.2 Nd Neodymium 60	145 Pm Promethium 61	150.4 Sm Samarium 62	152.0 Eu Europium 63	157.3 Gd Gadolinium 64	158.9 Tb Terbium 65	162.5 Dy Dysprosium 66	164.9 Ho Holmium 67	167.3 Er Erbium 68	168.9 Tm Thulium 69	173.0 Yb Ytterbium 70	175.0 Lu Lutetium 71
The Actinides	232.0 Th Thorium 90	231.0 Pa Protactinium 91	238.0 U Uranium 92	237.0 Np Neptunium 93	244 Pu Plutonium 94	243 Am Americium 95	247 Cm Curium 96	247 Bk Berkelium 97	251 Cf Californium 98	254 Es Einsteinium 99	257 Fm Fermium 100	256 Md Mendelevium 101	254 No Nobelium 102	260 Lr Lawrencium 103